Instructor's Guide with Solutions

for

Moore/Notz/Fligner's

The Basic Practice of Statistics

Sixth Edition

R. Scott Linder
Ohio Wesleyan University

W. H. Freeman and Company
New York

©2013 by W.H. Freeman and Company

ISBN-13: 978-1-4641-1406-9
ISBN-10: 1-4641-1406-4

Printed in the United States of America

First printing

W.H. Freeman and Company
41 Madison Avenue
New York, NY 10010
Houndmills, Basingstoke RG21 6XS England

www.whfreeman.com

Contents

Preface

This Instructor's Guide is meant to serve as a companion to the *Instructor's Edition* to the 6th edition of *Basic Practice of Statistics*. In the Instructor's Edition of the text, instructors will find plenty of tips aimed at making course ideas easier to grasp for students. In this Instructor's Guide, additional chapter notes are provided (largely distilled from the Instructor Edition content), along with a few sample tests. Most importantly, detailed solutions to all textbook problems are provided. I hope you find that these solutions aid in identifying problems that enhance class discussion, as well as in the administration of course assignments.

I welcome comments, corrections, and suggestions for improvement. Most importantly, I welcome an open discussion of ideas for classroom activities and examples designed to make a classroom more engaging. You can contact me using the following information:

Happy teaching,

R. Scott Linder

Department of Mathematics and Computer Science
Ohio Wesleyan University
Delaware, Ohio 43015
Telephone: (740) 368-3660
Email: rslinder@owu.edu

distributions of data (rather than from mathematical models) and from the variability of the results of random sampling. Chapters 10 and 11 briefly present all that is needed to read the rest of the book, with Chapter 11 building a crucial understanding of sampling distributions, necessary for what is to come. Chapters 12 and 13 allow a fuller treatment but can be omitted without loss of understanding material to come.

- There is more discussion of the major ideas of inference, which form the backbone of the course. Chapters 14 and 15 (each based on the material on sampling distributions presented in Chapter 11) provide introductions to confidence interval estimation and tests of significance, respectively, while Chapter 16 delves into practical issues that arise from their use. Notably, discussion of significance tests emphasizes P-values rather than probabilities of Type I and Type II errors and tests with fixed α. This reflects common practice and helps students understand the output of statistical software.

- Presentation of two-sample methods emphasizes their close connection with those developed for one sample. This is consistent with a de-emphasis on formula memorization.

- Scatterplots, correlation, and simple linear-regression models are presented early, with emphasis on describing a sample and building a descriptive model. Later in the text, after inferential methods have been developed, the regression model is revisited in the context of inference for a population.

Upon completion of a course based on *BPS*, successful students should be able to think critically about data, to apply basic statistical inference procedures, and to draw conclusions from such analyses. Importantly, they should be able to take a practical problem and write it in the language of statistics, then recognize a method that may apply to addressing the problem. Finally, the BPS student should also be a statistically literate citizen, able to consume information in the media with healthy skepticism.

Computing

The practice of statistics requires a good deal of graphing and numerical calculation. While doing some graphing and calculating by hand may build understanding of methods, as teachers we should rely heavily on the use of automation with calculator or computer to minimize pointless, tedious work. Struggling with computational aspects of a procedure can interfere with a full understanding of the concepts. Automating arithmetic greatly improves the typical student's ability to complete problems, and frees the student's energies for focus on important concepts, and on interpretation of results. We therefore favor automating calculations and graphics as much as possible, within reason.

All students should have a calculator that does two-variable statistics, that is, that calculates not only $\bar{x}$ and s but the correlation r and the least-squares regression line from keyed-in data. *BPS* is written so that a student with such a calculator will not often be frustrated by the required calculations. Even if you use computer software, students should have such a calculator for use at home and on exams. *BPS* does not present anachronistic computing formulas that would allow exhaustive and pointless computation of (say) the least-squares regression line with a simple four-function (+, −, ×, ÷) calculator.

Just about any graphing calculator sold today will automate almost all procedures discussed in a first statistics course, and will provide basic graphs. Furthermore, if everyone in the classroom has a graphing calculator, class discussions can be greatly enhanced.

Software retains some clear advantages in entering and editing data and in graphics not being constrained by the small window of a graphing calculator. Almost all students now have some familiarity with personal computers, so most are able to quickly learn how to use a menu-driven software package, such as Minitab, SAS, CrunchIt!, or even Excel. *BPS* presents output from such software packages, integrated into the discussion of concepts.

As an encouragement to software use, the CD-ROM packaged with the text includes all substantial data sets for examples and exercises in *BPS*. The data appear as plain text (ASCII) files and also in the special formats of several common software systems. Data set icons are found in the margin next to examples and at the ends of exercises. The descriptive names indicated by these icons correspond to the names of the data set files.

Using Video

One of the most effective ways to convince students that statistics is useful is to show them real people (not instructors) employing statistics in a variety of settings. Video allows instructors to do this in the classroom.

The Statistics Video Tool Kit, available for use with *The Basic Practice of Statistics,* consists of three types of videos aimed to illustrate key statistical concepts and help students visualize statistics in the real world:

- *Statistically Speaking Snapshots:* This set of brief videos contains many examples from the popular PBS series *Against All Odds: Inside Statistics* (described below), but also adds new examples and documentary footage.

- *StatClips* Lecture Videos: These 36 mini-lectures (three to five minutes each) provide multimedia tutorials to reinforce lectures by explaining specific statistical skills and concepts.
- *StatClips* Examples: The *StatClips* lecture videos are paired with step-by-step examples done on a whiteboard so students can see how a specific problem is solved.

The Video Tool Kit is available as a resource in StatsPortal or as a separate package that can be purchased online. For more information, visit www.whfreeman.com/statistics.

Longer videos designed to motivate students and present a considerable amount of the course content are also available for use with *The Basic Practice of Statistics.* These videos are more appropriate for distance learning and hybrid courses, where the video can serve as a lecture developed around the "on location" documentary.

- *Statistically Speaking: Introductory Statistics:* This full video-based statistics course of 32 half-hour episodes includes some of the documentary footage from *Against All Odds,* but with new examples and a new host. For ordering information, visit www.whfreeman.com/statistics.

This series is also available on DVD from COAST Learning, www.coastlearning.org.

Resources on the Internet

The World Wide Web has made great amounts of information easily available. Here are some worthwhile sites with resources for use in conjunction with *BPS*. Some of these sites have links to other interesting locations. The fluid nature of the Internet means that addresses may change, and other resources may show up from time to
time; Web searches for phrases such as "statistics tutor" or "statistics applets" will almost certainly yield some useful results.

First, some general collections:

- Carnegie-Mellon University maintains *StatLib*, an electronic repository of things of statistical interest, including data sets. To get started, visit lib.stat.cmu.edu. Note in particular the "Data and Story Library," an online source related to the EESEE collection of case studies that is included on the *BPS* CD-ROM.

- The *Journal of Statistics Education*, an electronic journal of the American Statistical Association, contains much of interest to teachers of statistics. For more information, visit www.amstat.org/publications/jse.

- The Chance Web site, hosted by Dartmouth College, provides timely "current events" material to supplement a statistics course. Find it at www.dartmouth.edu/~chance.

- If you want to find some examples of "bad statistics," visit www.junkscience.com.

It is useful for students to visit "real statistics" sites to get a glimpse of the richness of the subject:

- Ask students to locate facts about their home counties at the U.S. Census Bureau, www.census.gov, or read the latest press release about employment and unemployment from the Bureau of Labor Statistics at stats.bls.gov. Look under "Economic News Releases" and then under "Employment & Unemployment" for releases with the title "Employment Situation." Also, the unified gateway to   federal statistical agencies at www.fedstats.gov is comprehensive but a bit overwhelming.

- Find current Gallup poll press releases and Gallup's explanations of how sample surveys work at www.gallup.com. The National Council on Public Polls (www.ncpp.org) has statements on "Principles of Disclosure" and "20 Questions a Journalist Should Ask about a Poll" that make interesting reading.

- The abstracts of current medical research in the *New England Journal of Medicine* (www.nejm.org) demonstrate that you must know some statistics to read medical literature. Choose a clinical trial and an observational study from the available abstracts, then ask students to search for them by subject and to write a description of the design, the explanatory and response variables, and the conclusions.

You can find a large number of attractive, interactive animated simulations that demonstrate important facts about probability and statistics. We recommend these for class demonstrations as well as for student work, particularly if you are not using software in your course. Most are at university locations, and their URLs change often. We mention just a few; searching for "statistics applet" or a similar term will reveal many more.

- First, we must mention the StatsPortal applets at www.whfreeman.com/bps6e, the *BPS* companion Web site. Some exercises in the text refer to these applets.

- http://onlinestatbook.com/stat_sim/ (David Lane, Rice University), www.stat.sc.edu/rsrch/gasp (Todd Ogden, Columbia University, and R.Webster West, University of South Carolina), http://www.stat.tamu.edu/jhardin/applets/ and http://www.stat.tamu.edu/jhardin/StatConcepts.html (James Hardin, Texas A&M University), and surfstat.anu.edu.au/surfstat-home/surfstat-main.html (University of Newcastle, Australia).

- www.math.csusb.edu/faculty/stanton/m262/probstat.html (Charles Stanton, California State University–San Bernardino) and www.math.uah.edu/stat (Kyle Siegrist, University of Alabama at Huntsville) are especially strong in probability.

- Want to select an SRS or do experimental randomization, even for large samples, and bypass the table of random digits? Visit the Research Randomizer at www.randomizer.org.

PLANNING A COURSE

Introduction

In preparing to teach from *BPS*, look carefully at each **Chapter Summary**. There you will find a detailed list of the essential skills that students should gain from study of each chapter. Additionally, each larger group of chapters (Part I, consisting of Chapters 1 to 6, etc.) concludes with a **Part Summary Chapter**, listing the skills and knowledge covered in that set of chapters. These learning objectives are given at the end of the chapters and parts because they would make little sense to students in advance. However, you can use them for advance planning as you decide what to emphasize and how much time to devote to each topic.

Also, look at the **APPLY YOUR KNOWLEDGE** exercises, short sets of exercises that cover the specific content of the preceding exposition. Their location tells students, "You should be able to do this right now." They also show the instructor what students can be expected to do at each step. The longer sets of **Chapter Exercises** at the end of each chapter ask students to integrate their knowledge, if only because their location does not give as clear a hint to the skills required. The **Review Exercises** in the last chapter of each part add another level of integration. You can help students by judicious selection of exercises from all three locations.

Course Outline

For a one-semester course, the core material consists of Chapters 1–7 (data analysis and descriptive methods); Chapters 8 and 9 (experimental design and sampling methods); Chapter 10 (basics of probability); Chapter 11 (sampling distributions); Chapters 14–16 (basics of inference, including confidence intervals and tests of significance); Chapter 18 (inference about a mean using the t distribution); Chapter 19 (comparing two means); Chapters 20 and 21 (inference for one and two proportions); and Chapter 24 (Inference for regression).

The material in Chapters 6 and 23 tie together nicely, and relate very well to the important material on experimental design in Chapters 8 and 9. Hence, covering Chapter 23 near the end of class forms a bookend for the course content. The material in Chapter 25 on Analysis of Variance is important, but it is sometimes omitted for time constraints. If your student audience consists of budding psychology or sociology majors, ANOVA is especially useful, while if your student audience contains more economics or business majors, the regression chapters will be more important.

If time allows, some of the nonparametric methods discussed in supplemental Chapter 26 can be woven in with other chapters, especially the material on two-sample methods, or on matched pairs. It adds depth to the course when students can point to methods suitable for use when standard methods are not applicable.

Meanwhile, you should be able to steer clear of the material in Chapters 12 and 13, as these topics are not necessary for understanding the remainder of material.

CHAPTER COMMENTS

Chapter 1: Picturing Distributions with Graphs

The first two chapters of this text concern themselves with describing data – a practice known as exploratory data analysis. The goal here is to describe data, and to discover questions worthy of further investigation. Chapter 1 concerns graphical displays of data – typically a first and simple approach to analysis of data. Graphical displays can convey sophisticated or subtle messages simple numbers cannot convey. The right graph or plot can reveal surprising results that may inspire a different line of questioning, or it may reveal previously unknown truths. In examining a distribution by using a graph, we concern ourselves with the distribution's shape, spread and center. The shape of a distribution provides a crude description of where common values lie, and where rare values lie. The center of a distribution describes its "typical" values, and its spread describes variation in the distribution. We may also be able to recognize outliers by examining a graphical display of data.

For categorical data, the two most important types of graphs are bar graphs and pie charts. Bar graphs are usually more informative, because pie charts rely on perception of area – something often difficult for people.

For quantitative data, the most important types of graphs are histograms and stemplots, though later we will learn about boxplots. Both stemplots and histograms can be used to address the important features of shape, center and spread, discussed above. They can also be used to identify the kinds of numerical summaries are appropriate in addressing future research questions. These numerical summaries are the subject of Chapter 2.

Chapter 2: Describing Distributions with Numbers

In this chapter we move from graphical to numerical description of data. The two should always be used together: Graphical methods provide a visual impression of the data, and can often reveal features that summary numerical descriptive values cannot, while, conversely, descriptive summaries provide information that graphical displays cannot.

Numerical summaries are typically designed to provide insight about one of several different qualities of interest: There are measures of center, which get at a list's "typical" value, and measures of spread, which get at the amount of variability (lack of consistency) in the data. There are also measures of relative standing, which measure how unusual an individual is from a norm.

There are typically several reasonable choices for which numerical description one would use to get at a question of interest. For example, one could use the median or mean to describe a "typical" value in a list. The decision of which measure to use depends on properties of the measures. For example, the mean and median are both measures of center but if a data set is skewed, the median is generally preferred. The same is true with measures of spread. Sample standard deviation and sample range may both be used to describe variability, but almost always the sample standard deviation is preferred over the sample range.

When we examined graphical displays, we typically described the center, spread, and shape of a distribution. These properties may be determined from numerical summaries as well. The boxplot, based on the five-number summary, provides another graphical display of the data.

Chapter 3: The Normal Distribution

This chapter is primarily about using density curves to model the distribution of a random variable. In applications, researchers may use histograms to get some insight into the shape of such a model, and there are a great many different density curves one may fit to a histogram.

The Normal distribution is certainly the most widely used distribution (and therefore most important) an introductory level statistics student will use. However, the reason for the Normal distribution's importance usually has little to do with the populations from which we sample. Instead, Normal distributions attain their importance as large sample size approximations to the sampling distributions of most of the important statistics we use for decisions – sample means (and therefore proportions), as well as sums. Essentially, if the statistic is a sum or average, then its sampling distribution is approximately Normal, provided the sample size is large enough. It is also true that some population distributions are Normal or can be approximated by the Normal distribution, and here students develop the technical skills of obtaining percentiles or proportions under a Normal density curve. These skills will be critical later, when they study sampling distributions.

A common density curve that may be used to model many real-world variables is symmetric and bell-shaped. This is the basic shape of a Normal random variable. A Normal distribution is fully described through its two parameters: μ and σ, the mean and standard deviation, respectively. In order to compute proportions or percentiles for an arbitrary normal distribution, we use the important result is that any normal variable can be converted to a *standard* normal variable, having mean 0 and standard deviation 1 through the equation $z = \dfrac{x - \mu}{\sigma}$.

As students learn about the Normal distributions, it will be helpful for them to relate μ and σ through the 68-95-99.7 rule, which describes what percent of observations lie within one, two and three standard deviations of the mean, respectively. Students will encounter two varieties of applied problems: given values, a and b, find the proportion of the population between those values; and given a proportion, p, find the value a, such that p is the proportion of the population less than a. Both problems will require access to a standard normal distribution, either through a table or through software.

Chapter 4: Scatterplots and Correlation

From Chapters 1 and 2, students are familiar with the use of graphical displays and summary statistics to summarize data. Here we begin to explore the relationship between two variables first graphically, then numerically.

The scatterplot is used to graphically represent the relationship between two variables. If summarizing the relationship is all that matters, it is not important to identify an explanatory or response variable. However, if we plan to use the scatterplot to inspire a model relating the variables, then this distinction is necessary. Fortunately, this is typically straightforward, made clear from the context of a problem.

Constructing a scatterplot is simple and should be left to the computer. However, interpreting a scatterplot takes a bit of practice. The important task is to look for an overall pattern (Is the pattern roughly linear? Is it curved? What is the general direction of the relationship? Is it a strong relationship?). We also take time to look for deviations from this pattern (are there any influential values?).

We measure the strength and direction of any linear relationship between two variables by use of correlation. Students need to be mindful of caveats when interpreting correlation: If two variables are strongly correlated, there is not necessarily a strong cause and effect relationship. Be mindful of correlations based on aggregation of data (ecological correlation). Finally, beware of the influence of outliers on correlation.

Chapter 5: Regression

This chapter picks up where Chapter 4 (Scatterplots and Correlation) left off. If we find a strong linear relationship between two variables, as suggested by a scatterplot of the data and by correlation, then we may be interested in summary of the overall pattern by drawing a line on the scatterplot. We use the least-squares regression line to describe the straight-line relationship between the variables. The regression line provides a numerical summary of this relationship.

There are essentially three issues examined in this chapter. First, the question of how to fit a simple linear regression line is considered. Students need to understand that the least-squares regression line is the one that minimizes the total of squared prediction errors. Second, the question of how to measure the regression line's goodness of fit is considered. We often used the squared correlation (often called the coefficient of determination) to measure this, but this number is an incomplete summary. We should also plot the data, along with the regression line and consider any potential undue influence of outliers. Third, we consider how to use the regression line to describe the relationship between response and explanatory variables, or to make a prediction of the response variable, given a known value of the explanatory variable.

The slope of the regression line is the expected (predicted) change in the response variable associated with an increase by one unit of the explanatory variable. The intercept of the regression line is the predicted value of the response variable when the explanatory variable is zero… but this is not often useful, since such a prediction would be extrapolation in many settings.

Before using the regression line to make predictions or to summarize the relationship between two variables, it is wise to examine a residual plot, which plots residuals (prediction errors) against the explanatory variable. Using this plot, one can more easily identify outliers, influential observations or detect any patterns of non-linearity in the data that might suggest a straight-line model is inappropriate. Regression models have limitations, as discussed at the end of the chapter. It is virtually always unreasonable to extrapolate beyond the range of the explanatory variable constrained by previous experience. And, regression models built using plots of data averaged over the response mask variation and lead to a false sense of good fit.

Instructors are well advised to steer students away from intensive computation, as students are better served with examples providing output from statistical software and interpreting it. Provided with output, or creating it themselves using the software, students can then demonstrate understanding of (1) whether conditions for use of the line are met; (2) obtaining the least-squares regression line and using it to make a prediction; (3) interpreting the slope and intercept of the regression line in context of the problem; (4) interpreting the meaning of r^2 and using it to compute the correlation between the variables; and (5) understanding the limitations of regression.

Chapter 6: Two-Way Tables

This chapter is concerned with revealing relationships between two categorical variables, as opposed to that of Chapters 4 and 5 on regression, which dealt with relating two quantitative variables.

The computation required in this chapter is minimal. Students only need to compute proportions and percentages, but they need to be careful to distinguish between marginal and conditional proportions. Indeed, the distinction between these two proportions, and consideration of which is appropriate for use in a particular application, is the most important subject of the chapter. Perhaps the most interesting revelation for students is the notion that a marginal distribution may reveal a different relationship than the conditional distribution. It probably suffices to spend one or two class periods on this material, all of which can be described using one compelling example.

There are interesting connections between the material presented here and that covered in later chapters. We will learn about comparing two proportions, about the chi-square test for homogeneity, and about simple experimental design. All of these subjects are related to categorical data described in a contingency table. As well, covering this material gives one the chance to review bar graphs.

Chapter 7: Exploring Data: Part I Review

This chapter serves as an overview of the material covered thus far in the text, which covers exploratory methods (graphical and numeric) of describing data. These methods are used to summarize important qualities of a given data set, such as describing its center and spread. At this point, students should be connecting all of the ideas from Chapters 1 – 6, using them to paint an informative picture of data, and possibly discovering new lines of topics for investigation. Some students in an introductory course will tend to view chapters as disjoint, and this can lead to a failure to grasp the larger picture. Hence, think of this chapter as an attempt to bring all of these concepts together, and select problems for thorough class discussion that allow students to combine these topics . Notice that the examples are more thorough, and require the use of several approaches simultaneously, rather than one or two. In this way, the problems in the Supplementary Exercises section of the chapter provide example problems useful for in-class review or student study.

Many of the concepts and techniques learned in Part I will be used throughout the text. It is always worth foreshadowing topics the students may encounter repeatedly. Students have seen and will see again the importance of the roles variables play in a study and also the dangers and other effects that lurking variables may have on results. Finally students are reminded that the key steps in any data analysis are to State, Plan, Solve, and Conclude. These key steps will be used in future chapters as well.

Chapter 8: Producing Data: Sampling

While Chapters 1–7 were concerned with describing data, the next two concern themselves with collecting it. The quality of any decision, estimate or judgment about a population based upon a sample – any statistical inference – depends upon the sample being representative of the population. Chapters 8 and 9 are all about collecting data sensibly – making the sample more likely to represent the population. There are two primary ways in which data are collected: Surveys through random samples (the topic of Chapter 8), and both observational studies and experiments, (the topics of Chapter 9).

Introductory courses often fail to devote enough attention to these important concepts. However, in an age in which we are exposed to claims or summaries of studies in the media, questioning the source of data is a component of basic statistical literacy. This requires an understanding that if an experiment, observational study or sample survey is poorly designed, nothing meaningful can be extracted. Students should learn to be skeptical of claims made in the media, and learning to distinguish good studies from bad studies is essential to this.

The sampling methods presented here start with the simplest and easiest, and build to more complicated, but often more useful methods. Convenience samples and voluntary response samples are both straightforward and tempting because of their ease of use, but they are among the least favorable sample designs, and generally produce useless data, as they are unlikely to provide a representative sample of the target population. The simple random sample (SRS) is the first proper random sampling design students will see, and is the easiest to understand. Stratified random samples are more complicated, but are often more efficient than simple random samples.

Students should be constantly reminded of some of the cautions associated with sampling. Confounding variables are defined here and discussed again in future chapters. Well-designed samples will suffer from random (sampling) error – if you repeat the survey, results will vary by random chance. Badly designed samples may also suffer from nonsampling, systematic error – types of bias due to undercoverage and nonresponse, for example.

Chapter 9: Producing Data: Experiments

In this chapter students learn to distinguish between observational study (in which subjects assign themselves to groups, and no variables are manipulated or controlled by the researcher) and experiments (in which the researcher assigns subjects to comparison groups and manipulates one or more variables). Observational studies are poorly equipped for determining a cause and effect relationship between variables simply because there may be lurking variables driving people to assign themselves to comparison groups in such a way that the groups differ in more than one way. For example, people that choose to smoke may also tend to have different exercise or diet habits, so it is difficult to conclude that any difference in health is due to smoking, or to diet or exercise differences.

Good design of experiments is central to research, especially in the sciences and in psychology (in many social science settings – economics, for example – observational studies are more typical sources of data). Experimental design is concerned with efficiently collecting data, so that the maximum amount of information about a problem of interest can be obtained, given constraints (a budget, for example). Unfortunately, this subject is often given sparse coverage in introductory courses. In this chapter, we focus on the most basic principles of experimentation.

Whereas observational studies may be used to determine if a relationship exists between two variables, it is only through formal experimentation that cause in a relationship can be determined. Many of the experiments discussed in this chapter are used in the life sciences, agriculture, medicine and many other fields.

The roles of subjects, treatment, and response are key in any experimental design, so students should be reminded throughout the chapter of the importance and roles of these concepts. The simplest designs, randomized comparative experiments, and completely randomized designs, are introduced first; then more advanced and thus complicated designs, such as matched pair and block designs, are covered.

Chapter 10: Introducing Probability

In this chapter, students are formally introduced to probability. There have been hints pointing to this chapter throughout preceding chapters. For example, the proportions computed in Chapter 6 (Two-Way Tables) are sometimes regarded as estimates of probabilities.

In fact, in most introductory courses little formal treatment of probability is covered. Formal rules for computing more complicated probabilities are typically skipped. Without question, the most important concept for beginning students to grasp is that the probability of an event represents a long-run proportion of times the event would occur if the random experiment is repeated endlessly. Later, when we interpret a *P*-value or a confidence interval, this notion will be central, as all of these are interpreted in terms of repeating the experiment endlessly. Other concepts, such as formulas for computing probabilities, are less important, but some of them (such as the probability of a complementary event, or of the union of two events) will be used in the future also. Additionally, it is useful to understand the concept of a random variable.

One of the central ideas of probability is that chance behavior, or occurrences that happen at random, are unpredictable in the short run but have regular and predictable patterns over the long run. So, when a fair coin is flipped twice, we may not observe one head and one tail; however, we know that if the coin is flipped continually, the proportion of heads will converge to 0.5.

Statistical reasoning is inductive in nature – we make statements of uncertainty about a population based on information in a sample, so we're generalizing to the whole from the part. Probabilistic reasoning is deductive – we make statements about uncertainty in a sample based on information (all of it) in a population. These are inverse problems, and understanding the probabilistic statements we make in the practice of statistics requires understanding something about probability. In an introductory course such as this, students don't need to grasp much of probability in order to understand statistical principles.

Chapter 11: Sampling Distributions

The material presented in this chapter forms the backbone for much of the material on statistical inference to follow; namely, confidence intervals and significance tests based on large samples. One cannot understand the meaning of a *P*-value, for example, without understanding sampling distributions. It isn't easy for students to grasp the idea that a statistic has its own probability distribution, and concepts such as "the mean of a sample mean" confuse many newcomers. But, time invested here will yield rewards repeatedly as we continue to study.

It is in this chapter that students are, at last, formally introduced to the distinction between a statistic and parameter – for here we begin to turn toward inference from sample to population. A common population parameter of interest is the population mean μ. The sample mean $\bar{x}$ is commonly used to estimate μ, so its sampling distribution is important.

In this chapter we examine several important results concerning this particular sampling distribution: (1) The mean of the statistic $\bar{x}$ is the same as the mean of the population we're sampling from, μ; (2) the standard deviation of the statistic $\bar{x}$ is $\sigma/\sqrt{n}$; (3) because of this result, the Law of Large Numbers states that the statistic $\bar{x}$ has less variability (greater consistency) when based on a larger sample size; and (4) the Central Limit Theorem states the sampling distribution of $\bar{x}$ will be approximately normal, no matter what population the sample is taken from, provided the sample size is large enough.

It will be a good idea to provide plenty of examples asking students to distinguish between questions that ask for probability for a single value taken from the population, and those asking about the probability for a sample mean. Students often confuse these problems, resulting in use of the "wrong standard deviation" in computing a *z*-score.

As importantly, instructors should require students to articulate the reason for using the standard normal distribution in referring to the table (or software). For example, "the population is Normal, so the sampling distribution of $\bar{x}$ is Normal regardless of the sample size," or "the sample size is large, so the sampling distribution of $\bar{x}$ is approximately Normal regardless of the population's skew." These reasons are important to distinguish – and the distinction bears on understanding when one uses the *t*-distribution for inference, covered soon.

Chapter 12: General Rules of Probability

This chapter is often omitted from introductory courses, especially when students have weaker backgrounds in mathematics. The statistical ideas to be explored next do not require an understanding of the addition or multiplication rules, or of conditional probability discussed in this chapter. However, understanding these rules will enrich one's capacity for combining or linking several statistical results together. In addition, an understanding of conditional probability greatly enhances an understanding of statistical modeling. The notion of independence, explored at greater depth here, is central to the Binomial distribution.

Many of the concepts of this chapter can be illustrated with simplistic examples that students may already be familiar with, and many of the concepts in this chapter are intuitively obvious (the addition rule, for example).

Chapter 13: Binomial Distributions

As with Chapter 12, this material is also often regarded as optional. In practice, we're often interested in the number of *successes* in a fixed number of independent trials. For example, we may be interested in the chance that no more than 4 of 25 randomly selected parts are defective. The probability distribution describing this count is often the binomial distribution, depending on conditions being met: trials must be independent, and each trial must result in a success or failure outcome with the same probabilities on each trial. The structure of the binomial distribution is intuitively appealing, at least for students with a reasonable mathematical background.

The mean and standard deviation of a binomial random variable will be seen to appear within the mean and standard error of the sample proportion when we discuss inference for a population proportion, p. Hence, when we learn about the sampling distribution of a sample proportion (Chapter 20), stronger students will recognize that this sampling distribution is simply a special case of the Central Limit Theorem for sample means, and it is recommended that such students learn to think of it this way. Indeed, this chapter concludes with the Normal approximation to the binomial distribution – an application of the Central Limit Theorem, not stated as such. Second, the structure of the binomial distribution is intuitively appealing, at least for students with a reasonable mathematical background.

Chapter 14: Confidence Intervals: The Basics

Chapter 11 (Sampling Distributions) marked the beginning of a turn toward statistical inference. This chapter marks the first such application, and moves directly from that material. Hence, here we begin a sequence of applied chapters forming the heart of the course. The problems encountered by students will feel somewhat inverted to students – where we previously used information about the entire population to characterize likely samples, now we'll make inferences about the population using information in a sample. It is this inversion that forms the link between sampling distributions and application of confidence intervals to parameter estimation.

Confidence intervals are used to estimate unknown population parameters by providing a set of a plausible values and attaching a level of certainty to that set. A strong understanding of sampling distributions is the single key to understanding both construction and properties of confidence intervals.

In constructing a confidence interval for a population parameter, we invoke the sampling distribution of an estimator of the parameter. The sampling distribution of the statistic (the estimator) yields a margin of error associated with the point estimate. The margin of error is a function of the estimator's standard error (standard deviation).

As you introduce students to confidence intervals, consider explaining their construction from the context of repeated sampling. Invoke the Central Limit Theorem and get students to describe that (for example) about 95% of sample means will lie within $1.96\,\sigma/\sqrt{n}$ of the population mean μ. Get them to see that when and only when this occurs, the construction $\bar{x} \pm 1.96\,\sigma/\sqrt{n}$ will capture μ. The notion of repeated sampling is crucial here, as it is with interpreting all inferential methods described in these chapters.

An important first step in many studies is to determine the sample size needed to meet certain predetermined criteria. One method of determining such sample size is presented here. This material emphasizes the idea that the margin of error of estimation is related to sample size. A possible later formal course on experimental or sample survey design will rely on variations of the formula presented here.

Chapter 15: Tests of Significance: The Basics

With confidence intervals, we were interested in determining a set of plausible values of a parameter – values consistent with the sample observed. In this chapter, students encounter a second primary inferential method – significance testing. With tests of significance, the focus is on a particular value of the parameter, with an interest in whether the particular value of interest is plausible or may be rejected upon seeing the sample. There is a duality between confidence intervals and hypothesis tests.

Many students will find that the terminology and symbols encountered in this chapter are almost overwhelming. Regardless, however, there are only a handful of crucial ideas here, the most important being the concept of a *P*-value. The *P*-value is a measure of how supportive of the alternative hypothesis a sample was, under the assumption of the null hypothesis. Common abstract challenges for students include: (1) Correct specification of hypotheses; (2) Understanding that smaller *P*-values indicate stronger evidence against the null hypothesis; and (3) Understanding that the action is on rejecting the null hypothesis or not rejecting it – failure to reject the null hypothesis is not evidence that it is true.

Chapter 16: Inference in Practice

In the two previous chapters, students were introduced to the two primary vehicles for inference about a population mean - confidence intervals and significance tests. Both methods are based on the sampling distribution of the parameter's estimator – in this case, the sample mean, $\bar{x}$. In this chapter, we focus on developing a sense for when it is valid to apply these methods, and learn about the kinds of practical problems that can threaten the validity of inferences made using them.

If the researcher's objective is to make inferences about the population, it is important to consider how the data are collected. All of the methods for statistical inference are based on an assumption that the sample selected is random, or that the data come from a randomized comparative experiment. If the method of selecting a sample induces bias, then the integrity of inference is threatened, and the margin of error associated with a confidence interval does not account for this kind of error. In significance testing, a statistically significant result may not be practically significant, while lack of statistical significance does not mean that the null hypothesis is true. In interpreting a *P*-value, one should reflect on whether it is best to require less evidence to reject the null hypothesis (select a larger level of significance), or best to require more evidence (select a lower level of significance). It helps to consider the meaning of Type I and Type II errors in selecting a level of significance in choosing an appropriate level of significance for testing. The chapter ends with a discussion of the power of a test of hypotheses – the probability that a false null hypothesis will be rejected.

Chapter 17: From Exploration to Inference: Part II Review

This chapter serves as an overview of the material covered in Chapters 8 through 16. This material included here is expansive, ranging from basic experimental and sample survey design to probability to sampling distributions, and concluding with a first exposure to the two main vehicles for statistical inference – confidence intervals and significance tests. This chapter provides the instructor with the opportunity to place the most important of this material (experimental design, sampling plans, sampling distributions, confidence intervals and significance tests) into perspective.

Take time to select some problems from this chapter to simultaneously review material covered, and to provide a unity of context for these chapters, which students sometimes struggle to see. Most importantly, be sure that students can move comfortably between the ideas of Chapters 11 (sampling distributions), 14 (confidence intervals), 15 (significance tests) and 16 (pragmatic issues in inference). Less important are details associated with the binomial distribution (Chapter 13) and probability (Chapter 12).

Chapter 18: Inference About a Population Mean

In Chapters 14 – 16, we developed a basic overview of hypothesis tests and confidence intervals for this parameter. In this chapter students are exposed to more realistic applications of statistical inference about a population mean. Fortunately, the ideas we'll discuss here are essential modifications to those developed earlier – if students understand the meaning of a *P*-value, for example, they'll have little trouble adapting the methods of Chapter 15 to computing *P*-values here. The major ideas and methods, as well as their interpretation, remain unchanged.

In this chapter you may well discover that many students are able to follow procedure, but lack the ability to articulate a reason for the procedure's validity. If you've required such articulation in Chapters 11 (Why is the sampling distribution of the sample mean approximately Normal?), Chapter 14 (Why is the large sample confidence interval valid?) or Chapter 15 (Why is the Normal distribution appropriate for computing a *P*-value?), students will have an easier time understanding the assumptions required for use of the *t* distribution, introduced here. Again, the more often you require students to articulate the distinction between assuming the population is Normal and the assumption that the sampling distribution of a statistic is Normal, the better.

Here we grapple with the more realistic scenario in which the population standard deviation, σ, is unknown. We estimate σ by the sample standard deviation, *s*. This leads to the introduction of a new distribution that must be used in such cases: the *t* distribution. The *t* distribution is similar to the standard Normal distribution in that it has mean 0 and is symmetric and bell-shaped. However, the *t*-distribution has more variation, and this spread depends upon the sample size through *degrees of freedom*. One ramification of this is that use of the *t*-distribution will result in wider confidence intervals and lower power in hypothesis testing. However, when σ is unknown our inference should reflect this additional uncertainty.

Most students will find that the computational procedures of this chapter are easily learned, since they are very similar to those taught in Chapters 14 and 15; only some of the small details in the processes change. For this reason, this chapter serves as an opportunity to review previous concepts, even as new material is covered. Even the matched pairs procedure covered at the end of the chapter should not be taught as a new topic, but rather as an extension of what students have already seen. This material serves as a prelude to the material to be covered in the next chapter, concerning inference for two samples.

The *t* procedures are based on an assumption that the population being sampled from is Normal. However, the chapter ends with a discussion of the robustness of these procedures, emphasizing that they perform well even if data is non-normal, unless extreme outliers or skewness are present. It is this robustness that makes the *t* procedures so applicable.

Chapter 19: Two-Sample Problems

One of the canonical applications of applied statistics is the comparison of two groups. The subject of comparing two population means, covered in this chapter, represents something of a keystone topic in the course for this reason. Researchers are often concerned with problems such as which of two drugs is more effective, or whether a new teaching method is superior to an old teaching method in teaching children to read.

We compare the means of two population means, μ_1 and μ_2, through estimation of their difference, $\mu_1 - \mu_2$, rather than (say) their ratio. This is for mathematical reasons – the sampling distribution of the ratio of sample means is generally unknown, for example. If this difference is estimated to be a large positive number, the conclusion may be reached that μ_1 is larger than μ_2. Similarly, if the difference is estimated to be near zero, the conclusion can be made that the populations may have nearly the same mean. Here, the words "large" and "near" are determined, as always, by reflecting on the standard error of the estimator, $\bar{x}_1 - \bar{x}_2$.

Here we have two SRS's, each taken from different populations. Consistent with Chapter 18, we assume that these populations are Normally distributed, but it is enough in practice that the distributions have similar shapes and that the data have no strong outliers.

There are two options for computing degrees of freedom when using a two-sample *t* procedure. When technology is used, the software can obtain accurate critical values using degrees of freedom obtained via an advanced method. Details of this initial option for the *t* distribution are addressed in an optional section later in the chapter. When technology is not used, the more conservative, but simple option of basing degrees of freedom on the size of the smaller sample is suggested.

The chapter ends with a few advanced topics presented in optional sections. A discussion of "pooling" is worth having if your class is mathematically strong: The pooled two-sample *t*-test is identical to one-way analysis of variance with two populations; and the two-sample test for comparing proportions (discussed later) invokes pooling. The advice to avoid inference about comparing two population standard deviations is useful. The old-fashioned F-test for a ratio of two sample variances in order to make inferences about two population variances is still used in some circles, but since its widespread use, the test has been shown to be highly sensitive to even slight non-Normality, and therefore non-robust.

Chapter 20: Inference about a Population Proportion

We turn our attention here to inference about the proportion of "successes" in a population of "successes" and "failures." In many applications, a researcher is interested in estimation of a population proportion. We label this parameter p. For example, p could denote the proportion of all parts manufactured by a factory that are defective. In all such problems, the researcher is observing qualitative data ("yes" versus "no", or "success" versus "fail" outcomes), rather than quantitative data. Here, for qualitative data, we'll use the sample proportion, $\hat{p}$, to estimate the population proportion, p. This is just as the case for quantitative data, where we used the sample mean, $\bar{x}$, to estimate the population mean, μ.

This chapter covers confidence intervals and significance tests for a population proportion. In a larger sense, the concepts covered here are largely the same as those covered earlier, when we were interested in estimating a population mean, μ. For example, a *P*-value remains the measured probability of observing a sample as supportive of the alternative hypothesis as our sample is, assuming that the null hypothesis is true. However, the formulas used to work inference problems will seem completely new to most students at this introductory level.

Depending on the mathematical background of your students, and on the time you spent in Chapter 15 examining details for the binomial distribution, students may benefit from restating the Central Limit Theorem in terms of p, instead of $\bar{x}$. This comparison will allow students to see immediately that the confidence interval formula, or the *P*-value computations of this chapter mirror those developed earlier.

Chapter 21: Comparing Two Proportions

In this chapter we discuss comparison of two population proportions using two independent samples. The material here compares well with that of Chapter 19, where we discussed comparing two population means using two samples. If the two population proportions are p_1 and p_2, we compare them by estimating their difference, $p_1 - p_2$. In this chapter we develop confidence intervals and significance tests for this difference.

We begin by considering the sampling distribution of the difference in sample proportions, $\hat{p}_1 - \hat{p}_2$. Because the two populations are heavily non-Normal (each population consists of "successes" and "failures"), t distribution based methods are not appropriate. However, since sample proportions are simply sample means, the Central Limit Theorem provides that the sampling distribution of $\hat{p}_1 - \hat{p}_2$ is approximately Normal if each sample size is large enough.

Ideally, students will feel a sense of redundancy in studying this material. The ideas explored here are, in essence, repackaged and reformulated for the particular setting in question – this material does for two population proportions as the material in Chapter 19 did for two population means. The more students grasp this, the better they understand the material overall.

Students should be able to articulate that the populations are non-Normal, but if the samples are large, the sampling distributions of both $\hat{p}_1$ and $\hat{p}_2$ are approximately Normal, and therefore the sampling distribution of $\hat{p}_1 - \hat{p}_2$ is approximately Normal.

Chapter 22: Inference About Variables: Part III Review

Here, again, we have the opportunity to provide students with a set of problems requiring them to place the methods developed recently in context. In Part III students have learned how inferences are conducted in practice. They have seen one-sample and two-sample inferences for the most common settings – estimating population means and proportions. Hopefully, they have also realized that the basic concepts driving these methods are the same across these settings, and are beginning to see the redundancy of these ideas. If this is the case, then groundwork has been laid for understanding other inferential statistical methods, possibly in future courses.

The discussion in "Part III Summary" of the chapter provides a kind of flowchart students can use to organize the different kinds of problems they have encountered recently. This is particularly useful because students often struggle to recognize the kinds of formulas and methods that should be applied to different kinds of problems.

This chapter also provides a good reminder of the importance of checking conditions for specific procedures. This typically involves recognizing that a sample or samples are random and that either (1) they are large enough for the sample mean(s) or proportion(s) to have approximately Normal sampling distributions, or (2) the population(s) being sampled from are not highly non-Normal.

Chapter 23: Two Categorical Variables: The Chi-Square Test

This chapter links directly to Chapter 6, in which we discussed two-way tables and some associated topics, such as bar graphs and Simpson's paradox. This was an early exposure to categorical data. In this chapter we use statistical inferential methods to analyze data in two-way tables. On the surface, the formulas used (to construct the test statistic, for example) will be unfamiliar to students. However, like all test statistics, it measures the "distance" between observed data and data expected under a hypothesis, and interpreting the *P*-value remains essentially unchanged.

The chapter begins with a discussion of two-way tables and the problem of multiple comparisons. The hypothesis of no relationship between the categorical variables imposes expected cell counts on cells in the table. The chi-square test statistic measures the "distance" between counts expected and counts observed across the table. There is a discussion of assumptions and conditions required for the test's validity. There is also discussion of chi-square test statistic's use as a test for goodness of fit, which is particularly useful in modeling.

This chapter provides opportunity for the instructor to establish connections to topics possibly included in the course to date. The expected cell counts under the model of independence, for example, are easily explained as coming from the Multiplication Rule for Independent Events, possibly studied in Chapter 12. In a r x 2 table, with one dimension (columns, without loss of generality) viewed as success or failure, the number of observations in each cell has the Binomial distribution (Chapter 13) with number of trials equal to row total. In fact, in a more general r x c table, individual cell counts have the more general *multinomial* distribution. The chi-square test statistic, when computed, is equal to the square of the z-test statistic for comparing two proportions, studied in Chapter 21. Hence, the test for independence studied here yields exactly the same P-value in the two-sided test $H_0 : p_1 = p_2$ vs. $H_a : p_1 \neq p_2$. More generally, it can be viewed as good for students to see examples of test statistic constructions that don't follow the same formulaic mold as those T or Z statistics examined earlier.

Chapter 24: Inference for Regression

In Chapters 4 and 5, students learned about scatterplots, correlation, and about fitting the least squares regression line $\hat{y} = a + bx$ to bivariate data. This chapter demonstrates the use of statistical inference in this setting, where now students will view bivariate data as being a random sample taken from a population.   Some students will struggle with the notion of a bivariate population, even though we have spent many chapters studying applications with univariate populations. The heavily symbolic nature of this material is also a challenge. Nevertheless, this material is applied extensively across the social sciences and in some physical sciences.

We propose that the population of bivariate pairs is described by a population regression line, $\mu_y = \alpha + \beta x$, and that the least squares regression line fit earlier is an estimate of this population line.

Conditions necessary for inference are presented to students early in the chapter, when the formal model is presented. We discuss the regression standard error in this context. A computational formula is presented, but requires tedious calculations, so the use of technology is emphasized. Students then encounter their first formal inference regarding regression, which is a significance test on the slope parameter. The hypothesis $H_o : \beta = 0$ is the claim that no linear relationship exists between the explanatory and response variables. Inference is based on an underlying t-distribution. The test statistic here is equivalent to that for testing H_0: Population Correlation $= 0$. Confidence intervals for the regression slope, β, are discussed. Finally, inference is concluded when confidence intervals for the mean response and prediction intervals are explained. The chapter ends with another discussion of checking conditions for inference.

Chapter 25: One-Way Analysis of Variance: Comparing Several Means

In this chapter students learn to compare three or more population means, the objective of Analysis of Variance (ANOVA). Note that in Chapter 19 the primary objective was inference for comparing two population means, but the direct connection of ANOVA to that material lies through the pooled two-sample t-test, which may not have been covered. Analysis of Variance (ANOVA) is concerned with comparing group or treatment means in different samples by comparing variation *between* groups to variation *within* groups.

The early part of the chapter provides motivation for the method to be described – the problem of multiple comparisons. If there are I populations being compared, then there are $I(I-1)/2$ different pairwise comparisons of population means possible (1 vs. 2, 1 vs. 3, 2 vs. 3, etc.). Hence, when there are more than two or three populations being compared, application of the pairwise comparison methods of Chapter 19 will break down – we can't safely compare many parameters by comparing two at a time. This is the problem of multiple comparisons. The F-test for ANOVA looks for evidence of any differences among the I population means. If necessary, we follow with an analysis to decide which of the means differ.

The ANOVA F-test measures evidence for differences between population means by comparing two different kinds of variation in the sample: variation among the group sample means (measured by MSG, the mean square for groups), and variation among individuals within the same group (measured by MSE). If MSG is large compared with MSE, there is stronger evidence of a difference between population means. These two sources of variation in the sample are central to the method. The ANOVA table provides a summary of these sources of variation, along with other components of the analysis – degrees of freedom, the F-statistic and a P-value corresponding to the test.

If the hypothesis of equal means is rejected in favor of differences between means, the next job is to determine which groups differ. We use descriptive statistics and plots (typically boxplots) to determine this.

Throughout the chapter, as with all inferential methods, we focus on conditions necessary for inference. Equal sample sizes are not necessary, although balanced designs offer some advantages (they provide greater power for the ANOVA F-test, for example). Equality of population standard deviations is necessary, and rules of thumb for checking this based on the sample standard deviations are provided.

SAMPLE TESTS

Sample Test for Part I

1. During the years 1058 to 1714, there were 25 different Kings and Queens of an independent Scotland. The durations of their reigns (rounded to the nearest whole year) are given:

4	4	6	12	13	13	16
17	19	23	23	24	25	25
27	28	29	29	31	35	36
37	42	49	58			

   (a) Make a histogram of these data, using 10-year classes, starting with $0 < \text{reign} \le 10$ years, $10 < \text{reign} \le 20$, ..., $50 < \text{reign} \le 60$ years.

   (b) Describe the overall shape of the distribution of reign durations. Is it roughly symmetric, skewed right, skewed left, etc.? Are there any outliers?

   (c) For a brief summary of this distribution, would it be better to use the five-number summary or the mean and standard deviation? Explain your choice, and compute it.

2. The number of eggs laid by a female housefly during her lifetime averages around 400. Suppose that the number of eggs laid varies with a Normal distribution, with mean 400 and standard deviation 50.

   (a) What proportion of female houseflies lay at least 510 eggs?

   (b) What proportion of female houseflies lay between 410 and 480 eggs?

   (c) Complete the following sentence: Only 2% of female houseflies lay more than _____ eggs.

3. Whiskey is aged in oak barrels because the wood induces chemical changes in the whiskey that enhance its flavor. One of these changes is the whiskey's alcohol content, measured as "proof." For example, a "100 proof" whiskey is 50% alcohol by volume, while a "120 proof" whiskey is 60% alcohol by volume.

   In an experiment, 11 batches of whiskey were aged in caskets for varying durations. After aging, each whiskey's proof concentration was measured.

Age:	0	0.5	1	2	3	4	5	6	7	8	9
Proof:	105	104	104	105	106	107	108	110	111	112	113

(a) Make a scatterplot of whiskey Proof against Age. Is there an overall straight-line relationship between Proof and Age?

(b) What is the correlation between Age and Proof? What percent of the observed variation in Proof content is explained by Age?

(c) Find the least-squares regression line for predicting whiskey Proof from the number of years it is aged in an oak casket. What does the slope of the regression line mean in context of this problem?

(d) Use your least-squares regression line computed in (c) to predict the proof content of a whiskey aged in an oak casket for 8 years. Explain why it would not be reasonable to make such a prediction for a whiskey aged 15 years in an oak casket.

4. The following table classifies all flights on Alaska Airlines and America West Airlines departing from 5 western United States Cities during June 1991. Flights are classified by airline (Alaska or America West), by City of Departure (Los Angeles, Phoenix, San Diego, San Francisco, Seattle), and by whether the departure was on time or late.

	Alaska		America West		
	On Time	Late	On Time	Late	
Los Angeles	497	62	694	117	
Phoenix	221	12	4840	415	
San Diego	212	20	383	65	
San Francisco	503	102	320	129	
Seattle	1841	305	201	61	
Total	**3274**	**501**	**6438**	**787**	

(a) For each airline, compute the proportion of flights that were late to depart.
    Alaska Airlines   _____% late
    America West Airlines   _____% late

(b) In each city, compare the proportion of late departs for each airline:

	Alaska Airlines	America West Airlines
Los Angeles	_____% late	_____% late
Phoenix	_____% late	_____% late
San Diego	_____% late	_____% late
San Francisco	_____% late	_____% late
Seattle	_____% late	_____% late

(c) Compare your results in (a) and (b) – you'll notice that the results are somewhat surprising. What phenomenon is demonstrated here? Looking at the original data, can you explain these results?

Sample Test I Solutions

1. (a) A histogram and stemplot are provided.

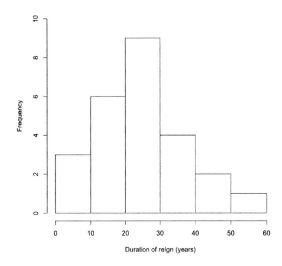

```
0 | 446
1 | 233679
2 | 334557899
3 | 1567
4 | 29
5 | 8
```

(b) The distribution of reign durations is skewed right, with no outliers. (c) Because the distribution is skewed right, the five-number summary provides a better description. The five-number summary is given by: Min = 4, Q1 = 14.5 (average of 13 and 16), Median = 25, Q3 = 33 (average of 31 and 35), and Max = 58 years.

2. Let E denote the number of eggs laid by a randomly selected female housefly. Then E has the Normal distribution with mean 400 and standard deviation 50.

(a) $P(E \geq 510) = P\left(Z \geq \dfrac{510 - 400}{50}\right) = P(Z \geq 2.20) = 1 - 0.9861 = 0.0139$.

(b) $P(410 \leq E \leq 480) = P\left(\dfrac{410 - 400}{50} \leq Z \leq \dfrac{480 - 400}{50}\right) = P(0.20 \leq Z \leq 1.60) = 0.9452 - 0.5793$
$= 0.3659$. (c) We seek the value of E so that the area under the Normal curve to the right of E is 0.02, and the area to the left is 0.98. Hence, $Z = 2.05$ (or $Z = 2.0537$ using software). Hence, E $= 400 + 2.05(50) = 502.5$ eggs. A fly would have to lay about 503 eggs to be in the top 2%.

3. (a) A scatterplot follows. There is a fairly strong straight-line relationship between Age and Proof content.

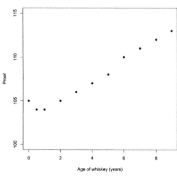

(b) Correlation = r = 0.980. Since R^2 = $(0.980)^2$ = 0.960, or 96%, we say that 96% of the overall variation in Proof content is explained by Age. (c) The regression line is given by $\hat{y} = 103.4475 + 1.0347x$. In context of this problem, each additional year of aging in an oak casket increases the proof content of whiskey by 1.0347. (d) For an 8-year-old whiskey, we predict a proof content of 103.4475 + 1.0347(8) = 111.725. Such a prediction for a 15-year-old whiskey would not be reasonable because we do not have reason to believe that the linear relationship between Age and Proof would extend far beyond 10 years (the maximum in the sample). This would be extrapolation.

4. (a) For Alaska Airlines, 501 out of 501 + 3274 flights were late. This is 501/3775 = 0.133, or 13.3%. For America West Airlines, we have 787/7225 = 0.109, or 10.9% late. (b) For example, in Los Angeles, Alaska Airlines' late rate is 62/(62+497) = .111, or 11.1%. Continuing, we get

	Alaska Airlines	America West Airlines
Los Angeles	11.1% late	14.4 % late
Phoenix	5.2% late	7.9% late
San Diego	8.6% late	14.5% late
San Francisco	16.7% late	28.7 % late
Seattle	14.2% late	23.3 % late

(c) In (a) we determined that, overall, Alaska Airlines has a higher percentage of late flights. In (b) we determined that in each city America West has a higher percentage of late flights. This would seem to be contradictory, and is an example of Simpson's Paradox. The explanation is that Alaska Airlines has more flights departing from San Francisco and Seattle – cities that suffer from higher late rates due to frequent poor weather conditions. Meanwhile, America West flies more out of Los Angeles, Phoenix and San Diego – cities that enjoy lower late rates due to better weather conditions.

Sample Test for Part II

1. Lifetimes of a certain type of light bulb are Normally distributed with mean 2000 hours and standard deviation 240 hours.

    (a) If a single bulb is randomly selected, what is the probability that its lifetime is less than 1900 hours?

(b) If 25 light bulbs are selected randomly, what is the probability that their average lifetime is less than 1900 hours?

2.   At a convenience store, the amount of money customers spend has a right-skewed distribution with mean $6.42 and standard deviation $3.82. If we randomly select 100 customers and record the amount these customers spend, what is the approximate sampling distribution of the sample mean? Explain.

3.   A pharmaceutical company synthesizes a new drug designed to lower blood pressure. In order to investigate the drug's efficacy, it will conduct an experiment. The company has 100 potential subjects of similar age and medical background. Outline the design of an experiment appropriate for determining whether the drug is effective.

4.   For a certain kind of scientific instrument, the standard deviation for measurements of weight is 0.2 grams.

(a) Suppose you weigh an object 100 times and observe a sample mean weight of 31.345 grams. Construct a 90% confidence interval for the weight of this object.

(b) In context of this problem, explain what is meant by 90% confidence.

5.   A soda-bottling machine is calibrated to dispense 20 ounces of soda to each bottle. The actual amount of soda dispensed varies Normally with standard deviation 0.12 ounces. In a random sample of 84 bottles, we observe a mean soda volume of 19.91 ounces. Does this sample provide evidence that the mean volume of soda dispensed to bottles differs from 20 ounces? Carry out a test of hypotheses at the 3% level of significance. Be sure to include appropriate null and alternative hypotheses, a computed *P*-value, and a conclusion stated in context of this problem.

Solutions to Sample Test II

1. (a) We have a single observation, so $P(L < 1900) = P\left(Z < \dfrac{1900 - 2000}{240}\right) = P(Z < -0.42) =$ 0.3372.

(b) We have 25 observations and the question concerns the sample mean, $\bar{L}$. $\mathrm{SE}_{\bar{L}} = \dfrac{240}{\sqrt{25}} = 48$ hours. Hence, $P(\bar{L} < 1900) = P\left(Z < \dfrac{1900 - 2000}{48}\right) = P(Z < -2.08) = 0.0188$.

2. Even though the distribution for individual customer purchases is right skewed, the sampling distribution of the mean of 100 customer purchases will be approximately Normal with mean $6.42 and standard deviation $\dfrac{\sigma}{\sqrt{n}} = \dfrac{3.82}{\sqrt{100}} = \$0.382$.

3. The 100 subjects should be assigned to two groups randomly. It doesn't matter whether you toss a fair coin for each subject (which may lead to groups of unequal size), or simply draw 50

names randomly for assignment to each group. One group of 50 will be given the new drug. The other group will be given a placebo. Subjects will not know which group they've been assigned to. Also, the individuals measuring blood pressure or performing other medical evaluations will not know which group a subject belongs to. We compare average blood pressure reduction in the two groups. This is a randomized, double-blind experiment.

4. (a) For a 90% confidence interval, use $z^* = 1.645$. Hence, the confidence interval is given by

$$\bar{x} \pm z^* \frac{\sigma}{\sqrt{n}} = 31.345 \pm 1.645 \frac{0.2}{\sqrt{100}} = 31.345 \pm 0.033 = 31.312 \text{ to } 31.378 \text{ grams.}$$

(b) If we repeated this experiment, each time measuring the object 100 times and producing a 90% confidence interval for the weight of the object, then in the long run 90% of these intervals would capture the true weight.

5. We test $H_0 : \mu = 20$ ounces vs. $H_a : \mu \neq 20$ ounces. With $\text{SE}_{\bar{x}} = \frac{\sigma}{\sqrt{n}} = \frac{0.12}{\sqrt{84}} = 0.0131$ ounces,

the test statistic is $Z = \frac{19.97 - 20}{0.0131} = -2.29$, so the P-value is $P = 2P(Z \leq -2.29) = 2(0.0110) = 0.0220$. At the 3% level of significance, there is enough evidence to conclude that the mean volume of soda dispensed to all bottles is different from 20 ounces. **Note:** *This is a good example of how statistical significance is not the same as practical significance.*

Sample Test for Part III

1. In an experiment on the effect of brisk, prolonged walking on hemoglobin levels in blood, six subjects were used. The subjects were all similar with respect to many important characteristics. In the experiment, the hemoglobin level of each patent was measured twice: once before a long, brisk walk, and once immediately afterward. The data follow:

Subject:	1	2	3	4	5	6
Pre-walk hemoglobin level	1460	1730	1090	1280	1660	1220
Post-walk hemoglobin level	1380	1540	1130	1160	1640	1260

   Is there enough evidence to conclude that hemoglobin levels decrease on average during prolonged, brisk walking? Conduct a test of hypotheses at the 5% level of significance.

2. Some researchers have investigated whether the air in carpeted rooms contains more bacteria than air in uncarpeted rooms. For an experiment, we have 5 rooms that are carpeted and 5 that are uncarpeted. The rooms are similar in size. After a suitable period of time, the concentration of bacteria in the air is measured in all of the rooms (units are bacteria per cubic foot). The data and summaries are provided:

						$\bar{x}$	s
Carpeted Rooms:	220	210	160	200	230	204	27.0
Uncarpeted Rooms:	160	150	170	190	190	172	17.9

(a) Is there enough evidence to conclude at the 10% level of significance that the air in carpeted rooms contains a higher average concentration of bacteria than that of uncarpeted rooms?

(b) Construct a 90% confidence interval for the difference in mean concentration of bacteria in the air between carpeted rooms and uncarpeted rooms.

3.   In a recent survey, 91 of 149 randomly selected college-aged men indicated that they would be willing to marry a woman of "lower social class." Of 236 randomly selected college-aged women, 117 indicated a willingness to marry a man of lower social class.

(a) Can we conclude that men and women differ in a willingness to marry somebody of lower social class? Carry out a test of hypotheses based on a level of significance of your choice.

(b) Construct a 95% confidence interval for the difference in proportions of men and women willing to marry a person of lower social class.

Solutions to Sample Test III

1. The experiment is a matched pairs design, since each subject is measured before walking and after walking. The six differences (post-walk hemoglobin level – pre-walk hemoglobin level) are given by
$$-80 \quad -190 \quad 40 \quad -120 \quad -20 \quad 40.$$
Let μ denote the population mean reduction in hemoglobin level due to brisk, prolonged walking. If, on average, post-walk hemoglobin level is less than pre-walk hemoglobin level, then $\mu < 0$. The hypotheses of interest are then $H_0 : \mu = 0$ vs. $H_a : \mu < 0$.

From the data, $\bar{x} = -55$ and $s = 92.0326$. Hence, SE $= \dfrac{s}{\sqrt{n}} = \dfrac{92.0326}{\sqrt{6}} = 37.572$. The test statistic is $t = \dfrac{\bar{x} - 0}{\text{SE}} = \dfrac{-55}{37.572} = -1.464$. With df $= 6-1 = 5$, we have $P = 0.1015$ (using software), or $P > 0.10$ using Table C. We do not have enough evidence to reject H_0 at the 5% level of significance. There is not enough evidence to conclude that brisk, prolonged walking reduces hemoglobin level, on average.

2. Let μ_C denote the mean concentration of bacteria in the air for carpeted rooms, and let μ_U denote the corresponding mean for uncarpeted rooms.

(a) We test $H_0 : \mu_C = \mu_U$ vs. $H_a : \mu_C > \mu_U$. Then SE $= \sqrt{\dfrac{s_C^2}{n_C} + \dfrac{s_U^2}{n_U}} = \sqrt{\dfrac{27.0^2}{5} + \dfrac{17.9^2}{5}} = 14.487$.

The test statistic is $t = \dfrac{\bar{x}_C - \bar{x}_U}{\text{SE}} = \dfrac{204 - 172}{14.487} = 2.209$. With df $= \min(5-1, 5-1) = 4$ (using the more conservative Option 2), we have $0.025 < P < 0.05$. Using software, df $= 6.947$ and $P = 0.032$. There is enough evidence to conclude at the 10% level of significance that on average, carpeted rooms have a greater concentration of bacteria in the air than uncarpeted rooms.

(b) We construct a 90% confidence interval for $\mu_C - \mu_U$. With df = 4, we use $t^* = 2.132$. The interval is then $\bar{x}_C - \bar{x}_U \pm t^* SE = (204 - 172) \pm 2.132(14.487) = 32 \pm 30.886 = 1.114$ to 62.886 bacteria per cubic foot. We estimate with 90% confidence that the mean concentration of bacteria in the air of carpeted rooms is exceeds that of uncarpeted rooms by between 1.1 and 62.9 bacteria per cubic foot.

3. Let p_w denote the proportion of women willing to marry a man of lower social class. Let p_m denote the proportion of men willing to marry a woman of lower social class. Our sample proportions are $\hat{p}_m = \dfrac{91}{149} = 0.6107$ and $\hat{p}_w = \dfrac{117}{236} = 0.4958$.

(a) We test $H_0 : p_m = p_w$ vs. $H_a : p_m \neq p_w$. The pooled sample proportion is $\hat{p} = \dfrac{91 + 117}{149 + 236} = 0.5403$, leading to SE $= \sqrt{\hat{p}(1 - \hat{p})\left(\dfrac{1}{n_w} + \dfrac{1}{n_m}\right)} = \sqrt{0.5403(1 - 0.5403)\left(\dfrac{1}{236} + \dfrac{1}{149}\right)} = 0.0521$. The test statistic is then $z = \dfrac{\hat{p}_m - \hat{p}_w}{SE} = 1.35$, and $P = 2P(Z \geq 1.35) = 0.177$. There is little or no evidence in support of a conclusion that men and women differ in their willingness to marry a person of lower social class. Random chance easily explains the observed difference in sample proportions. **Note**: *Students were asked to select a level of significance. This choice should be made before computing a P-value. Remind students that reasonable researchers would not test at the 20% level of significance, for example.*

(b) For 95% confidence, $z^* = 1.96$, and the confidence interval is given by

$$\left(\hat{p}_m - \hat{p}_w\right) \pm 1.96\sqrt{\dfrac{\hat{p}_m\left(1 - \hat{p}_m\right)}{n_m} + \dfrac{\hat{p}_w\left(1 - \hat{p}_w\right)}{n_w}} = (0.6107 - 0.4958) \pm$$

$$1.96\sqrt{\dfrac{0.6107(1 - 0.6107)}{149} + \dfrac{0.4958(1 - 0.4958)}{236}} = 0.0714 \pm 0.1009 = -0.0305 \text{ to } 0.1713.$$ With 95% confidence, the difference between men and women in the proportion willing to marry a person of lower social class is between –0.0305 and 0.1713, or –3.05% and 17.13%. Notice that 0 is contained in this confidence interval, which is consistent with the conclusion reached in (a).

Sample Test for Part IV

1. Does shelf level of display influence sales? A new brand of cereal was sold at 12 different stores of a popular grocery store chain. The 12 stores were assigned randomly to three groups – in 4 stores, the cereal was displayed on a low shelf; in 4 stores it was displayed on a medium-height shelf, and in the other 4 stores it was displayed on a high shelf. The number of units (boxes) of cereal sold was recorded. The data is provided below, along with Minitab output for an ANOVA analysis.

Low:	47	43	46	40	→	$\bar{x}_L = 44$
Medium:	62	68	67	71	→	$\bar{x}_M = 67$
High:	41	39	42	46	→	$\bar{x}_H = 42$

Overall Mean = 51

One-way ANOVA: Sales versus Shelf

```
Source  DF     SS      MS      F       P
C2       2   1544.0   772.0   70.90   0.000
Error    9     98.0    10.9
Total   11   1642.0

S = 3.300   R-Sq = 94.03%   R-Sq(adj) = 92.71%
```

```
                            Individual 95% CIs For Mean Based on
                            Pooled StDev
Level  N    Mean   StDev   --+----------+----------+----------+------
High   4  42.000   2.944   (----*----)
Low    4  44.000   3.162    (----*----)
Med    4  67.000   3.742                             (----*----)
                           --+----------+----------+----------+------
                            40         50         60         70
```

```
Pooled StDev = 3.300
```

Researchers are interested in knowing whether the mean number of units of cereal sold depends on height of the display.

(a) Write the null and alternative hypotheses corresponding to the research question of interest.

(b) State the conditions necessary for use of the ANOVA F test useful for testing these hypotheses. Do these assumptions seem to be reasonable here?

(c) Carry out the test and reach a conclusion in the context of this problem.

2.   A sample of 20 apartments located near a large university is selected. For each apartment, the monthly cost of rent is recorded, along with the size of the apartment (measured in square feet). The output provided summarizes a simple regression model for predicting monthly rent ("Rent", measured in dollars) from apartment size ("Footage", measured in square feet). Refer to that output in answering the following questions.

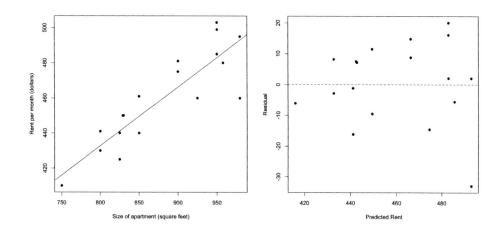

The regression equation is
Rent = 165.42 + 0.334 Footage

Predictor	Coef	SE Coef	T	P
Constant	165.41991	39.40347	4.198	0.001
Footage	0.33424	0.04488	7.447	0.000

S = 13.57   R-Sq = 75.5%   R-Sq(adj) = 74.1%

Additional Information: $\sum (x - \bar{x})^2 = 91352.55$ and $\bar{x} = 875.35$ feet.

(a) Is there significant evidence of a straight-line dependence between size of apartment and rent? Carry out the appropriate test of significance.

(b) Interpret the slope of the fitted regression line in the context of this problem. Construct a 90% confidence interval for the increase in rent associated with an increase in apartment size by one square foot.

(c) Construct a 90% prediction interval for the rent of a 900 square-foot apartment.

(d) Interpret the meaning of R^2 in the context of this problem.

Solutions to Sample Test IV

1. (a) We test $H_0 : \mu_H = \mu_L = \mu_M$ against H_a: The three means are not all equal. Here, μ_L, μ_M, and μ_H represent the mean number of boxes of cereal sold when displayed at low, medium and high shelf heights, respectively. (b) First, we need SRS's from each population, or a randomized comparative experiment. Here we assigned 12 stores to the three groups randomly, so this is a randomized comparative experiment. Second, the three populations need to be Normal, but the ANOVA F test is robust, so it is safe to use with samples this small, provided that there are no outliers. Examining the data, there are clearly no outliers, as every observation lies close to its group mean. Third, the population standard deviations should be the same. Since the ratio of

largest to smallest sample standard deviations is (3.742/2.944 = 1.271) is less than two, we find no evidence against this assumption. All three conditions seem to be met.
(c) From the output, $F = 70.90$. We compare this statistic to the F-distribution with 2 and 9 degrees of freedom, yielding P-value $P < 0.001$ (in the output, P = 0.000). There is overwhelming evidence against H0, and we conclude that the mean sales at different shelf heights are not the same. It seems that sales at the medium shelf height exceed sales at low and high shelf heights on average.

2. (a) We test $H_0 : \beta = 0$ vs. $H_a : \beta \neq 0$. The plot of residuals indicates no evidence of non-linearity, and just one minor outlier. From the output, we find T = 7.447 with df = 20–2 = 18, yielding P = 0.000. There is overwhelming evidence of a linear relationship between apartment size and rent. (b) Each square foot increase in apartment size is associated with an increase in rent of $0.334. With df = 18, we have $t^* = 1.734$. From the output, $b = 0.334$ and $SE_b = 0.04488$. Our 90% confidence interval for β is then $b \pm t^* SE_b = 0.334 \pm 1.734(0.04488) = 0.256$ to 0.412. With 90% confidence, the average increase in rent for each additional square foot of apartment size is $0.256 to $0.412. (c) For a 900 square-foot apartment, we predict a rent of $\hat{y} = \$165.42 + \$0.334(900) = \$466.02$. With df = 18, we have $t^* = 1.734$. Now,

$$SE_{\hat{y}} = s\sqrt{1 + \frac{1}{n} + \frac{\left(x^* - \bar{x}\right)^2}{\sum\left(x - \bar{x}\right)^2}} = 13.57\sqrt{1 + \frac{1}{20} + \frac{\left(900 - 875.35\right)^2}{91352.55}} = 13.949.$$ Hence, a 90%

prediction interval for rent for a 900 square-foot apartment is $466.02 \pm 1.734(\$13.95) = \$441.83$ to 490.21. (d) From the output, $R^2 = 75.5\%$. This means that our straight-line regression model explains 75.5% of the total variation in rent.

Chapter 1 Solutions

1.1: (a) The individuals are the car makes and models. (b) For each individual, the variables recorded are Vehicle type (categorical), Transmission type (categorical), Number of cylinders (usually treated as quantitative), City mpg (quantitative), Highway mpg (quantitative), and Carbon footprint (tons, quantitative).

1.2: Answers will vary. Some possible categorical variables: Whether or not student plays on a sport team or club; Sex; Whether or not the student smokes; Attitude about exercise, etc. Some possible quantitative variables: Weight (kilograms or pounds), Height (centimeters or inches); Resting heart rate (beats per minute); Body mass index (kg/m^2 or lb/ft^2).

1.3: (a) These shares sum to 67.3%. Hence, 100% − 67.3% = 32.7% of the radio audience listens to stations with other formats. (b)

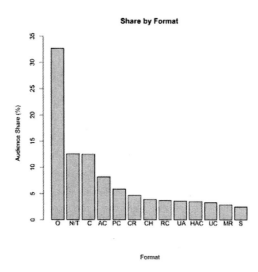

(c) A pie chart would be inappropriate based only on the data presented because the areas of the pie wedges would be relative to the total of the categories presented (67.3%). If you include a wedge for "other" that accounts for 32.7% of the total, a pie chart would be reasonable.

33

1.4: (a) Individuals fall into more than one of the categories. (b) A bar graph follows:

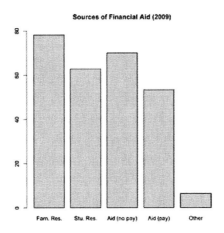

1.5:

A pie chart would make it more difficult to distinguish between the weekend days and the weekdays. Some births are scheduled (induced labor, for example), and probably most are scheduled for weekdays.

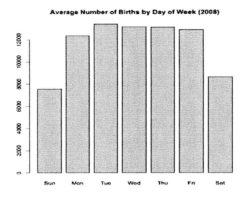

1.6:

Make this histogram by hand, as the instructions suggest:

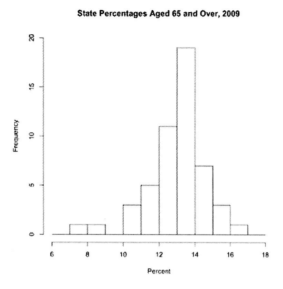

1.7: Use the applet to answer these questions.

1.8: The distribution is roughly symmetric, although one could argue that it is very slightly left-skewed. The center is around 13%. The statewide percentages range from about 7% to 17%. One state has only about 7% of its residents aged 65 or older (Alaska, 7.0%), while another has almost 17% of its residents aged 65 or older (Florida, 16.9%).

1.9: (a) The District of Columbia is the center of Federal government and hence has many, many young professionals, many of whom may not be married. (b) The 26th ordered value falls between 26 and 28. The values in this distribution fall between 20 and 54, but virtually all are between 20 and 34. Again, the District of Columbia is an outlier.

1.10: A stemplot for the state percentages of residents aged 65 years and over:

7	0
8	8
9	
10	0139
11	378888
12	1114456689999
13	012222334556688
14	0011367
15	035
16	9

The midpoint is 13.0%. The spread is 7.0% to 16.9%.

1.11: Here is a stemplot for health expenditure per capita (PPP). Data are rounded to units of hundreds. For example, Argentina's "1332" becomes 13. Stems are thousands, and are split, as prescribed.

```
0   1  1  2  3
0   7  7  7  8  8  8  8  8
1   0  3
1   7
2   3
2   7  7  7  7  8
3   0  3  3  4  4
3   5  5  6  7  8  9
4   4
4   8
5
5
6
6
7   3
```

This distribution is somewhat right-skewed, with a single high outlier (United States). There are two clusters of countries. The center of this distribution is around 25 ($2500 spent per capita), ignoring the outlier. The distribution's spread is from 1 ($100 spent per capita) to 73 ($7300 spent per capita).

1.12: (a) A time plot of Average tuition follows:

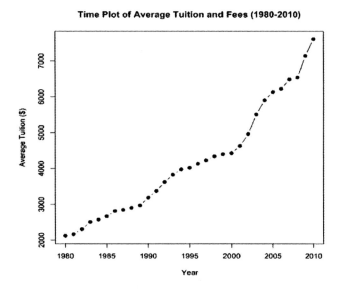

Time Plot of Average Tuition and Fees (1980-2010)

(b) Tuition has steadily climbed during the 30-year period, with sharpest absolute increases in the last 10 years. (c) It would be better to use percent increases, rather than dollar increases. A 10% increase in tuition in 1980 should correspond to a 10% increase in tuition in 2005, but the absolute dollar increases in these cases are very different.

1.13: (a) the students.

1.14: (c) either a pie chart or a bar graph.

1.15: (b) Square footage and average monthly gas bill are both quantitative variables.

1.16: (b) Zip code is a categorical variable. Zip codes are equivalent to town (or zone) names or identifications, and you can't do arithmetic meaningfully with them.

1.17: (b) 20% to 22%.

1.18: (a) 0, 1, 2, 3, 4, 5, 6, 7, 8, 9.

1.19: (c) 30.9 minutes.

1.20: (b) roughly symmetric.

1.21: (b) close to 23.4 minutes. Take the 26th ordered value.

1.22: (c) skewed to the right.

1.23: (a) Individuals are students who have finished medical school. (b) 6, including "Name." "Age" and "USMLE" are quantitative. The others are categorical.

1.24: The categorical variables are (a) Type of wood, (b) Type of water repellent, (d) Paint color. The quantitative variables are (c) Paint thickness and (e) Weathering time.

1.25: "Other colors" should account for 4%. A bar graph would be an appropriate display:

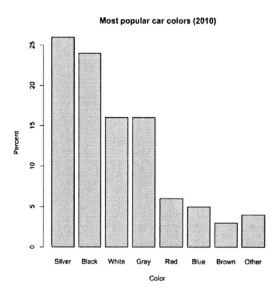

1.26: (a) Bar graphs for the age distribution of Facebook and MySpace users follow.

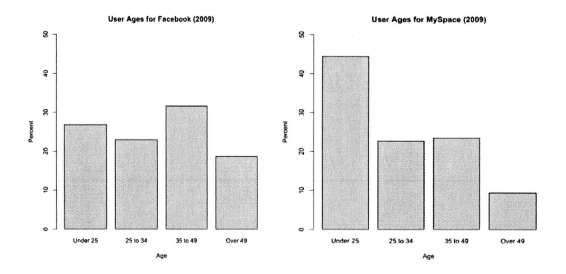

 (b) Comparing these distributions, notice that Facebook users are almost evenly distributed across the age categories, while MySpace users are more heavily concentrated among the youngest demographic. Keeping the age groups arranged in order is important here.

(c) Pie charts follow, and are appropriate since the percentages in each distribution sum to 100%, though note that the percentages for Facebook categories sum to 100.1% due to rounding. Many feel that it is easier to compare distributions using bar graphs. Bar graphs invite comparison by heights, while pie charts require comparing areas. Comparing areas is difficult for many people.

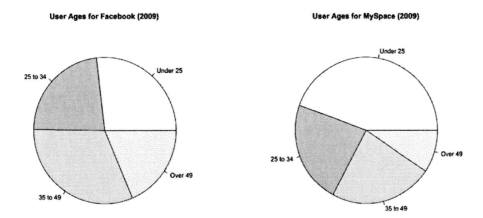

1.27: (a) A bar graph follows. (b) To make a pie chart, you would need to know the total number of deaths in this age group, or (equivalently) the number of deaths due to "other" causes.

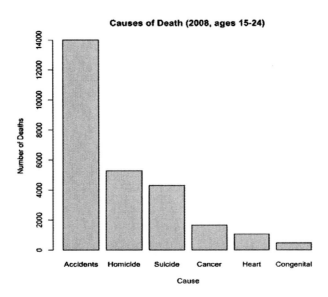

1.28: Perhaps 60-65% of the Hispanic population in the United States is Mexican, while perhaps 10% is Puerto Rican.

1.29: (a) A bar graph is provided below. (b) A pie chat would be inappropriate, because these percentages aren't "shares." That is, the percentages don't sum to 100%.

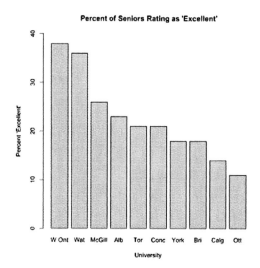

1.30: This distribution is right-skewed, with center around 2 servings, and spread from 0 to 8 servings. There are no outliers. About 12% (9 out of 74) consumed 6 or more servings, and about 35% (26 out of 74) ate fewer than 2 servings (which means 0 or 1 serving).

1.31: (a) Ignoring the four lower outliers, the distribution is roughly symmetric, centered at a score of about 110, and having spread in scores of 86 to 136. (b) 64 of the 78 scores are more than 100. This is 82.1%.

1.32: (a) The distribution is slightly left-skewed. (b) The center is somewhere between 0% and 2.5%. (c) The smallest value is somewhere between –10% and   –12.5%, and the largest value is between 12.5% and 15%. (d) There are about 130 negative returns, although your estimate could differ. This corresponds to about 42%.

1.33:

1. Are you male or female → Histogram (c). There are two outcomes possible, and the difference in frequencies is likely to be smaller than the right-handed/left-handed difference in (2).

2. Are you right-handed or left-handed → Histogram (b), since there are more right-handed people than left handed people, and the difference is likely larger than the sex difference in (1).

3. Heights → Histogram (d). Height distribution is likely to be symmetric.

4. Time spent studying → Histogram (a). The variable takes on more than one value, and time spent studying may well be a right-skewed distribution, with most students spending less time studying, and some students spending more time studying.

1.34: (a) A histogram is provided below. (b) This is an extremely right-skewed distribution. Ratios greater than 1 correspond to an acid with more omega-3 than omega-6. Hence, this would be 7 of the 30 acids, or 23.3%. Most foods' oils aren't this healthy. (c) Of the 7 healthier foods, 5 are types of fish. Furthermore, all of the fish in the list have ratios higher than 1. Clearly, fish provide a healthier ratio of omega-3 to omega-6 acids.

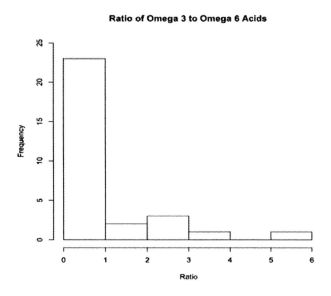

1.35:

(a) States vary in population, so you would expect more nurses in California than in New Hampshire, for example. Nurses per 100,000 provides a better measure of how many nurses are available to serve a state's population. (b) A histogram is provided below. The District of Columbia, South Dakota, and Massachusetts are the three states different from the others. Perhaps they could be considered outliers. It's difficult to know why these states would have more nurses than other states.

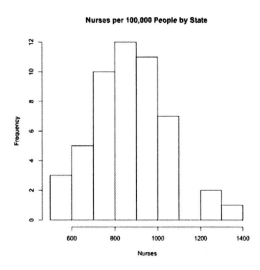

1.36: (a) Since the countries have varying populations, it is easier to compare them by emissions per person than by total emissions. (b) Round data to the nearest tenth place, and use whole numbers as stems. The United States and Canada are the extreme outliers in this data set – a larger economy tends to coincide with more fuel consumption. The distribution is right-skewed, with center near 4 and a range of 0 to about 19.

0	001113333689
1	344589
2	3
3	
4	011479
5	
6	089
7	7
8	2378
9	68
10	58
11	
12	
13	
14	
15	
16	9
17	
18	9

1.37: Here is a stemplot for the pups data, using split stems at the tens place. This is a right-skewed distribution, with center around 25 pups and spread of 17 pups to 56 pups. There were several extremely good years for pups, resulting in more than 45 births.

```
1   777789
2   0122344
2   555579
3   12333
3   899
4   3
4   77
5   4
5   6
```

1.38: (a) It is natural for people to round to common multiples like 5 and 10. In fact, multiples of 5 are the other common occurrence.

Women		Men
	0	033334
986	0	66679999
22222221	1	222222
88888888755555	1	5558
4440	2	44300
7	2	
	3	0
6	3	

Both distributions are somewhat right-skewed. The women's distribution is shifted a bit to the right of the men, suggesting that they tend to study a bit more. One woman claimed to study 360 minutes (6 hours) per night.

1.39: A time plot of seal pups. The decline in population is not described by the stemplot made in Exercise 1.37.

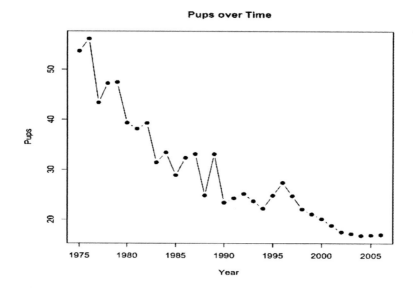

1.40: Rates are appropriate (rather than number of accidents) because the group sizes are different. If marijuana did not increase with the rate of accidents, then you would still have more accidents (by count) in the largest groups.

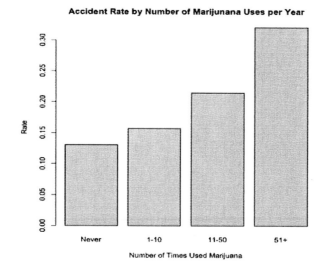

Accident rates go up with the number of times drivers use marijuana. The data are "observational," and no cause-and-effect conclusion is reasonable.

1.41: Coins with earlier (lower) dates are older, and rarer. Hence, there are more coins with larger dates (newer coins) than with smaller dates (older coins).

1.42: (a) Here are stem and split-stem plots. In both cases, stems denote the hundreds place. The slight right skew in the distribution is more apparent in the original version, but can be seen in both versions of the stem plot.

```
6  0 3 5 5 7
7  0 1 2 4 4 8 8 9 9 9
8  1 1 3 6 6 7
9  0 6
```

```
6  0 3
6  5 5 7
7  0 1 2 4 4
7  8 8 9 9 9
8  1 1 3
8  6 6 7
9  0
9  6
```

(b) The center of this distribution is around 780 millimeters. The distribution is somewhat right-skewed. There are no outliers. (c) It seems that El Niño strength is associated with volume of monsoon rains. No cause-and-effect relationship can be established, however, since there may be another factor driving both strong El Niño weather patterns and reduced monsoon rain volume.

1.43: (a) Graph (a) appears to show the greatest increase, even though both plots describe the same data. Vertical scaling can impact one's perception of the data. (b.) In both graphs, tuition starts around $2000 and rises to $7700. Again, both plots describe the same data.

1.44: (a) It seems as though winter quarters are typically associated with lower housing starts. (b) and (c) Over the long run, housing starts have risen, except for the most recent years, which correspond with the 2007–10 economic "crisis."

1.45: (a) A time plot of ozone hole size (area) is provided below. There is a trend, as well as year-to-year variability. The hole has grown a lot over the period studied, but may have leveled out in recent years.

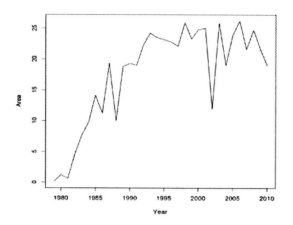

(b) A stemplot of ozone hole size (area) is provided below. The midpoint is 19.3 millions of km^2. A stemplot fails to capture the relationship between size of hole and year.

0	0004
0	79
1	0114
1	899999
2	11222333444
2	5556

1.46: Use the Applet to investigate this problem.

1.47 and 1.48 are Web-based exercises.

Chapter 2 Solutions

2.1: Mean breaking strength = 30841 pounds. Only 6 pieces have strengths less than the mean. The mean is so small relative to the data because of the sharp left skew (low outliers).

2.2: The mean expenditure for all countries including the United States is $2332.20. The mean when the United States is excluded is $2186.53. Hence the United States as an outlier increases the mean by about $145.67, even with as many as 34 other countries.

2.3: The mean travel time is 31.25 minutes. The median travel time is 22.5 minutes. The mean is significantly larger than the median due to the right skew in the distribution of times.

2.4: The mean is larger than the median, for surely the distribution of home prices is right skewed.

2.5: A histogram is given below. Note the right skew. Hence, the mean is larger than the median. Here, the mean is 4.61 and the median is 3.95 tons per person.

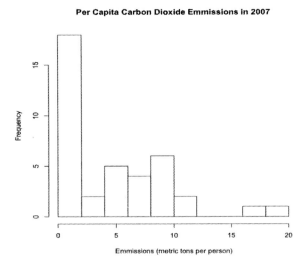

2.6: (a) and (b) A back to back stemplot is provided. The five-number summaries are tabulated. (c) It seems that the offensive line players are heavier. Perhaps there is one outlier—one 325-pound defensive lineman.

	Minimum	Q1	Median	Q3	Maximum
Offensive line	304	309.5	319	331.5	344 pounds
Defensive line	280	285	300	305	325 pounds

Offensive line		Defensive line
	28	0 5
	29	8
4 4	30	0 5 5
9 8 5	31	
5 4	32	5
8	33	
4	34	

2.7: (a) Minimum = 9, Q1 = 16, Median = 18, Q3 = 22, Maximum = 51. (b) The boxplot shows right skew in the distribution of MPG values.

2.8: For these data, Q1 = 10, Q3 = 30, and so IQR = 30 – 10 = 20 minutes. Hence, Q1 – 1.5 x IQR = 10 – 1.5 × 20 = –20 minutes. Obviously no times can be negative, so no outliers are in the left tail. Q3 + 1.5 × IQR = 30 + 1.5 × 20 = 60 minutes. Hence, the "60" would not be considered an outlier, but it's close.

2.9: IQR = 22 – 16 = 6, so Q3 + 1.5 × IQR = 22 + 1.5 × 6 = 31. There are 5 values greater than 31 that would be identified as potential outliers (33, 35, 41, 41, 51). Since Q1 – 1.5 × IQR = 16 – 1.5 × 6 = 7, there are no potential outliers below 7.

2.10: (a) $\bar{x}$ = (5.2 + 13.8 + 8.6 + 16.8)/4 = 44.4/4 = 11.1 picocuries. (b) The standard deviation can be computed in steps:

x	5.2	13.8	8.6	16.8
$x - \bar{x}$	–5.9	2.7	–2.5	5.7
$(x-\bar{x})^2$	34.81	7.29	6.25	32.49

Hence, $s^2 = \dfrac{1}{n-1}\sum(x-\bar{x})^2 = \dfrac{1}{4-1}(34.81+7.29+6.25+32.49) = 26.94667$

So $s = \sqrt{s^2} = \sqrt{29.94667} = 5.19$ picocuries.

2.11: Both data sets have the same mean and standard deviation (about 7.5 and 2.0, respectively). However, construct simple stemplots to reveal that Data A have a very left-skewed distribution, while Data B have a slightly right-skewed distribution.

2.12: (a) No. The distribution isn't symmetric. (b) Yes. The distribution is symmetric and mound-shaped with no severe outliers. (c) No. The distribution is strongly right-skewed.

2.13: Group 1: $\bar{x} = 23.7500$, $s = 5.06548$. Group 2: $\bar{x} = 14.0833$, $s = 4.98102$. Group 3: $\bar{x} = 15.7778$, $s = 5.76146$.

2.14: Both groups (developing countries and developed countries) have right-skewed distributions for unpaid parking tickets. Comparing, developing countries' diplomats tend to have more unpaid tickets. National income alone, however, does not explain countries whose diplomats have more or fewer unpaid tickets.

2.15: (b) 167.48

2.16: (b) 168.25

2.17: (b) 151.6, 163.5, 168.25, 174.3, 177.6

2.18: (c) the mean is greater than the median.

2.19: (b) 50%.

2.20: (c) the five-number summary.

2.21: (c) 8.2.

2.22: (a) $0 \le s$.

2.23: (b) seconds.

2.24: (a) the median.

2.25: The distribution of incomes in this group is almost certainly right-skewed, so the mean is $58,762 and the median is $46,931.

2.26: In both cases (for the under 35 crowd and for all families), the distribution of account sizes is right-skewed. Lots of people have very small retirement savings accounts.

2.27: With 842 colleges (an even number), the median location is (842 + 1)/2 = 421.5, so the median is computed by averaging the 421st and 422nd endowments sizes. The first quartile, Q1, is found by taking the median of the first 421 endowments (when sorted). This would be the (421+1)/2 = 211th endowment. Similarly, Q3 is found as the 632nd endowment (211 endowments above the median).

2.28: (a) Minimum = 23040, Q1 = 31975, Median = 31975, Q3 = 32710, Maximum = 33650. (b) Notice that the Minimum is much farther from Q1 than the Maximum is from Q3. This suggests a long left tail, consistent with a left-skewed distribution.

2.29: The five-number summaries for the three species are tabulated below. Boxplots don't add much information not already present in the stemplots.

	Minimum	Q1	Median	Q3	Maximum
Bihai	46.34	46.71	47.12	48.25	50.26
Red	37.4	38.07	39.16	41.69	43.09
Yellow	34.57	35.45	36.11	36.82	38.13

2.30: (a) Median = 2, Q1 = 1, Q3 = 4, (b) $\bar{x}$ = (15)(0) + (11)(1) + (15)(2) + (11)(3) + (8)(4) + (5)(5) + (3)(6) + (3)(7) + (3)(8)]/74 = 194/74 = 2.62 servings. This is larger than the median because the distribution is right-skewed.

2.31: A histogram of the survival times follows. The distribution is strongly right-skewed, with center around 100 days, and spread 0 to 600 days. (b) Because of the extreme right skew, we should use the five-number summary: 43, 82.5, 102.5, 151.5, 598 days. Notice that the median is closer to Q1 than to Q3.

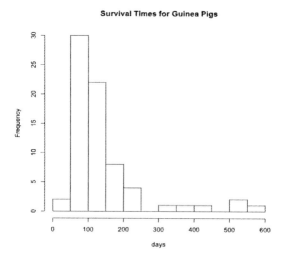

2.32: (a) If countries or years have very different numbers of babies born, it would be unreasonable to compare across years or across countries by counts. (b) 4,243,333 babies. (c) The distribution is left-skewed. (d) The median is the 2,121,667[th] baby weight, and falls in the interval 3000 to 3499 grams. Q3 is in the interval 3500 to 3999 grams. Q1 is in the interval 2500 to 2999 grams.

2.33: (a) Symmetric distributions. (b) Removing the outliers reduces both means and both standard deviations.

2.34: (a) Mean (green arrow) moves along with moving point. Median (red arrow) points to middle point (rightmost nonmoving point). (b) Mean follows moving point. When moving point passes rightmost fixed point, median moves with it until moving point passes leftmost fixed point—then median stays there.

2.35: (a) The 6th observation must be placed at median for the original 5 observations. (b) No matter where you put the 7th observation, the median is one of the two repeated values above.

2.36: Both distributions are very similar: On weekdays more babies are born, and there is from weekday to weekday, though Mondays appear to have slightly fewer births. On weekends, fewer births take place. Of course, many more births take place in the United States.

2.37: The mean for all 51 entries is 8.4%, far from the national percentage of 12.5%. You can't average averages. Some states, like California and Florida, are larger and should carry more weight in the national percentage. Indeed, there are more people over the age of 65 living in Florida than there are residents in Wyoming.

2.38: More than half of all American households do not carry credit card debt.

2.39: (a) Pick any four numbers all the same: for instance, (4,4,4,4) or (6,6,6,6). (b) (0,0,10,10). (c) There is more than one possible answer for (a), but not for (b).

2.40: The TI-89 calculator used by the author reported $s = 1$ for the list

100,000,000,001 100,000,000,002 100,000,000,003. At some point, the calculator will fail… but for virtually any practical setting, a decent calculator will correctly compute.

2.41: Lots of answers are possible. Start by insuring that the median is 7, by "locking" 7 as the 3rd smallest value. Then, adjust the minimum or maximum accordingly to acquire a mean of 10 (so they sum to 50). One solution: 5 6 7 8 24.

2.42: Lots of answers are possible. One solution: (–100, 1, 2, 3, 4, 5, 6).

2.43: (a) Weight losses that are negative correspond to weight *gains*. (b) A side-by-side boxplot (a version that reports suspected outliers using the 1.5 IQR rule) is provided below. Gastric banding seems to produce higher weight losses, typically. (c) It's better to measure weight loss relative to initial weight. (d) If the subjects that dropped out had continued, the difference between these groups would be as great or greater because many of the "lifestyle" dropouts had negative weight losses (i.e., weight gains), which would pull that group down.

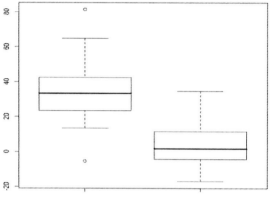

Treatment (1 = Gastric Banding, 2 = Lifestyle Intervention)

2.44: The distribution of Candiens players' salaries is very right-skewed. The median salary is $1,425,000 (while the mean is $2,520,646, consistent with a strong right-skew). The middle half of players earn between $756,250 and $4,416,500, although a handful earn more than $5,000,000.

2.45: The distribution of average returns is skewed-left. Most years, average return is positive. Returns range from about –40% to 40%, with the median return about 16%.

Average Performance

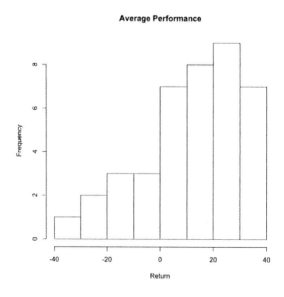

2.46: Comparing side-by-side boxplots, Lavender seems to produce the highest customer expenditures.

2.47: Based on side-by-side boxplots, lean people spend relatively more time active, but there is little difference in the time these groups spend lying down.

2.48: A side-by-side boxplot of tip results follows. Good weather forecasts generally yielded better tips, while there was little to no difference between a bad forecast and no forecast.

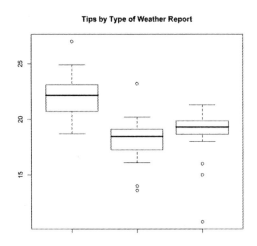

2.49: The distribution is also right-skewed. The median salary was $300, and the middle half of salaries were between $167.50 and $450. A handful of Canadians made $1000 or more. One earned $2200.

2.50: (a) 7.0, 12.1, 13.0, 13.6, 16.9. (b) A boxplot follows and suggests rough symmetry. There are three outliers (7.0% for Alaska, 8.8% for Utah, and 16.9% for Florida) using the 1.5 IQR rule.

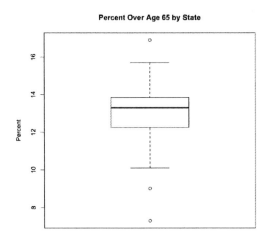

2.51: (a) Min = 0.0272, Q1 = 0.6449, Median = 3.954, Q3 = 8.1555, Max = 18.9144. Notice that the maximum is farther from Q3 than the minimum is from Q1. This suggests right skew. (b) IQR = 8.1555 – 0.6449 = 7.5106. Hence, 1.5 × IQR = 11.2659. Now Q1 – 1.5 × IQR = 0.6449 – 11.2659 <0, so no values are more than 1.5 IQR's below Q1. Also, Q3 + 1.5 × IQR = 8.1555 + 11.2659 = 19.4214, so there are no high outliers. This rule is rather conservative – most people would easily call the United States' value (18.9144) a far outlier, and perhaps Canada would be considered an outlier, too.

2.52: There are no salaries greater than $9,906,875. This is the salary that is 1.5 IQRs greater than Q3.

2.53: Any of the 11 incomes more than $873.75 would be considered an outlier by the 1.5 IQR rule.

2.54 and 2.55 are Web-based exercises.

Chapter 3 Solutions

3.1. Sketches will vary. Use them to confirm that students understand the meaning of (a) symmetric and (b) skewed to the left.

3.2. (a) It is on or above the horizontal axis everywhere, and because it forms a 1/5 × 5 rectangle, the area beneath the curve is 1. (b) One-fifth of accidents occur in the first mile: This is a 1/5 × 1 rectangle, so the proportion is 1/5, or 0.20. (c) The length of path along the stream is (1.3 – 0.8) = 1/2 mile. Hence, this is a (1/2)(1/5) rectangle, so the proportion is 1/10, or 0.10. (d) The part of the bike path more than a mile from either road is the 3-mile stretch from the 1-mile marker to the 4-mile marker. This is a (3)(1/5) rectangle, so the proportion is 3/5, or 0.6.

3.3: $\mu = 2.5$, which is the obvious balance point of the rectangle. The median is also 2.5 because the distribution is symmetric (so that median = mean), and half the area under the curve lies to the left and half to the right of 2.5.

3.4: (a) Mean is C, median is B (the right skew pulls the mean to the right). (b) Mean is B, median is B (this distribution is symmetric). (c) Mean is A, median is B (the left skew pulls the mean to the left).

3.5: Here is a sketch of the distribution of the Normal curve describing thorax lengths of fruit flies. The tick marks are placed at the mean, and at one, two and three standard deviations above and below the mean for scale.

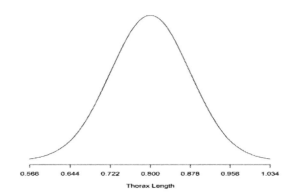

3.6: Use the sketch from Exercise 3.5 and shade in the appropriate areas to answer these questions. (a) 99.7% of all thorax lengths are within three standard deviations of the mean, or between 0.566 mm and 1.034 mm. (b) This is the area one or more standard deviations above the mean. Hence, 16% of thorax lengths exceed 0.878 mm.

3.7: (a) In 95% of all years, monsoon rain levels are between 688 and 1016 mm—two standard deviations above and below the mean: $852 \pm 2(82) = 688$ to 1016 mm. (b) The driest 2.5% of monsoon rainfalls are less than 688 mm; this is more than two standard deviations below the mean.

3.8: Alysha's standardized score is $z = \dfrac{670-516}{116} = 1.33$. John's standardized score is $z = \dfrac{26-21}{5.3} = 0.94$. Alysha's score is relatively higher than John's.

3.9: We need to use the same scale, so recall that 6 feet = 72 inches. A woman 6 feet tall has standardized score $z = \dfrac{72-64.3}{2.7} = 2.85$ (quite tall, relatively). A man 6 feet tall has standardized score $z = \dfrac{72-69.9}{3.1} = 0.68$. Hence, a woman 6 feet tall is 2.85 standard deviations taller than average for women. A man 6 feet tall is only 0.68 standard deviations above average for men.

3.10: (a) 0.0778. (b) 0.9222. (c) 0.9906. (d) 0.9906 – 0.0778 = 0.9128.

3.11: Let x be the monsoon rainfall in a given year. (a) $x \leq 697$ mm corresponds to $z \leq \dfrac{697-852}{82} = -1.89$, for which Table A gives 0.0294 = 2.94%. (b) $683 < x < 1022$

corresponds to $\dfrac{683-852}{82} < z < \dfrac{1022-852}{82}$, or $-2.06 < z < 2.07$. This proportion is

0.9808 – 0.0197 = 0.9611 = 96.11%.

3.12: (a) Let x be the MCAT score of a randomly selected student. Then $x > 30$ corresponds to $z > \dfrac{30-25.0}{6.4} = 0.78$, for which Table A gives 0.7823 as an area to the left. Hence, the answer is 1 – 0.7823 = 0.2177, or 21.77%. (b) $20 \leq x \leq 25$ corresponds to $\dfrac{20-25.0}{6.4} \leq z \leq \dfrac{20-25.0}{6.4}$, or – $0.78 \leq z \leq 0$. Hence, using Table A, the area is 0.5000 – 0.2177 = 0.2833, or 28.33%.

3.13: (a) We want the value such that the proportion below is 0.15. Using Table A, looking for an area as close as possible to 0.1500, we find this value has $z = -1.04$ (software would give the more precise $z = -1.0364$). (b) Now we want the value such that the proportion above is 0.70. This means that we want a proportion of 0.30 below. Using Table A, looking for an area as close to 0.3000 as possible, we find this value has $z = -0.52$ (software gives $z = -0.5244$).

3.14: Since the Normal distribution is symmetric, its median and mean are the same. Hence, the median MCAT score is 25.0. Now, following Example 3.11, the first quartile has $z = -0.67$, since the area under the curve to the left of the first quartile is 0.2500 (software gives $z = -0.6745$). Similarly, the third quartile has $z = 0.67$ since the area under the curve to the left of the third quartile is 0.7500. Hence, the first quartile is 25.0 – (0.67)(6.4) = 20.71, and the third quartile is 25.0 + (0.67)(6.4) = 29.29.

3.15. (b) Income distributions are typically skewed to the right. Also, in a forest, there are likely to be many more relatively short trees than there are relatively tall trees. Although the distribution of home prices in a very large metropolitan area tends to be right-skewed, perhaps in a suburb, where the houses tend to be similar, the distribution is more symmetric.

3.16. (a) Mean and standard deviation tell you center and spread, which is all you need for a Normal distribution.

3.17. (b) The curve is centered at 2.

3.18. (b) Estimating a standard deviation is more difficult than estimating the mean, but among the three options, 2 is clearly too small and 5 is clearly too large, so 3 seems to be the most reasonable for the standard deviation.

3.19. (b) $266 \pm 2(16) = 234$ to 298 days.

3.20: (c) 130 is two standard deviations above the mean, so 2.5% of adults have IQs of 130 or more.

3.21: (b) $z = \dfrac{127 - 100}{15} = 1.80.$

3.22: (c) $1 - 0.9664 = 0.0336.$

3.23: (a) 0.2266.

3.24: (c) About 96%. As in Exercise 3.21, $z = 1.80$, and by Table A, the proportion below is 0.9641.

3.25: Sketches will vary, but should be some variation on the one shown here: the peak at 0 should be "tall and skinny," while near 1, the curve should be "short and fat."

3.26. For each distribution, take the mean plus or minus two standard deviations. For mildly obese people, this is $373 \pm 2(67) = 239$ to 507 minutes. For lean people, this is $526 \pm 2(107) = 312$ to 740 minutes.

3.27. 70 is two standard deviations below the mean (that is, it has standard score $z = -2$), so about 2.5% (half of the outer 5%) of adults would have WAIS scores below 70.

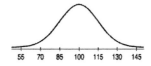

3.28: (a) 0.1056. (b) $1 - 0.1056 = 0.8944$. (c) $1 - 0.9850 = 0.0150$. (d) $0.9850 - 0.1056 = 0.8794$.

3.29: (a) We want the proportion less than z to be 0.60, so looking up a left-tail area of 0.6000 in the table, we find $z = 0.25$. (Software gives $z = 0.2533$.) (b) If 15% are more than z, then 85% are less than or equal to z. Hence, $z = 1.04$. (Software gives $z = 1.0364$.)

3.30: (a) Let x be the length of a thorax for a randomly selected fruit fly. (a) $x < 0.7$ mm corresponds to $z < \dfrac{0.7 - 0.800}{0.078} = -1.28$. Hence, the area is 0.1003, or 10.03%. (b) $x > 1$ mm corresponds to $z > \dfrac{1 - 0.800}{0.078} = 2.56$. Hence, the area is $1 - 0.9948 = 0.0052$, or 0.52%. (c) 0.7 mm $< x < 1$ mm corresponds to $-1.28 < z < 2.56$. Hence, the area is $0.9948 - 0.1003 = 0.8945$, or 89.45%.

3.31: About 0.2119: The proportion of rainy days with rainfall pH below 5.0 is about 0.2119: $x < 5.0$ corresponds to $z < \dfrac{5.0 - 5.43}{0.54} = -0.80$, for which Table A gives 0.2119.

3.32: (a) Less than 2% of runners have heart rates above 130 bpm: For the $N (104, 12.5)$ distribution, $x > 130$ corresponds to $z > \dfrac{130 - 104}{12.5} = 2.08$. Table A gives $1 - 0.9812 = 0.0188 = 1.88\%$. (b) About 50% of nonrunners have heart rates above 130 bpm: For the $N (130, 17)$ distribution, $x > 130$ corresponds to $z > 0$.

3.33: About 0.9876: For the $N (0.8750, 0.0012)$ distribution, $0.8720 < x < 0.8780$ corresponds to $\dfrac{0.8720 - 0.8750}{0.0012} < z < \dfrac{0.8780 - 0.8750}{0.0012}$, or $-2.50 < z < 2.50$, for which Table A gives $0.9938 - 0.0062 = 0.9876$.

3.34: Let x be the BMI for a randomly selected young woman aged 20 to 29. (a) Being underweight corresponds to $x < 18.5$. This gives $z < \dfrac{18.5 - 26.5}{6.4} = -1.25$. Hence, 0.1056, or 10.56% are underweight. (b) Being obese corresponds to $x > 30$. This gives $z > \dfrac{30 - 26.5}{6.4} = 0.55$. Hence, $1 - 0.7088 = 0.2912$, or 29.12% are obese.

For problems 3.35 – 3.38, let x denote the gas mileage of a randomly selected vehicle type from the population of 2010 model vehicles (excluding the high mileage outliers, as mentioned).

3.35: Cars with better mileage than the Camaro correspond to $x > 19$, which corresponds to $z > \dfrac{19 - 20.3}{4.3} = -0.30$. Hence, this proportion is $1 - 0.3821 = 0.6179$, or 61.79%.

3.36: We need the proportion below our vehicle's mileage to be 0.10. Looking for 0.1000 as a left-tail area in the table gives $z = -1.28$, so our vehicle would need mileage to be $20.3 - (1.28)(4.3) = 14.80$ mpg. A car would need to have gas mileage of 14.80 mpg or lower to be in the bottom 10% for all 2010 models.

3.37: As seen in Example 3.11, the first and third quartiles have $z = -0.67$ and $z = 0.67$, respectively. Hence, the first quartile is $20.3 - (0.67)(4.3) = 17.42$ mpg, and the third quartile is $20.3 + (0.67)(4.3) = 23.18$ mpg.

3.38: The first quintile is the mileage so that 20% of models have a lower mileage. This has $z = -0.84$ (find the number closest to 0.2000 in Table A as a left-tail area). Similarly, the second, third and fourth quintiles have $z = -0.25$, $z = 0.25$ and $z = 0.84$, respectively. The first quintile is then $20.3 - (0.84)(4.3) = 16.69$ mpg. Similarly, the second, third, and fourth quintiles are, respectively, 19.23 mpg, 21.38 mpg, and 23.91 mpg.

3.39: If William scored 32, his percentile is simply the proportion of all scores lower than 32. Let x be the MCAT score for a randomly selected student that took it. The event $x < 32$ corresponds to $z < \dfrac{32 - 25.0}{6.4} = 1.09$. Hence, 0.8621 is the corresponding proportion, or 86.21%. William's MCAT score is the 86.21 percentile.

3.40: About 0.0031: a score of 1600 standardizes to $z = \dfrac{1600 - 1021}{211} = 2.74$, for which Table A gives a proportion of 0.9969 below. Therefore, the proportion above 1600 (which are reported as 1600) is about 0.0031.

3.41: If x is the height of a randomly selected woman in this age group, we want the proportion corresponding to $x > 69.9$ inches. This corresponds to $z > \dfrac{69.9 - 64.3}{2.7} = 2.07$, which has proportion $1 - 0.9808 = 0.0192$, or 1.92%.

3.42: The distribution of weights of women is right-skewed. First, the mean weight is larger than the median weight. Another clue comes from the greater distance between the median and third quartile ($173.7 - 144.0 = 29.7$) than between the median and first quartile ($144 - 124.1 = 19.9$).

3.43: (a) Let x be a randomly selected man's SAT math score. $x > 750$ corresponds to $z > \dfrac{750 - 534}{118} = 1.83$. Hence, the proportion is $1 - 0.9664 = 0.0336$. (b) Let x be a randomly selected woman's SAT math score. $x > 750$ corresponds to $z > \dfrac{750 - 500}{112} = 2.23$. Hence, the proportion is $1 - 0.9871 = 0.0129$.

3.44: If the distribution is Normal, it must be symmetric about its mean—and in particular, the 10th and 90th percentiles must be equal distances below and above the mean—so the mean is 250 points. If 225 points below (above) the mean is the 10th (90th) percentile, this is 1.28 standard deviations below (above) the mean, so the distribution's standard deviation is 225/1.28 = 175.8 points.

3.45. (a) About 0.6% of healthy young adults have osteoporosis (the cumulative probability below a standard score of −2.5 is 0.0062). (b) About 31% of this population of older women has osteoporosis: The BMD level that is 2.5 standard deviations below the young adult mean would standardize to −0.5 for these older women, and the cumulative probability for this standard score is 0.3085.

3.46. (a) There are two somewhat low IQs—72 qualifies as an outlier by the $1.5 \times$ IQR rule, while 74 is on the boundary. However, for a small sample, this stemplot looks reasonably Normal. (b) We compute $x = 105.84$ and $s = 14.27$ and find:

23/31 = 74.2% of the scores in the range $x \pm 1s$, or 91.6 to 120.1, and

29/31 = 93.5% of the scores in the range $x \pm 2s$, or 77.3 to 134.4.

For an exactly Normal distribution, we would expect these proportions to be 68% and 95%. Given the small sample, this is reasonably close agreement.

```
 7  24
 7
 8
 8  69
 9  1 3
 9  68
10  023334
10  578
11  11222444
11  89
12  0
12  8
13  02
```

3.47: (a) 145,000/1,568,835 = 0.0924, or 9.24%. (b) There are 50,860 + 145,000 = 195,860 students with ACT score 28 or higher. This is 195,860/1,568,835 = 0.1248, or 12.48%. (c) If x is the ACT score, then $x > 28$ corresponds to $z > \dfrac{28 - 21.0}{5.2} = 1.35$, so the corresponding proportion is $1 - 0.9115 = 0.0885$, or 8.85%.

3.48: (a) The mean (5.43) is almost identical to the median (5.44), and the quartiles are similar distances from the median: $M - Q1 = 0.39$ while $Q3 - M = 0.35$. This suggests that the distribution is reasonably symmetric. (b) $x < 5.05$ corresponds to $z < \dfrac{5.05 - 5.43}{0.54} = -0.70$, and $x < 5.79$ corresponds to $z < \dfrac{5.79 - 5.43}{0.54} = 0.67$. Table A gives these proportions as 0.2420 and 0.7486. These are quite close to 0.25 and 0.75, which is what we would expect for the quartiles, so they are consistent with the idea that the distribution is close to Normal.

3.49: (a) A histogram is provided below, and appears to be roughly symmetric with no outliers. (b) Mean = 544.42, Median = 540, Standard deviation = 61.24, Q1 = 500, Q3 = 580. The mean and median are close, and the distances of each quartile to the median are equal. These results are consistent with a Normal distribution. (c) If x is the score of a randomly selected GSU entering student, then we are assuming x has the $N(544.42, 61.24)$ distribution. The proportion of GSU students scoring higher than the national average of 501 corresponds to the proportion of $x > 501$, or $z > \dfrac{501 - 544.42}{61.24} = -0.71$, or $1 - 0.2389 = 0.7611$, or 76.11%. (d) In fact, 1776 entering GSU students scored higher than 501, which represents 1776/2417 = 0.7348, or 73.48%. The nominal Normal probability in (c) fits the actual data well.

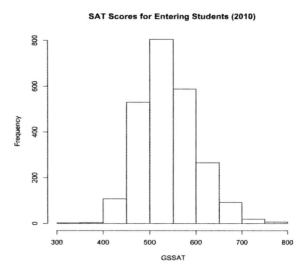

3.50: (a) One possible histogram is provided. The mean is 847.58 mm, and the median is 860.8 mm. (b) The histogram shows a left skew; this makes the mean lower than the median.

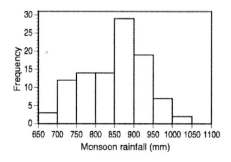

3.51: (a) The 65 Canadians with earnings greater than $375 represent $65/200 = 0.325$, or 32.5%. $x > 375$ corresponds to $z > \dfrac{375 - 350.30}{292.20} = 0.08$, which has proportion $1 - 0.5319 = 0.4681$, or 46.81% above.   (b) $x < 0$ corresponds to $z < \dfrac{0 - 350.30}{292.20} = -1.20$, or 0.1151, or 11.51%. (c) The Normal distribution model predicts 11.5% of Canadians to earn less than $0, while (of course) none do. This is a substantial error since the Normal model predicts 11.5% of values more than 375, where we actually observed 32.5% more than 375. The standard deviation ($292.20) is large relative to the average ($350.30), which suggests a strong right-skew in the distribution, given that no values can be negative. In this application, the data seem to be far from Normal in distribution.

3.52: (a) The applet shows an area of 0.6826 between -1.000 and 1.000, while the 68–95–99.7 rule rounds this to 0.68. (b) Between -2.000 and 2.000, the applet reports 0.9544 (compared with the rounded 0.95 from the 68–95–99.7 rule). Between -3.000 and 3.000, the applet reports 0.9974 (compared with the rounded 0.997).

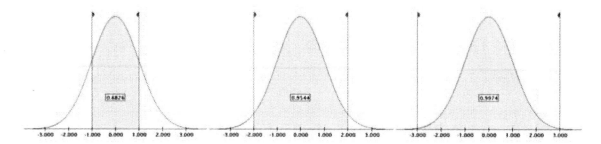

3.53: Because the quartiles of any distribution have 50% of observations between them, we seek to place the flags so that the reported area is 0.5. The closest the applet gets is an area of 0.5034, between −0.680 and 0.680. Thus the quartiles of any Normal distribution are about 0.68 standard deviations above and below the mean. **Note:** *Table A places the quartiles at about 0.67; other statistical software gives ±0.6745.*

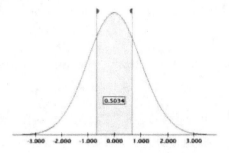

3.54: Placing the flags so that the area between them is as close as possible to 0.80, we find that the A/B cutoff is about 1.28 standard deviations above the mean, and the B/C cutoff is about 1.28 standard deviations below the mean.

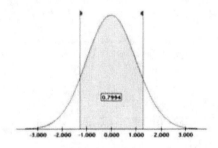

3.55 and 3.56 are Web-based exercises.

Chapter 4 Solutions

4.1: (a) Explanatory: time spent studying; response: grade. (b) Explore the relationship; there is no reason to view one or the other as explanatory. (c) Time spent online using Facebook is explanatory, GPA is the response variable. (d) Explore the relationship.

4.2: Sea-surface temperature is the explanatory variable; coral growth is the response variable. Both variables are quantitative.

4.3: For example: weight, sex, other food eaten by the students, type of beer (light, imported, . . .).

4.4: The researchers suspect that lean body mass is explanatory, so it should be on the horizontal axis.

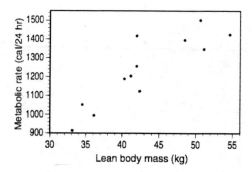

4.5: Outsource percent is the explanatory variable and should be on the horizontal axis. Delay percent is the response and should be on the vertical axis.

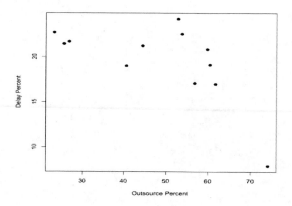

4.6: The scatterplot shows a positive direction, linear form, and moderately strong association.

4.7: There is an outlier (Hawaiian Airlines). Removing it, we would see no association between these variables. Without removing it, there is a very weak, negative association between the variables (which contradicts the suspicions described in Exercise 4.5).

4.8: (a) Below; speed is explanatory. (b) The relationship is curved—low in the middle, higher at the extremes. Because low "mileage" is actually *good* (it means that we use less fuel to travel 100 km), this makes sense: Moderate speeds yield the best performance. Note that 60 km/hr is about 37 mph. (c) Above-average (that is, bad) values of "fuel used" are found with both low and high values of "speed." (d) The relationship is very strong—there is little scatter around the curve, so the curve is very useful for prediction.

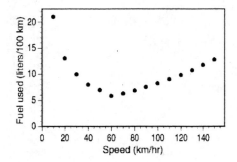

4.9: (a) Women are marked with filled circles, men with open circles. (b) For both men and women, the association is linear and positive. The women's points show a stronger association. As a group, males typically have larger values for both variables (they tend to have more mass, and tend to burn more calories per day).

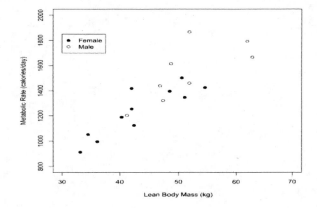

4.10: (a) Temperature is the explanatory variable. A scatterplot is provided below, and shows a fairly strong, *negative* linear association between Temperature and Coral growth. (b) $\bar{x} = 30.28$ degrees, $s_x = 0.43$ degrees, $\bar{y} = 2.46$ mm, $s_y = 0.16$ mm. See the table below for the standardized scores. The correlation is $r = -5.24/6 = -0.873$. This is consistent with the strong, negative association depicted in the scatterplot.(c) Software will give a value of -0.8914. The more precision you carry at each step, the closer you'll get to that value. The answer in (c) is erroneous at the hundredths place due to rounding.

z_x	z_y	$z_x z_y$
−1.40	+1.06	−1.48
−0.95	+0.75	−0.71
−0.28	+0.88	−0.25
−0.14	−0.13	0.02
+0.47	−1.25	−0.59
+0.86	−0.50	−0.43
+ 1.44	−1.25	−1.80

$$-5.24$$

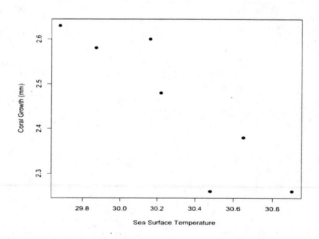

4.11: r would not change; units do not affect correlation.

4.12. (a) $r = 0.8765$. (b) With Point A included, the correlation increases to 0.9273; with Point B, it drops to 0.7257. (c) Point A fits in with the positive linear association displayed by the other points, and even emphasizes (strengthens) that association because, when A is included, the points of the scatterplot are less spread out (relative to the length of the apparent line suggested by the points). Meanwhile, Point B deviates from the pattern, weakening the association.

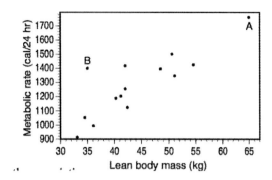

4.13: In computing the correlation, note that $\bar{x}$ = 50 mph, s_x = 15.8114 mph, $\bar{y}$ = 26.8 mpg and s_y = 2.6833 mpg. Refer to the table of standardized scores below, then note that r = 0/4 = 0. The correlation is zero because these variables do not have a straight-line relationship; the association is neither positive nor negative. Remember that correlation only measures the strength and direction of a *linear* relationship between two variables.

z_x	z_y	$z_x z_y$
−1.2649	−1.0435	1.3199
−0.6325	0.4472	−0.2828
0	1.1926	0
0.6325	0.4472	0.2828
1.2649	−1.0435	−1.3199
		0

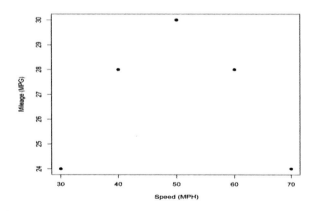

4.14: (a) We would expect that the price of a barrel of oil has an effect on the price of gasoline, rather than the reverse.

4.15: (a) The association should be positive (e.g., if oil prices rise, so do gas prices).

4.16: (b) IQ = 103, GPA = 0.5.

4.17: (a) 0.9. Without the outlier, there is a strong positive linear relationship.

4.18: (c) Correlations range from −1 to 1 inclusive.

4.19: (c) A correlation close to 0 might arise from a scatterplot with no visible pattern, but there could be a nonlinear pattern. See Exercise 4.13, for example.

4.20: (c) Because we are not told how the x and y values vary together, we cannot tell whether the correlation will be −1 or +1.

4.21: (a) 1. There would be a perfect, positive linear association.

4.22: (b) Correlation is unaffected by units.

4.23: (b) Computation with calculator or software gives $r = 0.8900$.

4.24: (a) The lowest first-round score was 66, scored by one golfer. This golfer scored 75 in the second round. (b) Lyle scored 86 in the second round, and 69 in the first round. (c) The correlation is very small, but positive... so closest to 0.1. Knowing a golfer's first-round score would not be useful in predicting a second-round score.

4.25: (a) Overall, there is a slightly negative association between these variables. (b) There is general disagreement — low BRFSS scores correspond to greater happiness, and these are associated with higher-ranked states (the least happy states, according to the objective measure). (c) It is hard to declare any of the data values as "outliers." It does not appear that any of the values are obviously outside of the general pattern. Perhaps one value (Rank = 8, BRFSS = 0.30) is an outlier, but this is hard to say.

4.26: (a) The scatterplot reveals a very strong, positive linear relationship between wine intake and relative risk for cancer. We expect correlation to be close to +1. (b) Using software, $r = 0.9851$. The data suggest that women who consume more wine tend to have higher risk of breast cancer. However, this is an observational study, and no causal relationship can be determined. The women who drink more wine may differ in many respects from women who drink less wine.

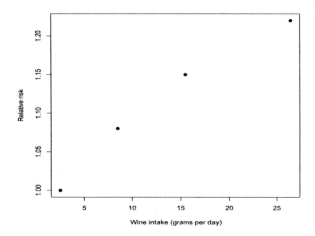

4.27: (a) The scatterplot suggests a strong positive linear association between distance and time with respect to the spread of Ebola. (b) $r = 0.9623$. This is consistent with the pattern described in (a). (c) Correlation would not change, since it does not depend on units.

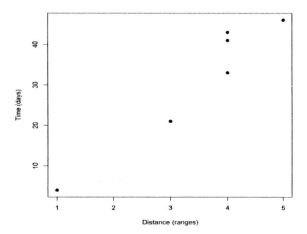

4.28: (a)The scatterplot shows a linear negative relationship. Because the relationship is linear, correlation is an appropriate measure of strength: $r = -0.7485$. (b)Because this association is negative, we conclude that the sparrow hawk is a long-lived territorial species.

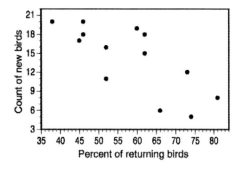

4.29: (a) The scatterplot is shown; note that neural activity is explanatory (and so should be on the horizontal axis). (b) The association is moderately strong, positive, and linear. The outlier is in the upper right corner. (c) For all points, $r = 0.8486$. Without the outlier, $r = 0.7015$. The correlation is greater with the outlier because it fits the pattern of the other points; if one drew the line suggested by the other points, the outlier would extend the length of the line and would therefore decrease the relative scatter of the points about that line.

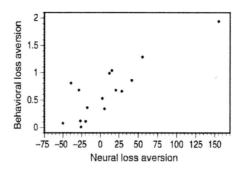

4.30: (a) SRD is the explanatory variable, so it should be on the horizontal axis. (b) The scatterplot shows a positive linear association. The correlation coefficient is $r = 0.9685$, which is consistent with the strength of the association visible in the scatterplot.

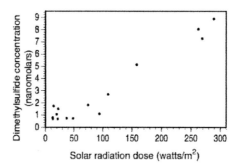

4.31: (a) The scatterplot is provided below. (b) The plot suggests that there is a strong relationship between alcohol intake and relative risk of breast cancer (again, this is an observational study, so no causal relationship is established here). It seems that type of alcohol has nothing to do with the increase since the same pattern and rate of increase is seen for both groups.

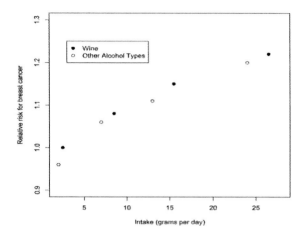

4.32: (a) The scatterplot is provided below. (b) The scatterplot suggests that there is not a linear relationship between relative growth rate and difference in begging intensity. Here, $r = -0.1749$. (c) Neither theory is strongly supported, but the latter is more strongly supported. That is, growth rate increases initially as begging intensity increases but then levels off or decreases as parents begin to ignore increases in begging by the foster babies.

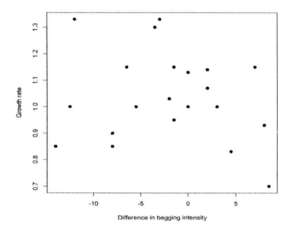

4.33: (a) A plot follows, and suggests that "Good" weather reports tend to yield higher tips. (b) The explanatory variable is categorical, not quantitative, so r cannot be used. Notice that we can arrange the categories any way, and these different arrangements would suggest different associations. Hence, it doesn't make sense to discuss a relationship direction here.

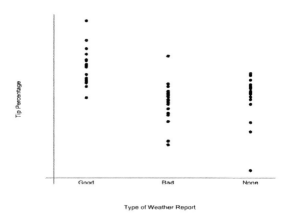

4.34: (a) Correlation would not change, as correlation does not depend on units. (b) Correlation would not change. By subtracting 0.25 from all risks, each point in the scatterplot moves "down" by 0.25, but the strength and direction of the linear relationship between risk and wine intake does not change. (c) There would be a perfect positive linear relationship with *r* = +1.

4.35: (a) The scatterplot is provided below. Changing the units has a dramatic impact on the plot. (b) Nevertheless, units do not impact correlation. For both data sets, *r* = 0.8900.

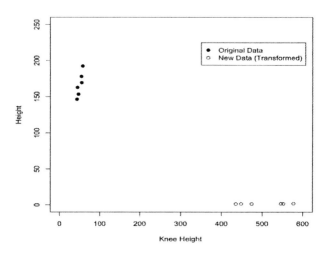

4.36: Explanations and sketches will vary, but should note that correlation measures the strength of the association, not the slope of the line. The hypothetical Funds A and B mentioned in the report, for example, might have a linear relationship having line of slope 2 or ½.

4.37: (a) Small-cap stocks have a lower correlation with municipal bonds, so the relationship is weaker. (b) She should look for a negative correlation (although this would also mean that this investment tends to *decrease* when bond prices rise).

4.38: The person that wrote the article interpreted a correlation close to 0 as if it were a correlation close to −1 (implying a negative association between teaching ability and research productivity). Professor McDaniel's findings mean there is little linear association between research and teaching ability. For example, knowing that a professor is a productive researcher gives little information about whether she is a good or bad teacher. Also, remember that correlation is only meaningful if both variables are quantitative — and here there is no guarantee that this is the case.

4.39: (a) Because gender has a nominal scale, we cannot compute the correlation between sex and any other variable. There is a strong *association* between sex and income. Some writers and speakers use "correlation" as a synonym for "association," but this is not correct. (b) A correlation of $r = 1.09$ is impossible, because r is restricted to be between −1 and 1. (c) Correlation has no units, so $r = 0.63$ centimeter is incorrect.

4.40: (a) The correlation will be closer to 1. One possible answer is shown. (b) Answers will vary, but the correlation will decrease, and can be made negative by dragging the point down far enough (see below, right).

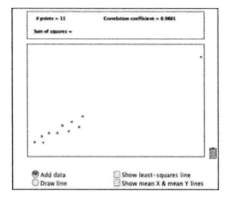 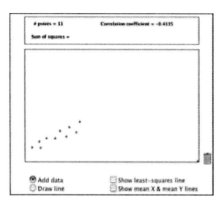

4.41: (a) Because two points determine a line, the correlation is always 1. (b) Sketches will vary; an example is shown. Note that the scatterplot must be positively sloped, but r is affected only by the scatter about the line, not by the steepness of the slope of that line. (c) The first nine points cannot be spread from the top to the bottom of the graph because in such a case the correlation cannot exceed about 0.66 (this is based on experience — lots of playing around with the applet). One possibility is shown. (d) To have $r = 0.7$, the curve must be higher at the right than at the left. One possibility is shown.

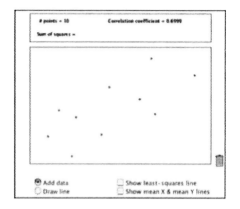

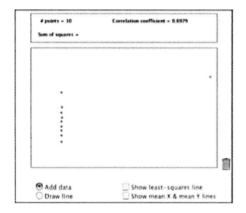

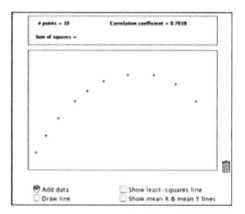

4.42: PLAN: To describe the change in solar radiation over time, we begin with a scatterplot (with year as the explanatory variable). If appropriate for the relationship, we compute the correlation coefficient to measure the strength of the association. SOLVE: The plot suggests that sunlight has brightened overall, and the increase has been relatively steady. Correlation is a useful measure here, and $r = 0.9454$. CONCLUDE: Over time, sunlight has gotten brighter.

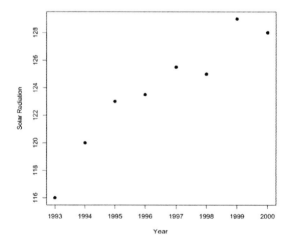

4.43: PLAN: To study the improvements in running times between men and women, we'll plot the data on the same scatterplot. We will not use correlation, but we will examine the plot to see if women are beginning to outrun men. SOLVE: The plot is provided below. By inspection, one might guess that the "lines" that fit these data sets will meet around 1998. This is how the researchers made this leap. CONCLUDE: Men's and women's times have, indeed, grown closer over time. Both sexes have improved their record marathon times over the years, but women's times have improved at a faster rate. In fact, as of 2011, the world record time for men has continued to be faster than the world record time for women. The difference is currently about 686 seconds (under 12 minutes), where in the data plotted, the difference was about 856 seconds.

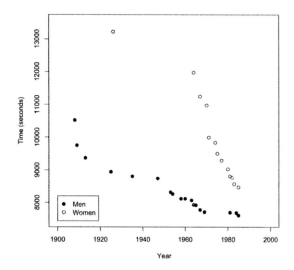

4.44: PLAN: To investigate the relationship between outside temperature and the percent of total heat loss due to beak, we plot heat loss from beak against outside temperature. We'll compute the correlation, if the relationship looks to be reasonably linear. SOLVE: The plot follows. Notice that there is a reasonably strong linear relationship. It seems reasonable to use correlation to describe this relationship's strength and direction. In fact, $r = 0.9143$. CONCLUDE: When the outside temperature increases, a greater percentage of total heat loss is due to beak heat loss. That is, the beak plays a more important role in cooling down the toco toucan as the weather outside becomes hotter.

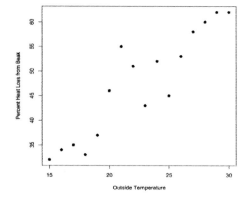

4.45: PLAN: We wish to explore the relationship between social distress and brain activity. We begin with a scatterplot, and compute the correlation if appropriate. SOLVE: A scatterplot shows a fairly strong, positive, linear association. There are no particular outliers; each variable has low and high values, but those points do not deviate from the pattern of the rest. The relationship seems to be reasonably linear, so we compute $r = 0.8782$. CONCLUDE: Social exclusion does appear to trigger a pain response: higher social distress measurements are associated with increased activity in the pain-sensing area of the brain. However, no cause-and-effect conclusion is possible since this was not a designed experiment.

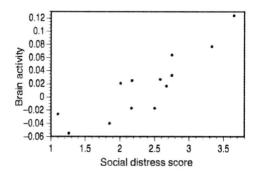

4.46: PLAN: We wish to explore the relationship between fish supply and animal population. We begin with a scatterplot, and compute the correlation if appropriate. SOLVE: A scatterplot shows a moderately strong, positive, linear association. There are no clear outliers, although a few points fall slightly above (and one slightly below) the cluster. Correlation ($r = 0.8042$) is an appropriate measure of the strength of the association. CONCLUDE: The positive association supports the idea that animal populations decline when the fish supply is low. The four years with the greatest fish supply were four of the five years in which biomass increased.

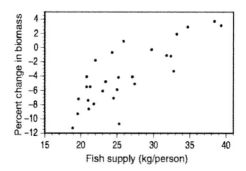

4.47 and 4.48 are Web-based exercises.

Chapter 5 Solutions

5.1: (a) The slope is 1.016. On average, highway mileage increases by 1.016 mpg for each additional 1 mpg change in city mileage. (b) The intercept is 6.554 mpg. This is the highway mileage for a nonexistent car that gets 0 mpg in the city. Although this interpretation is valid, such a prediction would be invalid, since it involves considerable extrapolation. (c) For a car that gets 16 mpg in the city, we predict highway mileage to be 6.554 + (1.016)(16) = 22.81 mpg. For a car that gets 28 mpg in the city, we predict highway mileage to be 6.554 + (1.016)(28) = 35.002 mpg. (d) The regression line passes through all the points of prediction. The plot was created by drawing a line through the two points (16, 22.81) and (28, 35.002), corresponding to the city mileages and predicted highway mileages for the two cars described in (c).

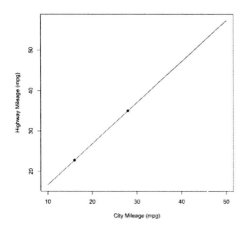

5.2: The equation is weight $= 80 - 5 \times$ days; the intercept is 80 grams (the initial weight), and the slope is –5 grams/day.

5.3: (a) $\bar{x} = 30.280$, $s_x = 0.4296$, $\bar{y} = 2.4557$, $s_y = 0.1579$, and $r = -0.8914$ Hence,

$b = r\dfrac{s_y}{s_x} = (-0.8914)\dfrac{0.1579}{0.4296} = -0.3276$, and $a = \bar{y} - b\bar{x} = 2.4557 - (-0.3276)(30.280) = 12.3754$.

(b) Software agrees with these values to 3 decimal places, since we rounded to the 4th decimal place.

5.4: (a) The scatterplot is shown. (b) The regression equation is $\hat{y} = 201.2 + 24.026x$. (c) The slope tells us that on the average, metabolic rate increases by about 24 calories per day for each additional kilogram of body mass. (d) For $x = 45$ kg, the predicted metabolic rate is $\hat{y} = 1282.4$ calories per day.

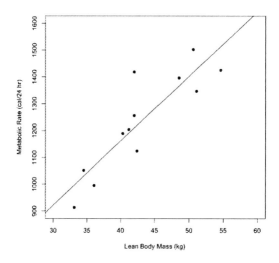

5.5: The farther *r* is from 0 (in either direction), the stronger the linear relationship is between two variables. In Exercise 4.30, the relationship between SRD and DMS is very strongly linear, and a regression line should enable relatively more accurate prediction.

5.6: (a) The scatterplot is provided, with the regression line. Regression gives $\hat{y} = 1.0284 - 0.004498x$ (see Minitab output). The plot suggests a slightly curved pattern, not a strong linear pattern. A regression line is not useful for making predictions. (b) $r^2 = 0.0306$. This confirms what we see in the graph: the regression line does a poor job summarizing the relationship between Difference in Begging Intensity and Growth Rate. Only 3% of the variation in Growth Rate is explained by the least-squares regression on Difference in Begging Intensity.

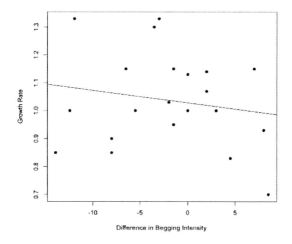

Minitab output

The regression equation is Growth = 1.028 − 0.0045 Difference

Predictor	Coef	Stdev	t-ratio	P
Constant	1.028409	0.039042	26.341	0
Difference	−0.004498	0.005808	−0.774	0.448

s = 0.1704 R^2 = 0.0306

5.7: (a) The residuals are computed in the table below using $\hat{y} = 12.3754 - 0.3276x$, as computed in Exercise 5.3.   (b) They sum to zero, except for rounding error.   (c) From software, the correlation between x and $y - \hat{y}$ is 0.000025, which is zero except for rounding.

x	y	$\hat{y}$	$y - \hat{y}$
29.68	2.63	2.652	−0.022
29.87	2.58	2.590	−0.010
30.16	2.60	2.495	0.105
30.22	2.48	2.475	0.005
30.48	2.26	2.390	−0.130
30.65	2.38	2.335	0.045
30.90	2.26	2.253	0.007

$$0$$

5.8: (a) Plot is provided below, on top.   (b) No; the pattern is curved, so linear regression is not appropriate for prediction.   (c) For $x = 10$, we estimate $\hat{y} = 11.058 - 0.01466(10) = 10.91$, so the residual is $21.00 - 10.91 = 10.09$. The sum of the residuals is −0.01.   (d) The first two and last four residuals are positive, and those in the middle are negative. Plot below.

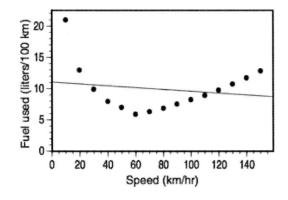
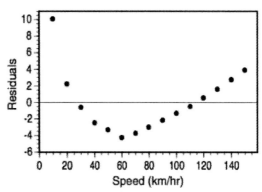

5.9: (a) Any point that falls exactly on the regression line will not increase the sum of squared vertical distances (which the regression line minimizes). Thus the regression line does not change. Possible output is shown, below left. Any other line (even if it passes through this new point) will necessarily have a higher total sum of squared prediction errors. The correlation changes (increases) because the new point reduces the relative scatter about the regression line. (b) Influential points are those whose *x* coordinates are outliers. An example is provided, below right.

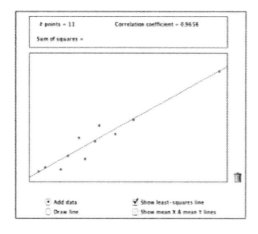
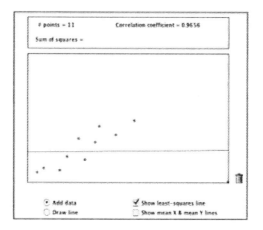

5.10: (a) Point A lies above the other points; that is, the metabolic rate is higher than we expect for the given body mass. Point B lies to the right of the other points; that is, it is an outlier in the *x* (mass) direction, and the metabolic rate is lower than we would expect. (b) In the plot, the solid line is the regression line for the original data. The dashed line slightly above that includes Point A; it has a very similar slope to the original line, but a slightly higher intercept, because Point A pulls the line up. The third line includes Point B, the more influential point; because Point B is an outlier in the *x* direction, it "pulls" the line down so that it is less steep.

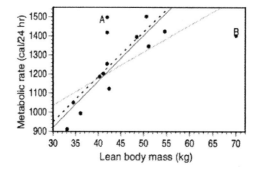

Since this

5.11: (a) In the plot, the outlier (Hawaiian Airlines) is the point identified with "H". Since this point is an outlier and falls outside the linear trend suggested by the other data points, it is influential, and will affect the regression line by "pulling" it. (b) With the outlier, $r = -0.624$. If the outlier is deleted from the data, $r = -0.441$. Notice that with the outlier, the correlation suggests a stronger linear relationship. (c) The two regression lines (one including the outlier, and the other without) are plotted. We see that the line based on the full data set (including the outlier) has been pulled down toward the outlier, indicating that the outlier is influential. Now, the regression line based on the complete (original) data set, including the outlier, is $\hat{y} = 27.486 - 0.164x$. Using this, when $x = 74.1$, we predict 15.33% delays. The other regression line (fit without the outlier), is $\hat{y} = 23.804 - 0.069x$, so our prediction would be 18.69% delays. The outlier impacts predictions because it impacts the regression line.

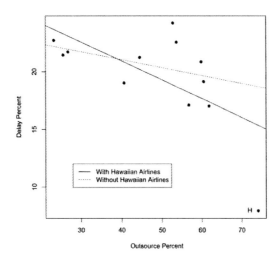

5.12: The correlation between *average* weight and height is an ecological correlation. There is far more variability among individuals than among the averages. Correlation would be much smaller if one calculated it based on weights of individuals and their heights.

5.13: (a) The regression line is $\hat{y} = -43.172 + 0.129x$. (b) If 975,000 boats are registered, then by our scale, $x = 975$, and $\hat{y} = -43.172 + (0.129)(975) = 82.6$ manatees killed. The prediction seems reasonable, as long as conditions remain the same, because "975" is within the space of observed values of x on which the regression line was based. That is, this is not extrapolation. (c) If $x = 0$ (corresponding to no registered boats), then we would "predict" –43.172 manatees to be killed by boats. This is absurd, since it is clearly impossible for fewer than 0 manatees to be killed. This illustrates the folly of extrapolation… $x = 0$ is well outside the range of observed values of x on which the regression line was based.

5.14: A student's intelligence may be a lurking variable: stronger students (who are more likely to succeed when they get to college) are more likely to choose to take these math courses, while weaker students may avoid them. Other possible answers might be variations on this idea; for example, if we believe that success in college depends on a student's self-confidence, and perhaps confident students are more likely to choose math courses.

5.15: Possible lurking variables include the IQ and socioeconomic status of the mother, as well as the mother's other habits (drinking, diet, etc.). These variables are associated with smoking in various ways, and are also predictive of a child's IQ.

Note: *There may be an indirect cause-and-effect relationship at work here: some studies have found evidence that over time, smokers lose IQ points, perhaps due to brain damage caused by toxins from the smoke. So, perhaps smoking mothers gradually grow less smart and are less able to nurture their children's cognitive development.*

5.16: Socioeconomic status is a possible lurking variable: children from upper-class families can more easily afford higher education, and they would typically have had better preparation for college as well. They may also have some advantages when seeking employment, and have more money should they want to start their own businesses.

This could be compounded by racial distinctions: some minority groups receive worse educations than other groups, and prejudicial hiring practices may keep minorities out of higher-paying positions. It could also be that some causation goes the other way: people who are doing well in their jobs might be encouraged to pursue further education or their employers might pay for them to get further education.

5.17: Age is probably the most important lurking variable: married men would generally be older than single men, so they would have been in the workforce longer, and therefore had more time to advance in their careers.

5.18: (b) 7.5. The regression line seems to pass through the point (110, 7.5).

5.19: (b) 0.2. Consider two points on the regression line, say (90,4) and (130,11). The slope of the line segment connecting these points is $\dfrac{11-4}{130-90}$ = 7/40.

5.20: (c) −3.

5.21: (a) $y = 1000 + 100x$

5.22: (b) will be less than 0. As the number of packs increases, average age at death decreases. Hence, correlation is negative, and so is the slope of the regression line.

5.23: (c) 16 cubic feet.

5.24: (a) 405 cubic feet.

5.25: (a) greater than zero. The slope of the line is positive.

5.26: (c) prediction of gas used from degree-days will be quite accurate.

5.27: (a) $\hat{y} = 42.9 + 2.5x$

5.28: (a) The slope is 0.0138 minutes per meter. On the average, if the depth of the dive is increased by one meter, it adds 0.0138 minutes (about 0.83 seconds) to the time spent underwater. (b) When D = 200, the regression formula estimates DD to be 5.45 minutes. (c) To plot the line, compute DD = 3.242 minutes when D = 40 meters, and DD = 6.83 minutes when D = 300 meters.

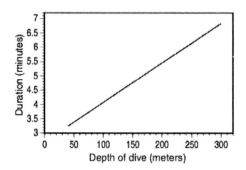

5.29: (a) Since the slope is 3721.02, the least-squares regression line says that increasing the size of a diamond by 1 carat increases its price by 3721.02 Singapore dollars. (b) A diamond of size 0 carats would have a predicted price of 259.63 Singapore dollars. This is probably an extrapolation, since the data set on which the line was constructed almost certainly had no rings with diamonds of size 0 carats. However, if the number is meaningful (dubious), then it refers to the cost of the gold content and other materials in the ring.

5.30: (a) The regression equation is $\hat{y} = -0.126 + 0.0608x$. For $x = 2.0$, this formula gives $\hat{y} = -0.0044$. (A student who uses the more precise coefficient estimates listed under "Coef" in the Minitab output might report the predicted brain activity as -0.0045.) (b) This is given in the Minitab output as "R-sq": 77.1%. The linear relationship explains 77.1% of the variation in brain activity. (c) Knowing that $r^2 = 0.771$, we find $r = \sqrt{r^2} = 0.878$; the sign is positive because it has the same sign as the slope coefficient.

5.31: (a) The regression equation is $\hat{y} = 0.919 + 2.0647x$. At 25 degrees Celsius, we predict beak heat loss of $\hat{y} = 0.919 + (2.0647)(25) = 52.34$ percent. (b) Since $r^2 = 0.836$, 83.6% of the total variation in beak heat loss is explained by the straight-line relationship with temperature. (c) $r = \sqrt{r^2} = \sqrt{0.836} = 0.914$. Correlation is positive here, since the least-squares regression line has a positive slope.

5.32: Since we wish to regress husbands' heights on wives' heights, the women's heights will be the x-values, and the men's heights will be the y-values. (a) $b = r\, s_y / s_x = (0.5)\left(\dfrac{3.9}{3.1}\right) = 0.629$, and $a = \bar{y} - b\bar{x} = 69.9 - (0.629)(64.3) = 29.46$ inches. Hence, the regression equation is $\hat{y} = 29.46 + 0.629x$. (b) If a wife is 67 inches tall, we predict her husband to have height $\hat{y} = 29.46 + (0.629)(67) = 71.603$ inches. The plot, with this pair identified, is provided. (c) We don't expect this prediction to be very accurate because the heights of men having wives 67 inches tall varies a lot.

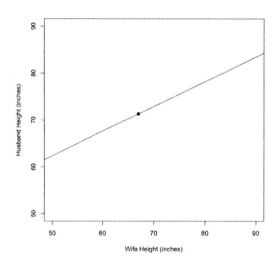

5.33: Not speaking to Professor Krugman's lack of professional or ethical values, the *x*-values will be pre-exam scores, and the *y*-values will be final exam scores. This is probably *not* the Princeton University, Nobel prize-winning economist Paul Krugman. (a) $b = r\, s_y / s_x = (0.5)\left(\dfrac{8}{40}\right)$ = 0.1, and $a = \bar{y} - b\bar{x} = 75 - (0.1)(280) = 47$. Hence, the regression equation is $\hat{y} = 47 + 0.1x$. (b) Julie's pre-final exam total was 300, so we would predict a final exam score of $\hat{y} = 47 + (0.1)(300) = 77$. (c) Julie is right… with a correlation of r = 0.5, $r^2 = (0.5)^2 = 0.25$, so the regression line accounts for only 25% of the variability in student final exam scores. That is, the regression line doesn't predict final exam scores very well. Julie's score could, indeed, be much higher or lower than the predicted 77. Since she is making this argument, one might guess that her score was, in fact, higher. Julie should visit the Dean.

5.34: $r = \sqrt{0.16} = 0.40$ (high attendance goes with high grades, so the correlation must be positive).

5.35: (a) The regression equation is $\hat{y} = 28.037 + 0.521x$. $r = 0.555$. (b) The plot is provided. Based on Damien's height of 70 inches, we predict his sister Tonya to have height $\hat{y} = 28.037 + (0.521)(70) = 64.5$ inches (rounded). This prediction isn't expected to be very accurate because the correlation isn't very large… so $r^2 = (0.555)^2 = 0.308$. The regression line explains only 30.8% of the variation in sister heights.

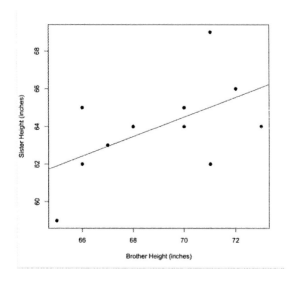

5.36: (a) A plot follows, and suggests that the relationship between Absorbence and Nitrates is extremely linear. From software, $r = 0.99994 > 0.997$, so the calibration does not need to be repeated. From software, the equation of the least-squares regression line for predicting Nitrates from Absorbence is $\hat{y} = -14.522 + 8.825x$. If the water sample has absorbence of 40, we predict Nitrate concentration of $-14.522 + (8.825)(40) = 338.478$ mg/liter. (c) We expect estimates of Nitrate concentration from Absorbence to be very accurate since the linear regression explains virtually all of the variation in Nitrate concentration. That is, $r^2 = (0.99994)^2 = 0.9999$, or 99.99% of the variation in Nitrate concentration is explained by the regression on Absorbence.

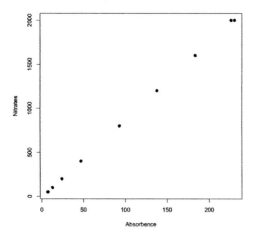

5.37: (a) The regression equation is $\hat{y} = 31.9 - 0.304x$. (b) The slope (-0.304) tells us that, on the average, for each additional 1% increase in returning birds, the number of new birds joining the colony decreases by 0.304. (c) When $x = 60$, we predict $\hat{y} = 13.66$ new birds will join the colony.

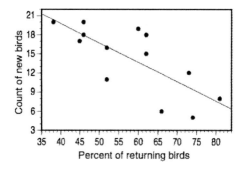

Minitab output

The regression equation is New = 31.9 – 0.304PctRtn

Predictor	Coef	Stdev	t-ratio	p
Constant	31.934	4.838	6.60	0.000
PctRtn	-0.30402	0.0812	-3.74	0.003

s = 3.667   R-sq = 56.0%   R-sq(adj) = 52.0%

5.38: (a) The outlier in the upper-right corner is circled because it is hard to see it with the two regression lines. (b) With the outlier omitted, the regression line is $\hat{y} = 0.586 + 0.00891x$. (This is the solid line in the plot.) (c) The line does not change much because the outlier fits the pattern of the other points; r changes because the scatter (relative to the line) is greater with the outlier removed, and the outlier is located consistently with the linear pattern of the rest of the points. (d) The correlation changes from 0.8486 (with all points) to 0.7015 (without the outlier). With all points included, the regression line is $\hat{y} = 0.585 + 0.0879x$ (nearly indistinguishable from the other regression line).

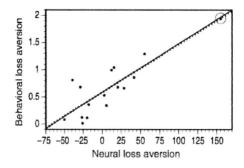

Minitab output: All points

The regression equation is Behave = 0.585 + 0.00879 Neural

Predictor	Coef	Stdev	t-ratio	p
Constant	0.58496	0.07093	8.25	0.000
Neural	0.008794	0.001465	6.00	0.000

With outlier removed

The regression equation is Behave = 0.586 + 0.00891 Neural

Predictor	Coef	Stdev	t-ratio	p
Constant	0.58581	0.07506	7.80	0.000
Neural	0.008909	0.002510	3.55	0.004

5.39: (a) To three decimal places, the correlations are all approximately 0.816 (for Set D, r actually rounds to 0.817), and the regression lines are all approximately $\hat{y} = 3.000 + 0.500x$. For all four sets, we predict $\hat{y} = 8$ when $x = 10$. (b) Plots below. (c) For Set A, the use of the regression line seems to be reasonable—the data seem to have a moderate linear association (albeit with a fair amount of scatter). For Set B, there is an obvious *non*linear relationship; we should fit a parabola or other curve. For Set C, the point (13, 12.74) deviates from the (highly linear) pattern of the other points; if we can exclude it, the (new) regression formula would be very useful for prediction. For Set D, the data point with $x = 19$ is a very influential point—the other points alone give no indication of slope for the line. Seeing how widely scattered the y-coordinates of the other points are, we cannot place too much faith in the y-coordinate of the influential point; thus we cannot depend on the slope of the line, and so we cannot depend on the estimate when $x = 10$. (We also have no evidence as to whether or not a line is an appropriate model for this relationship.)

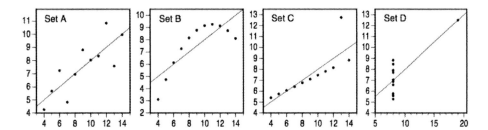

5.40: (a) The two unusual observations are indicated on the scatterplot. (b) The correlations are

$r_1 = 0.4819$ (all observations)

$r_2 = 0.5684$ (without Subject 15)

$r_3 = 0.3837$ (without Subject 18)

Both outliers change the correlation. Removing Subject 15 increases r because its presence makes the scatterplot less linear. Removing Subject 18 decreases r because its presence decreases the relative scatter about the linear pattern.

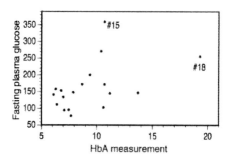

5.41: (a) The regression equation is $\hat{y} = 42.933 + 2.453x$. (b) The regression equation is $\hat{y} = 0.42933 + 0.002453x$. (c) Use the fact that 50 cm = 500 mm. When $x = 50$ cm, the first regression equation gives $\hat{y} = 165.583$ cm. Using the second equation, with $x = 500$ mm, $\hat{y} = 1.65583$ m. These are the same.

5.42: The scatterplot with regression lines added is given. The equations are

$\hat{y} = 66.4 + 10.4x$ (all observations)

$\hat{y} = 69.5 + 8.92x$ (without #15)

$\hat{y} = 52.3 + 12.1x$ (without #18)

While the equation changes in response to removing either subject, one could argue that neither one is particularly influential, because the line moves very little over the range of x (HbA) values. Subject 15 is an outlier in terms of its y value; such points are typically not influential. Subject 18 is an outlier in terms of its x value, but it is not particularly influential because it is consistent with the linear pattern suggested by the other points.

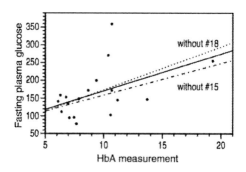

5.43: The correlation would be much lower, because there is much greater variation in individuals than in the averages. The correlation in Exercise 4.25 was an ecological correlation, which obscures the variability in individuals.

5.44: In this case, there may be a causative effect, but in the direction opposite to the one suggested: People who are overweight are more likely to be on diets, and so choose artificial sweeteners over sugar. (Also, heavier people are at a higher risk to develop Type 2 diabetes; if they do, they are likely to switch to artificial sweeteners.)

5.45: Responses will vary. For example, students who choose the online course might have more self-motivation or have better computer skills (which might be helpful in doing well in the class; e.g., such students might do better at researching course topics on the Internet).

5.46: For example, a student who in the past might have received a grade of B (and a lower SAT score) now receives an A (but has a lower SAT score than an A student in the past). While this is a bit of an oversimplification, this means that today's A students are yesterday's A and B students, today's B students are yesterday's C students, and so on. Because of the grade inflation, we are not comparing students with equal abilities in the past and today.

5.47: Here is a (relatively) simple example to show how this can happen: suppose that most workers are currently 30 to 50 years old; of course, some are older or younger than that, but this age group dominates. Suppose further that each worker's current salary is his/her age (in thousands of dollars); for example, a 30-year-old worker is currently making $30,000. Over the next 10 years, all workers age, and their salaries increase. Suppose every worker's salary increases by between $4000 and $8000. Then every worker will be making *more* money than he/she did 10 years before, but *less* money than a worker of that same age 10 years before. During that time, a few workers will retire, and others will enter the workforce, but that large cluster that had been between the ages of 30 and 50 (now between 40 and 60) will bring up the overall median salary despite the changes in older and younger workers.

5.48: We have slope $b = r\, s_y / s_x$, and intercept $a = \bar{y} - b\bar{x}$, and $\hat{y} = a + bx$. Hence, when $x = \bar{x}$, $\hat{y} = a + b\bar{x} = (\bar{y} - b\bar{x}) + b\bar{x} = \bar{y}$.

5.49: For a player who shot 80 in the first round, we predict a second-round score of

$\hat{y} = 52.74 + (0.297)(80) = 76.5$. For a player who shot 70 in the first round, we predict a second-round score of $\hat{y} = 52.74 + (0.297)(70) = 73.53$. Notice that the player who shot 80 the first round (worse than average) is predicted to have a worse-than-average score the second round, but better than the first round. Similarly, the player who shot 70 the first round (better than average) is predicted to do better than average in the second round, but not as well (relatively) as in the first round. Both players are predicted to "regress" to the mean.

5.50: Note that $\bar{y} = 46.6 + 0.41\,\bar{x}$. We predict that Octavio will score 4.1 points above the mean on the final exam: $\hat{y} = 46.6 + 0.41(\bar{x} + 10) = 46.6 + 0.41\,\bar{x} + 4.1 = \bar{y} + 4.1$. (Alternatively, because the slope is 0.41, we can observe that an increase of 10 points on the midterm yields an increase of 4.1 on the predicted final exam score.)

5.51: See Exercise 4.41 for the three sample scatterplots. A regression line is appropriate only for the scatterplot of part (b). For the graph in (c), the point not in the vertical stack is very influential – the stacked points alone give no indication of slope for the line (if indeed a line is an appropriate model). If the stacked points are scattered, we cannot place too much faith in the y-coordinate of the influential point; thus we cannot depend on the slope of the line, and so we cannot depend on predictions made with the regression line. The curved relationship exhibited by the scatterplot in (d) clearly indicates that predictions based on a straight line are not appropriate.

5.52: (a) Drawing the "best line" by eye is a very inaccurate process; few people choose the best line. (b) Most people tend to overestimate the slope for a scatterplot with $r = 0.7$; that is, most students will find that the least-squares line is less steep than the one they draw.

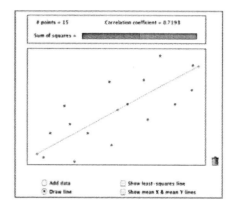
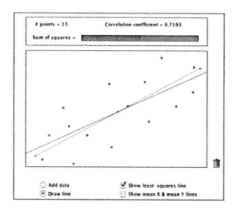

5.53: PLAN: We construct a scatterplot (with beaver stumps as the explanatory variable), and if appropriate, find the regression line and correlation. SOLVE: The scatterplot shows a positive linear association. Regression seems to be an appropriate way to summarize the relationship; the regression line is $=-1.286+11.89x$. The straight-line relationship explains $r^2 =83.9\%$ of the variation in beetle larvae. CONCLUDE: The strong positive association supports the idea that beavers benefit beetles.

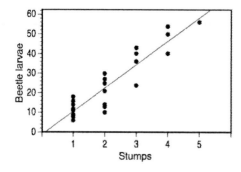

5.54: PLAN: We construct a scatterplot, with distance as the explanatory variable, using different symbols for the left and right hands, and (if appropriate) find separate regression lines for each hand. SOLVE: In the scatterplot, right-hand points are filled circles and left-hand points are open circles. In general, the right-hand points lie below the left-hand points, meaning the right-hand times are shorter, so the subject is likely right-handed. There is no striking pattern for the left-hand points; the pattern for right-hand points is obscured because they are squeezed at the bottom of the plot. While neither plot looks particularly linear, we might nonetheless find the two regression lines: For the right hand, $\hat{y} = 99.4 + 0.0283x$ ($r = 0.305$, $r^2 = 9.3\%$), and for the left hand, $\hat{y} = 172 + 0.262x$ ($r = 0.318$, $r^2 = 10.1\%$). CONCLUDE: Neither regression is particularly useful for prediction; distance accounts for only 9.3% (right) and 10.1% (left) of the variation in time.

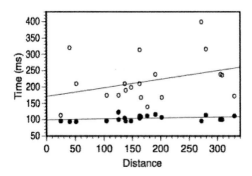

5.55: PLAN: We construct a scatterplot, with forecast as the explanatory variable, and Actual as the response variable. If appropriate, we find the least-squares regression line. We consider the impact of the potential outlier (2005 season). SOLVE: A scatterplot follows. There is a reasonable, but not very strong linear relationship between Forecasted and Actual hurricanes. In the plot, the 2005 season is noted with an open circle. It is an outlier, and influential, pulling the regression line somewhat. We might consider deleting this point and fitting the line again. Deleting the line, we obtain the dotted regression line, $\hat{y} = 2.6725 + 0.7884x$. If the forecasts were perfect, the intercept of this line would be 0, and the slope would be 1, for reference. Deleting the 2005 season, $r = 0.621$, and $r^2 = 38.5\%$. Hence, even after deleting the outlier, the regression line explains only 38.5% of variation in number of hurricanes. CONCLUDE: Predictions using the regression line are not very accurate. However, there is a positive association... so a forecast of many hurricanes may reasonably be expected to forebode a heavy season for hurricanes.

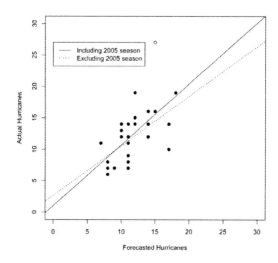

5.56: PLAN: We plot the data, producing a time-series plot. If appropriate, we consider fitting a regression line. SOLVE: The plot follows. We see that during the recent 10-15 years, the volume of discharge has increased more rapidly, but before then, the rate increased slowly, if at all. CONCLUDE: If there is a relationship between Year and Discharge, it isn't strongly linear, and use of a regression line would not be useful to predict Discharge from Year.

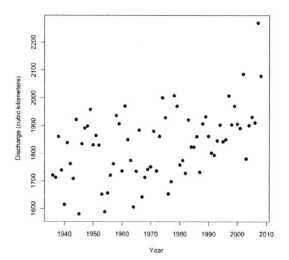

5.57: PLAN: We plot marathon times by year for each gender, using different symbols. If appropriate, we fit least-squares regression lines for predicting time from year for each gender. We then use these lines to guess when the times will concur. SOLVE: The scatterplot is provided below, with regression lines plotted. The regression lines are:

For men: $\hat{y} = 67,825.3 - 30.44x$

For women: $\hat{y} = 182,976.15 - 87.73x$

Although the lines appear to fit the data reasonably well (and the regression line for women would fit better if we omitted the outlier associated with year 1926), this analysis is inviting you to extrapolate, which is never advisable. CONCLUDE: Using the regression lines plotted, we might expect women to "outrun" men by the year 2010. Omitting the outlier, the line for women would decrease more steeply, and the intersection would occur sooner, by 1995.

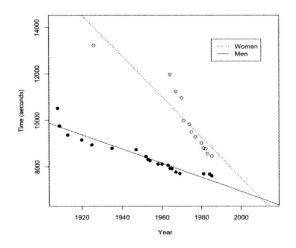

5.58 – 5.60 are Web-based exercises.

Chapter 6 Solutions

6.1: (a) This table describes $736 + 450 + 193 + 205 + 144 + 80 = 1808$ people. $736 + 450 + 193 = 1379$ played video games. (b) The percent of boys earning A's and B's is $(736 + 205)/1808 = 0.5205 = 52.05\%$. We do this for all three grade levels. The complete marginal distribution for grades is

Grade	Percent
A's and B's	52.05%
C's	32.85%
D's and F's	15.10%

Of all boys, $32.85\% + 15.10\% = 47.95\%$ received a grade of C or lower.

6.2: (a) The sum of all entries is 11,378. Hence, this table describes 11,378 undergraduates. (b) There are $2814 + 2648 = 5462$ undergraduates in the 20–24 age group. This represents $5462/11,378 = 0.4800 = 48.00\%$. The marginal distribution for ages of undergraduates follows:

Age group	Percent
15 to 19	35.16%
20 to 24	48.00%
35 to 34	10.89%
35 or older	5.95%

6.3: There are $736 + 450 + 193 = 1379$ players. Of these, $736/1379 = 53.37\%$ earned A's or B's. Similarly, there are $205 + 144 + 80 = 429$ nonplayers. Of these, $205/429 = 47.79\%$ earned A's or B's. Continuing in like manner, the conditional distribution of grades for players follows:

Grades	Players	Nonplayers
A's and B's	53.37%	47.79%
C's	32.63%	33.56%
D's and F's	14.00%	18.65%

It doesn't look like there's a big difference between these conditional distributions. If anything, players have slightly higher grades (slightly more A's and B's, slightly fewer D's and F's) than nonplayers, but this could be due to chance (more on that later).

6.4: STATE: How do the percents of women vary among age groups? PLAN: Starting with the two-way table from Exercise 6.2, find and compare the conditional distributions of gender for each age group. SOLVE: Shown in the table are the percents of women in each age group; for example, for the 15–19 age group, the proportion of women is 2124/(2124 + 1876) = 2124/4000 = 0.531, or 53.1%. Students might also report the percent of men in each age group, of course. CONCLUDE: The data support our suspicion — the percent of women in the 25–34 age group (53.1%) is, indeed, larger than the percent of women in the 20–24 age group (51.5%). Notice that the percent of women in the 35 or older age group is particularly high, at 76.5%.

Age group	Percent female
15 to 19	53.1%
20 to 24	51.5%
35 to 34	56.7%
35 or older	76.5%

6.5: Two examples are shown. In general, choose a to be any number from 10 to 50, and then all the other entries can be determined.

30	20
30	20

50	0
10	40

6.6: (a) Rubis made 119 + 36 = 155 field goals in 119 + 115 + 36 + 61 = 331 attempts. Hence, she made 115/331 = 0.347, or 34.7% of her field goal attempts. Similarly, Shearer made 47.6% of her field goal attempts. (b) The table below describes the percent of field goals made for each type of field goal, for each player. For example, for two-pointers, Rubis made 119/(119+115) = 0.5085, or 50.85% of attempts. (c) While Rubis's overall field goal percentage is lower than Shearer's, notice that Rubis's percentage is higher for both types of field goals. This is an example of Simpson's paradox — the comparison that holds for both field goal groups is reversed when the groups are combined into one group. Notice that Shearer took very few three-point shots.

	Rubis	Shearer
Two-pointers	50.85%	50.59%
Three-pointers	37.11%	23.81%

6.7: (a) For Rotura district, 79/8889 = 0.0089, or 0.9%, of Maori are in the jury pool, while 258/24,009 = 0.0107, or 1.07%, of the non-Maori are in the jury pool. For Nelson district, the corresponding percents are 0.08% for Maori and 0.17% for non-Maori. Hence, in each district, the percent of non-Maori in the jury pool exceeds the percent of Maori in the jury pool. (b) Combining the regions into one table:

	Maori	Non-Maori
In Jury Pool	80	314
Not in Jury Pool	10,138	56,353
Total	10,218	56,667

For the Maori, overall the percent in the jury pool is 80/10,218 = 0.0078, or 0.78%, while for the non-Maori, the overall percent in the jury pool is 314/56,667 = 0.0055, or 0.55%. Hence, overall the Maori have a larger percent in the jury pool, but in each region they have a lower percent in the jury pool. (c) The reason for Simpson's paradox occurring with this example is that the Maori constitute a large proportion of Rotura's population, while in Nelson they are small minority community.

6.8: (b) 612 people.

6.9: (b) 150 teens in schools that forbid cell phones.

6.10: (b) about 25% (150/612 = 0.245, or 24.5%).

6.11: (a) the marginal distribution of school permissiveness.

6.12: (c) about 65% (97/150 = 0.647, or 64.7%).

6.13: (c) the conditional distribution of the frequency that a teen brings a cell phone to school among the schools that forbid cell phones.

6.14: (b) about 21% (97/468 = 0.207, or 20.7%).

6.15: (b) the conditional distribution of school permissiveness among those who brought their cell phone to school every day.

6.16: (b) 4 bars.

6.17: (b) an example of Simpson's paradox.

6.18: The two distributions are given below. For example, the percentage of people that feel astrology is not at all scientific, the percent with JC degrees is 87/(87 + 198 + 111) = 0.2197, or 21.97%.

	Not at all Scientific	Very or sort of Scientific
Junior College	22.0%	33.6%
Bachelor's	50.0%	44.5%
Graduate	28.0%	21.9%

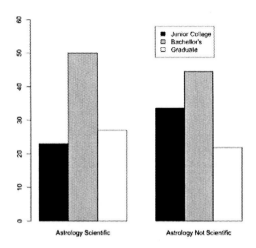

The bar chart and the tables above reveal that, loosely, adults that believe astrology is not at all scientific tend to have relatively more college education than adults that believe astrology is very or sort of scientific.

6.19: For each type of injury (accidental, not accidental), the distribution of ages is produced below.

	Accidental	Not accidental
8–13	19.0%	4.0%
14–18	42.2%	35.8%
19–22	15.4%	20.8%
23–30	23.4%	39.4%

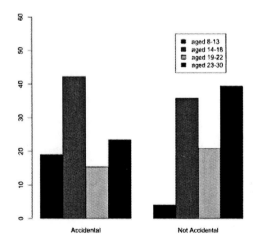

We see that among accidental weight lifting injuries, the percentage of relatively younger lifters is larger, while among the injuries that are not accidental, the percentage of relatively older lifters is larger.

6.20: The table gives the two marginal distributions. The marginal distribution of marital status is found by taking, for example, 337/8235 = 0.041, or 4.1% for the "Single" group. The marginal distribution of job grade is found by taking, for example, 955/8235 = 0.116, or 11.6%, for Grade 1. As rounded here, both sets of percents add to 100%.

Single	Married	Divorced	Widowed
4.1%	93.9%	1.5%	0.5%
Grade 1	Grade 2	Grade 3	Grade 4
11.6%	51.5%	30.2%	6.7%

6.21: The percent of single men in Grade 1 jobs is 58/337 = 0.172, or 17.2%. The percent of Grade 1 jobs held by single men is 58/955 = 0.0607, or 6.07%.

6.22: Divide the entries in the first column by the first column total; for example, from Problem 6.21, 17.2% is 0.172 = 58/337. These should add to 100%, except for possible rounding error.

Job Grade	1	2	3	4
% of Single Men	17.2%	65.9%	14.8%	2.1%

6.23: (a) We need to compute percents to account for the fact that the study included many more married men than single men, so we would expect their numbers to be higher in every job grade (even if marital status had no relationship with job level). (b) A table of percents is provided; descriptions of the relationship may vary. Single and widowed men had higher percents of Grade 1 jobs; single men had the lowest (and widowed men the highest) percents of Grade 4 jobs.

	Single	Married	Divorced	Widowed
Grade 1	17.2%	11.3%	11.9%	19.0%
Grade 4	2.1%	6.9%	5.6%	9.5%

6.24: Age is the main lurking variable: Married men would generally be older than single men, so they would have been in the workforce longer, and therefore had more time to advance in their careers.

6.25: (a) The two-way table of race (White, Black) versus death penalty (Death penalty, No death penalty) follows.

	White Defendant	Black Defendant
Death penalty	19	17
No peath penalty	141	149

(b) For black victims: The percentage of white defendants given the death penalty is 0/9 = 0, or 0%. The percentage of black defendants given the death penalty is 6/103 = 0.058, or 5.8%. For white victims: The percentage of white defendants given the death penalty is 19/151 = 0.126, or

12.6%. The percentage of black defendants given the death penalty is $11/63 = 0.175$, or 17.5%. Hence, for both victim races, black defendants are given the death penalty relatively more often than white defendants. However, overall, referring to the table in (a), $19/160 = 0.119$, or 11.9%, of white defendants got the death penalty, while $17/166 = 0.102$, or 10.2%, of black defendants got the death penalty. This illustrates Simpson's paradox. (c) For white defendants, $(19 + 132)/(19 + 132 + 0 + 9) = 0.9438 = 94.4\%$ of victims were white. For black defendants, only $(11 + 52)/(11 + 52 + 6 + 97) = 0.3795$, or 37.95%, of victims were white. Meanwhile, the death penalty was predominantly assigned to cases involving white victims: 14.0% of all cases with a white victim, while only 5.5% of all cases with a black victim had a death penalty assigned to the defendant. Hence, because most white defendants' victims are white, and cases with white victims carry additional risk of a death penalty, white defendants are being assigned the death penalty more often overall.

6.26: Examples will vary. Here is one very simple possibility. The key is to be sure that the three-way table has a lower percent of overweight people among the smokers than among the nonsmokers.

Smoker	Early Death	
	Yes	No
Obese	1	0
Not obese	4	2

Nonsmoker	Early Death	
	Yes	No
Obese	3	6
Not obese	1	3

Combined	Early Death	
	Yes	No
Obese	4	6
Not obese	5	5

6.27: PLAN: From the given two-way table of results, find and compare the conditional distributions of outcome (success, no success) for each treatment (Chantix, Bupropion, and Placebo). SOLVE: The percentages for each column are provided in the table. For example, for Chantix, the percentage of successes (no smoking in weeks 9–12) is $155/(155 + 197) = 0.4403$, or 44.0%. Since we're comparing success rates, we'll leave off the row for "% Smoking in weeks 9–12" since this is just 100% – % no Smoking in weeks 9–12.

	Chantix	Bupropion	Placebo
% No smoking in weeks 9–12	44.0%	29.5%	17.7%

CONCLUDE: Clearly, a larger percentage of subjects using Chantix were not smoking during weeks 9 – 12, compared with results for either of the other treatments. In fact, as we'll learn later, this result is statistically significant… random chance doesn't easily explain this difference, and we might conclude that Chantix use increases the chance of success.

6.28: PLAN: From the given two-way table of response by sex, find and compare the conditional distributions of response for men alone and women alone. SOLVE: The table represents the responses of 516 men and 636 women. To find the conditional distributions, divide each entry in the table by its column total. These percents are given in that table; for example, 76/516 = 0.1473, or 14.73%. CONCLUDE: Men are more likely to view animal testing as justified if it might save human lives: over two-thirds of men agree or strongly agree with this statement, compared to slightly less than half of women. The percents who disagree or strongly disagree tell a similar story: 16% of men versus 30% of women.

Response	Male	Female
Strongly agree	14.7%	9.3%
Agree	52.3%	38.8%
Neither	16.9%	21.9%
Disagree	11.8%	19.3%
Strongly disagree	4.3%	10.7%

6.29: PLAN: Calculate and compare the conditional distributions of sex for each degree level. SOLVE: We compute, for example, the percentage of women earning associate's degrees: 519/823 = 0.631, or 63.1%. The table shows the percent of women at each degree level, which is all we need for comparison. CONCLUDE: Women constitute a substantial majority of associate's, bachelor's, and master's degrees, a scant majority doctor's degrees, and slightly less than 50% of professional degrees.

Degree	% female
Associate's	63.1%
Bachelor's	57.5%
Master's	61.1%
Professional	49.5%
Doctor's	53.3%

6.30: PLAN: Find and compare the conditional distributions of type of complication for each of the three treatments. SOLVE: The table provides the percents of subjects with various complications for each treatment. For example, for subjects with Gastric banding, 81/5380 = 0.0151, or 1.5%, had non-life-threatening complications. CONCLUDE: Without question, gastric bypass surgery carries the greatest risk for both non-life-threatening and serious complications. Gastric banding seems to be the safest procedure, with the lowest rates for both types of complications.

	Non-life-threatening	Serious	None
Gastric banding	1.5%	0.9%	97.6%
Sleeve gastrectomy	3.6%	2.2%	94.1%
Gastric bypass	6.7%	3.6%	89.7%

6.31: PLAN: Find and compare the conditional distributions for health (self-reported) for each group (smokers and non-smokers). SOLVE: The table provides the percent of subjects with various health outlooks for each group. CONCLUDE: Clearly, the outlooks of current smokers are generally bleaker than that of current non-smokers. Much larger percentages of non-smokers reported being in "excellent" or "very good" health, while much larger percentages of smokers reported being in "fair" or "poor" health.

| | Health Outlook | | | | |
	Excellent	Very good	Good	Fair	Poor
Current smoker	6.2%	28.5%	35.9%	22.3%	7.2%
Current non-smoker	12.4%	39.9%	33.5%	14.0%	0.3%

6.32: (a) The two-way table is provided. (b) PLAN: Compare the conditional distribution of hatching given temperature. SOLVE: In order of increasing temperature, the proportions hatching are 16/27 = 0.593, or 59.3%, 38/56 = 0.679, or 67.9%, and 75/104 = 0.721, or 72.1%. (We could also construct a bar graph of these percents.) CONCLUDE: The percent hatching increases with temperature; the cold temperature did not prevent hatching, but made it less likely. The difference between the percents hatching at hot and neutral temperatures is fairly small, and may not be big enough to be called significant. (Statistical tests say that it is not.)

| | Temperature | | |
	Cold	Neutral	Hot
Hatched	16	38	75
Did not hatch	11	18	29

6.33–6.35 are Web-based exercises.

Chapter 7 Solutions

Test Yourself Exercise Answers are sketches. All of these problems are similar to ones found in Chapters 1–6, for which the solutions in this manual provide more detail.

7.1: (c)

7.2: Answers vary. Some suggestions for questions with a categorical response: "What is your class level (Freshman, Sophomore, etc.)?" or "Is this your first Statistics class?" Some suggestions for questions with a quantitative response: "How many hours per week do you work at a paying job?" or "How many hours do you spend studying in a typical week?"

7.3: (c)

7.4: (d)

7.5: (b)

7.6: (a)

7.7: (a)

7.8: (c)

7.9: (d)

7.10: (c)

7.11: (b)

7.12: (a) centimeters; (b) centimeters; (c) centimeters; (d) grams^2.

7.13: (b)

7.14: (d) 5 years is 60 months, and there are 10 of 40 observations below 60.

7.15: (a)

7.16: (d)

7.17: $P(X > 90) = P(Z > 1.81) = 1 - 0.9649 = 0.0351$, or 3.51%. (b) The middle 50% of all observations lie between the first and third quartiles, so the IQR is the range in which these observations lie. In Chapter 3, we see that the first and third quartiles are 0.67 standard deviations above and below average. Hence, these values are $75 - 0.67(8.3) = 69.44$ and $75 + 0.67(8.3) = 80.56$ ksi. The range (IQR) in which the middle values lie is therefore $80.56 - 69.44 = 11.12$ ksi.

7.18: (a) $P(X > 20) = P(Z > 0.33) = 1 - 0.6293 = 0.3707$. (b) $Z = 1.64$ (or 1.65), so allow $19 + 1.65(3) = 23.95$, or about 24 minutes.

7.19: (a) Minimum = 7.2, Q1 = 8.5, M = 9.3, Q3 = 10.9, Maximum = 12.8. (b) M = 27. (c) 25% of values exceed Q3 = 30. (d) Yes. Virtually all Torrey pine needles are longer than virtually all Aleppo pine needles. There is no overlap in the distributions, as seen by comparing, say, Minimum for Torrey pine needles (21) to Maximum for Aleppo pine needles (12.8).

7.20: (d)

7.21: (b)

7.22: (a)

7.23: (c)

7.24: (c)

7.25: (c)

7.26: (a)

7.27: (d)

7.28: (b)

7.29: (d)

7.30: (c)

7.31: (c)

7.32: (b)

7.33: (a)

7.34: The increased correlation suggests that the two types of stocks (American and European) now tend to rise together and fall together, which reduces the ability of one to hedge risk of the other.

7.35: (a) No. (b) $r^2 = 0.64$, or 64%.

7.36: (a) The least squares regression line is given by $\hat{y} = 10.07 + 86.03x$. (b) If $x = 0.60$, we predict $\hat{y} = 10.07 + (86.03)(0.60) = 61.688$ introspective ability. (c) For $x = 0.99$, we predict $\hat{y} = 95.24$ introspective ability. Since $r^2 = (0.448)^2 = 0.201$, only 20.1% of the variation in introspective scores are explained by our regression model. Predictions using this model aren't very reliable.

7.37: (a) 8.683 kg. (b) 10.517 kg. (c) Such a comparison would be unreasonable because the lean group is less massive, and therefore would be expected to burn less energy on average. (d) A plot follows. (e) Based on the plot, it appears that the rate of increase in energy burned per kilogram of mass is about the same for both groups. Of course, the obese monkeys are more massive, and therefore, on average, burn more energy, as computed in (a) and (b).

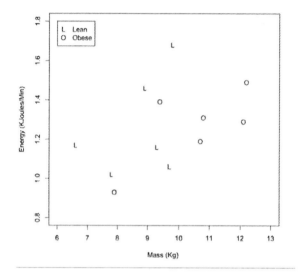

7.38: (a) The scatterplot is provided below. (b) There is a very strong, negative linear relationship between "Year" and "Percent of Smokers." There are no real outliers, but the rate of decline in smoking has varied over time… in the late 1980s, for example, there was a very sharp decline, while in the 1990s the decline slowed. (c) The least-squares regression line is given by $\hat{y} = 1017.009 - 0.497x$. (d) Over this time, on average, smoking declined by 0.497% per year (about 1% every two years). (e) $r^2 = (-0.98)^2 = 0.9604$, or 96.04%. (f) In the year 2010, we predict that $1017.009 - (0.497)(2010) = 18.04\%$ of adults smoke. The goal hasn't been achieved. (g) Such a prediction would be unreasonable because the year 2050 is far outside the range of years on which this model was based. This would be terrible extrapolation. In fact, the prediction is –1.8%, which is clearly impossible.

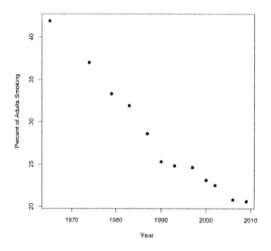

7.39: (a) 190/8474 = 0.0224, or 2.24%. (b) 633/8474 = 0.0747, or 7.47%. (c) 27/633 = 0.0427, or 4.27%. (d) 4621/8284 = 0.5578, or 55.78%. (e) The conditional distribution of CHD for each level of anger is tabulated below. The result for the high anger group was computed in (c), for example. Clearly, angrier people are at greater risk of CHD.

Low anger	Moderate anger	High anger
1.70%	2.33%	4.27%

7.40: (a) A graph (either a stemplot or histogram) shows that the distribution is slightly right-skewed; one observation is somewhat low, but not really an outlier. (b) Because of the slight right skew, we might expect the mean to be slightly larger, but the low observation will tend to counteract that. We find that $\bar{x}$ = 563.1 and M = 560 km^3 of water. (c) Because the distribution is not too skewed, one could choose the mean and standard deviation. Here, s = 136.5 km^3 of water. Alternatively, use the five-number summary: Min = 290, Q1 = 445, M = 560, Q3 = 670, Max = 900 (all km^3 of water).

```
2 | 9
3 |
3 | 6999
4 | 1222234
4 | 5678
5 | 00114
5 | 5566889
6 | 0001344
6 | 778889
7 | 011
7 | 7
8 | 0
8 | 8
9 | 0
```

7.41: The time plot shows a lot of fluctuation from year to year, but also shows a recent increase: Prior to 1972, the discharge rarely rose above 600 km^3, but since then, it has exceeded that level more than half the time. A histogram or stemplot cannot show this change over time.

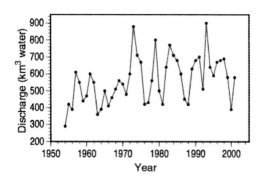

7.42: A stemplot is shown; a histogram would also be a good choice. The distribution is roughly Normal, though with enough irregularity that students may not be willing to call it Normal. The two low numbers and one high number are not extreme enough to be called outliers. The mean, standard deviation and five-number summary (all in days) are $\bar{x}$ = 15.287, s = 5.918, and Min = 1, Q1 = 11, M = 16, Q3 = 19, Max = 31. The median date is therefore May 5.

```
0 | 11
0 |
0 | 455
0 | 77
0 | 88999
1 | 00000000111111111
1 | 22222333
1 | 4445555
1 | 66666666777777
1 | 8899999999
2 | 0001111
2 | 2222333333
2 | 455
2 | 67
2 |
3 | 1
```

7.43: (a) The plot is provided. (b) The least-squares regression line is $\hat{y}$ = 160.79 – 0.07410x. The slope is negative, suggesting that the ice breakup day is decreasing (by 0.07410 day per year). (c) The regression line is not very useful for prediction, as it accounts for only about 11.7% (r^2 = 0.117) of the variation in ice breakup time.

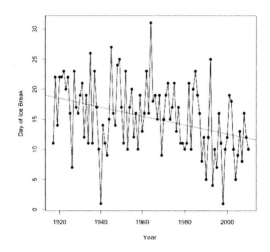

7.44: The five-number summaries are:

	Min	Q_1	M	Q_3	Max
1917 – 1939	7	12	19	22	26
1940 – 1962	1	11	16	20	27
1963 – 1985	9	11	17	20	31
1986 – 2010	1	8	11	16	25

Boxplots are also provided below. There is clearly no discernible pattern in the boxes, but the minimum values suggest a cyclic pattern (the minimum is 1 in every other group of years). This is also seen in the time plot above in Exercise 7.43.

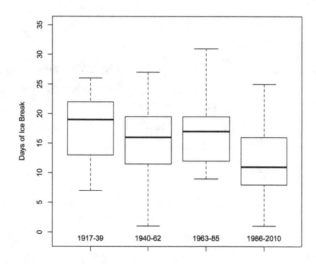

7.45: (a) and (b) Two stemplots are provided. The first shows all the data points, and the second omits the three highest countries, which are identified as outliers by use of the 1.5 × IQR criterion. In the absence of those outliers, the distribution is roughly symmetric. (c) The mean and standard deviation are $\bar{x} = 18.2447\%$ and $s = 7.0451\%$. Some students may instead report the five-number summary, which is Min = 3.14%, Q1 = 13.64%, M = 18.27%, Q3 = 24.08%, Max = 34.83%. (d) The U.S. share of G.D.P. is small compared to the other countries in this list; more than one standard deviation below the mean and below the first quartile of the distribution.

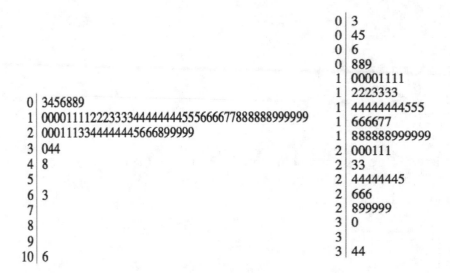

```
 0 | 3456889
 1 | 0000111122233334444444455566667778888888999999
 2 | 00011133444444445666899999
 3 | 044
 4 | 8
 5 |
 6 | 3
 7 |
 8 |
 9 |
10 | 6
```

```
0 | 3
0 | 45
0 | 6
0 | 889
1 | 00001111
1 | 2223333
1 | 44444444555
1 | 666677
1 | 888888999999
2 | 000111
2 | 33
2 | 44444445
2 | 666
2 | 899999
3 | 0
3 |
3 | 44
```

7.46: STATE: Do dead cicadas make good fertilizer? PLAN: Compare the seed masses for the two groups of plants (with and without cicadas), both graphically (using stemplots, histograms, or boxplots) and numerically (with appropriate statistics). SOLVE: Back-to-back stemplots show little difference overall. Both shapes are somewhat irregular, but neither is clearly higher or lower. Means and medians are also similar.

Cicada plants		Control plants
0	1	
	1	3
4	1	445
7	1	77
99	1	89999
111100	2	0111
3333332222	2	2
5544	2	4444445555
7777666	2	66666
999	2	89
110	3	
	3	
5	3	

CONCLUDE: The data give little reason to believe that cicadas make good fertilizer, at least on the basis of this response variable.

	$\bar{x}$	M
Cicada group	0.2426 mg	0.2380 mg
Control group	0.2221 mg	0.2410 mg

7.47: STATE: How does angle of deformity vary among young HAV patients requiring surgery? PLAN: Display the distribution with a graph and compute appropriate numerical summaries. SOLVE: A stemplot is shown; a histogram could also be used. The distribution seems to be fairly Normal apart from a high outlier of 50°. The five-number summary is preferred because of the outlier: Min = 13°, Q1 = 20°, M = 25°, Q3 = 30°, Max = 50°. (The mean and standard deviation are $\bar{x}$ = 25.4211° and s = 7.4748°.) CONCLUDE: Student descriptions of the distribution will vary. Most patients have a deformity angle in the range of 15° to 35°.

```
1 | 34
1 | 66788
2 | 000111123
2 | 55556666888
3 | 00012224
3 | 88
4 |
4 |
5 | 0
```

7.48: STATE: Do the data support the principle that "more prey attract more predators, who drive down the number of prey"? PLAN: We will examine the relationship with a scatterplot and (if appropriate) provide correlation and regression lines. SOLVE: The scatterplot suggests a positive linear association, albeit with lots of scatter, so correlation and regression are reasonable tools to summarize the relationship. The correlation is r = 0.6821, and the least-squares regression line is $\hat{y}$ = 0.1205 + 0.008569x. The regression line explains r^2 = 46.5% of the variation in the proportion killed. CONCLUDE: The analysis provides weak support for the idea that the proportion of perch killed rises with the number of perch present.

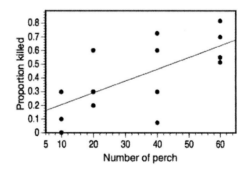

7.49: STATE: Can severity of MA be used to predict severity of HAV? PLAN: We examine the relationship with a scatterplot and (if appropriate) correlation and regression line. SOLVE: MA angle is the explanatory variable, so it should be on the horizontal axis of the scatterplot. The scatterplot shows a moderate to weak positive linear association, with one clear outlier (the patient with HAV angle 50°). The correlation is r = 0.3021, and the regression line is $\hat{y}$ = 19.723 + 0.3388x. CONCLUDE: MA angle can be used to give (very rough, imprecise) estimates of HAV angle, but the spread is so wide that the estimates would not be very reliable. The linear relationship explains only r^2 = 9.1% of the variation in HAV angle.

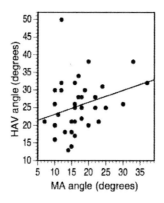

7.50: STATE: Do the data support the idea that more wildebeest reduce the percent of grasslands that are burned? PLAN: We will examine the relationship with a scatterplot and (if appropriate) correlation and regression line. SOLVE: The scatterplot suggests a fairly strong, negative linear association, so correlation and regression are reasonable tools to use here. The correlation is $r = -0.8035$, and the regression equation is $\hat{y} = 92.29 - 0.05762x$; the equation explains $r^2 = 64.6\%$ of the variation in burned grassland. CONCLUDE: The claim is supported: When wildebeest numbers are higher, the percent of grassland burned tends to be lower. Each additional 100 wildebeest decrease burned area by about 0.058% on the average.

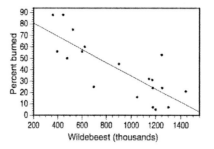

7.51: STATE: How does the cylinder wall thickness influence the gate velocity chosen by the skilled workers? PLAN: We will examine the relationship with a scatterplot and (if appropriate) correlation and regression line. SOLVE: The scatterplot, shown with the regression line $\hat{y} = 70.44 + 274.78x$, shows a moderate, positive linear relationship. The linear relationship explains about $r^2 = 49.3\%$ of the variation in gate velocity. CONCLUDE: The regression formula might be used as a rule of thumb for new workers to follow, but the wide spread in the scatterplot suggests that there may be other factors that should be taken into account in choosing the gate velocity.

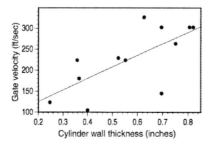

7.52: STATE: How do parent opinions of schools vary among these racial/ethnic groups?
PLAN: We will compare the groups using graphs and appropriate conditional distributions.
SOLVE: Student analyses will vary, as will choices of graphs. Some possible observations: all
three groups were basically identical in the percent rating schools as "poor." Hispanics appear to
be more likely to rate their children's schools as "excellent" but less likely to call them "good."
CONCLUDE: Student conclusions will vary also.

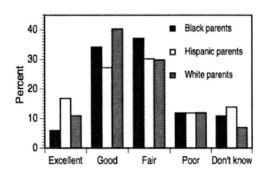

7.53: (a) The scatterplot of 2003 returns against 2002 returns shows (ignoring the outlier) a
strong negative association. (b) The correlation for all 23 points is $r = -0.6230$; with
the outlier removed, the correlation is $r = -0.8722$. The outlier deviates from the linear pattern of
the other points; removing it makes the negative association stronger, and so r moves closer to -1. (c) Regression formulas are given in the table on the right. The first line is solid in the plot,
the second is the dashed line. The least-squares regression line makes the sum of the squares of
the vertical deviations of the points from the line as small as possible. The line for the 22 other
funds is so far below Fidelity Gold that the squared deviation is very large. The line must pivot
up toward Fidelity Gold in order to minimize the sum of squares for all 23 deviations. Fidelity
Gold is very influential.

	r	Equation
All 23 funds	-0.6230	$\hat{y} = 29.2512 - 0.4501x$
Without Fidelity Gold	-0.8722	$\hat{y} = 18.1106 - 0.9429x$

7.54: (a) The regression equation is $\hat{y} = 93.92 + 0.7783x$. The third point (pure tone 241, call 485 spikes/second) is A (circled in plot). The first point (474 and 500 spikes/second) is B; it is marked with a square. (b) The correlation drops only slightly (from 0.6386 to 0.6101) when A is removed; it drops more drastically (to 0.4793) without B. (c) When either point is removed, the slope decreases. Without A, the line is $\hat{y} = 98.42 + 0.6792x$; without B, it is $\hat{y} = 101.1 + 0.6927x$.

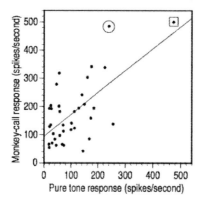

7.55: (a) Fish catch (on the horizontal axis) is the explanatory variable. The point for 1999 is at the bottom of the plot. (b) The correlations are given in the table below. The outlier decreases r because it weakens the strength of the association. (c) The two regression lines are given in the table; the solid line in the plot uses all points, while the dashed line omits the outlier. The effect of the outlier on the line is small: it pulls the line down on the left side (and increases the slope) very slightly, but for making predictions, both lines would give similar results.

	r	Equation
All points	0.6724	$\hat{y} = -21.09 + 0.6345x$
Without 1999	0.8042	$\hat{y} = -19.05 + 0.5788x$

Chapter 8 Solutions

8.1: (a) The population is (all) college students. (b) The sample is the 104 students at the researcher's college who returned the questionnaire.

8.2: The population is all the artifacts discovered at the dig. The sample is those artifacts (2% of the population) that are chosen for inspection.

8.3: (a) The population is all 45,000 people who made credit card purchases. (b) The sample is the 137 people who returned the survey form.

8.4: It is a convenience sample; she is only getting opinions from students who are at the student center at a certain time of day. This might underrepresent some group: commuters, graduate students, or nontraditional students, for example.

8.5: Since all the students surveyed are enrolled in a special senior honors class, these students may be more likely to be interested in joining the club (and more willing to pay \$35 to do so). The direction of bias is likely to overestimate the proportion of all psychology majors willing to pay to join this club. This is a convenience sample.

8.6: Number from 01 to 30 alphabetically (down the columns). With the applet: Population = 1 to 30, select a sample of size 4, then click Reset and Sample. With Table B, enter at line 122 and choose 13 = Crestview, 15 = Fairington, 05 = Brandon Place, and 29 = Village Square.

8.7: Number from 01 to 26 alphabetically (down the columns). With the applet: Population = 1 to 26, select a sample of size 5, then click Reset and Sample. With Table B, enter at line 134 and choose 16 = Ippolito, 18 = Jung, 13 = Gupta, 21 = Modur, and 04 = Bonds.

8.8. (a) Assign five-digit labels to each record, from 00001 to 55914. (b) With Table B, enter at line 120 and choose 35476, 39421, 04266, 35435, and 43742.

8.9: With the election close at hand, the polling organization wants to increase the accuracy of its results. Larger samples provide better information about the population.

8.10: The sample size for the general public is larger than the sample size for Pentecostals. Larger samples yield more information, which means more accuracy, which means a smaller margin of error.

8.11: Label the suburban townships from 01 to 30, down the columns. With Table B, enter at line 105 and choose 29 = Wheeling, 07 = Elk Grove, 19 = Orland, 14 = New Trier, and 17 = Norwood Park. Next, label the Chicago townships from 1 to 8, down the columns. With Table B, enter at line 115 and choose 6 = Rogers Park, 1 = Hyde Park, and 4 = Lake View.

8.12: Label the students in each class as shown in the table below. If Table B (starting at line 122) is used to choose the samples, the students selected are those listed in the table.

Class	Labels	First five students in sample
Freshmen	0001 to 1127	0529, 0908, 0815, 0727, 1025
Sophomores	001 to 989	602, 755, 892, 330, 634
Juniors	001 to 943	184, 281, 868, 710, 350
Seniors	001 to 895	143, 367, 494, 271, 758

8.13: The higher no-answer was probably the second period—more families are likely to be gone for vacations, or to be outside enjoying the warmer weather, and so on. Nonresponse of this type might underrepresent those who are more affluent (and are able to travel). In general, high nonresponse rates always make results less reliable, because we do not know what information we are missing.

8.14: Question A asks whether existing law should be overturned. Question B simply asks whether openly gay men and women should be allowed to serve. Anybody who answers "yes" to Question A would surely answer "yes" to Question B, but the converse is not true. Hence, Question A is slanted toward a more negative response on gays in the military.

8.15: (a) and (b) Features will vary depending on the website chosen. (c) The weakness of any online poll is that it relies on voluntary response. Most online poll samples are not representative of any larger population of use or interest to the researcher.

8.16: Answers will vary. One possible answer follows. (a) One might guess that the population of people that own only a cell phone and no landline phone is more likely to regularly text, and would therefore be more likely to approve of texting while driving. (b) As explained, this group would be more supportive of texting while driving, so the sample percentage that favors making texting while driving illegal would decrease. (c) This is, indeed, bias. We're likely to overestimate the percentage of all adults that favor making texting while driving illegal.

8.17: (a) all customers who have purchased something in the last year.

8.18: (b) the 152 voters returning the questionnaire.

8.19: (b) 5458, 0815, 0727, 1025, 6027.

8.20: (b) the poll uses voluntary response, so the results tell us little about the population of interest.

8.21: (b) a stratified random sample (plots are stratified by terrain).

8.22: (a) 001, 002, 003, …, 439, 440. Each member of the population needs a 3-digit label, and we need 440 of them (not 441, as in (b)).

8.23: (c) 04, 18, 07, 13, 02, 05. (Notice that in (b) "07" appears in the sample twice.)

8.24: (b) undercoverage.

8.25: (b) The result for the entire sample is more accurate because both come from the same sample.

8.26: The population is all adults, aged 18 and older, living in the United States. The sample consists of the 1,014 adults randomly selected.

8.27: The population is the 1000 envelopes stuffed during a given hour. The sample is the 40 envelopes selected.

8.28: Numbering from 01 to 35 alphabetically (down the columns), we enter Table B at line 131 and choose 05 = Burke, 32 = Vore, 19 = Kessis, 04 = Bower, 25 = Prince, 29 = Shoepf, 20 = Lu, and 16 = Heaton. (Note: Using the table, "19" comes up a few times. After the first time "19" appears, it needs to be discarded for an alternate value.)

8.29: With the applet: Population = 1 to <u>287</u>, select a sample of size <u>20</u>, then click <u>Reset</u> and <u>Sample</u>. Using Table B, number the area codes 001 to 287. Then, enter at line 135, and pay attention to the instructions that if we use the table, we'll pick only 5 numbers. The selected area codes are 255, 100, 120, 126, 008.

8.30: (a) Assign labels 0001 through 1410. (b) Beginning at line 105, we choose plots 0769, 1315, 0094, 0720, and 0906.

8.31: (a) Alphabetize the 6168 names (using middle initials or a student ID to distinguish between two people with the same name). Label these students with an ID 0001 to 6168. (b) Using Table B, entering at line 135, the sample is 5556, 5839, 1007, 1120, 1513, 1260, 0842, and 1447.

8.32: If one always begins at the same place, then the results would not really be random.

8.33: (a) False. Such regularity holds only in the long run. If it were true, you could look at the first 39 digits and know whether or not the 40th digit was a 0. (b) True. All pairs of digits (there are 100, from 00 to 99) are equally likely. (c) False. Four random digits have chance 1/10,000 to be 0000, so this sequence will occasionally occur. The sequence 0000 is no more or less random than 1234 or 2718, or any other four-digit sequence.

8.34: (a) The population is (something like) adult residents of the United States. (b) The nonresponse rate is 1169/2000 = 58.45%. (c) This question will likely have response bias; specifically, many people will give an inaccurate count of how many movies they have seen in the past year.

8.35: Online polls, call-in polls, and voluntary response polls in general tend to attract responses from those who have strong opinions on the subject, and therefore are often not representative of the population as a whole. On the other hand, there is no reason to believe that randomly chosen adults would over-represent any particular group, so the responses from such a group give a more reliable picture of public opinion.

8.36: The response rate was 5029/45,956 = 0.1094, so the nonresponse rate was 0.8906 = 89.1%.

8.37: (a) Assign labels 0001 through 5024, enter the table at line 104, and select: 1388, 0746, 0227, 4001, and 1858. (b) More than 171 respondents have run red lights. We would not expect very many people to claim they *have* run red lights when they have not, but some people will deny running red lights when they have.

8.38: People likely claim to wear their seat belts because they know they should; they are embarrassed or ashamed to say that they do not always wear seat belts. Such bias is likely in most surveys about seat belt use (and similar topics).

8.39: (a) Each person has a 10% chance: 4 of 40 men, and 3 of 30 women. (b) This is not an SRS because not every group of 7 people can be chosen; the only possible samples are those with 4 men and 3 women. 8.40: Label the members of District 1 001, 002, …, 997. Label those of District 2 001, 002, …, 803. Continue in like manner for each district. Now, to sample 5 members from District 1, using Table B, entering at line 122, our sample is: 138, 738, 159, 895, and 052. To sample 5 members from District 2, using Table B, entering at line 131, our sample is: 050, 071, 663, 281, and 194. We use different lines so that the samples will be independent.

8.41: Sample separately in each stratum; that is, assign separate labels, then choose the first sample, then continue on in the table to choose the next sample, etc. Beginning with line 102 in Table B, we choose:

Forest type	Labels	Parcels selected
Climax 1	01 to 36	19, 27, 26, 17
Climax 2	01 to 72	09, 55, 32, 22, 69, 56, 52
Climax 3	01 to 31	13, 07, 02
Secondary	01 to 42	27, 40, 01, 18

8.42: (a) The sample size for the public is much larger, so the survey is more accurate for this group. (b) It's likely that people working health-related fields have opinions that differ from those of the public. The researchers probably want to examine this.

8.43: (a) Since 200/5 = 40, we will choose one of the first 40 names at random. Beginning on line 120, the addresses selected are 35, 75, 115, 155, and 195. (Only the first number is chosen from the table.) (b) All addresses are equally likely; each has chance 1/40 of being selected. To see this, note that each of the first 40 has chance 1/40 because one is chosen at random. But each address in the second 40 is chosen exactly when the corresponding address in the first 40 is, so each of the second 40 also has chance 1/40. And so on. This is not an SRS because the only possible samples have exactly one address from the first 40, one address from the second 40, and so on. An SRS could contain any 5 of the 200 addresses in the population. Note that this view of systematic sampling assumes that the number in the population is a multiple of the sample size.

8.44: (a) This design would omit households without telephones, those with only cell phones, and those with unlisted numbers. Such households would likely be made up of poor individuals (who cannot afford a phone), those who choose not to have phones, and those who do not wish to have their phone numbers published. (b) Those with unlisted numbers would be included in the sampling frame when a random-digit dialer (RDD) is used. (Additionally, RDDs exclude cell phones, although students may not be aware of this fact. For a discussion of this issue, see http://www.mysterypollster.com/main/2004/10/arianna_huffing.html.)

8.45: (a) Automated random digit dialing is a fast, economical way to randomly dial landline telephone numbers. (b) In some families, the adult that answers the phone regularly may be systematically different from an adult that does not. For example, people not working at a job may be at home more often, and therefore may be more likely to answer the phone. (c) There could be (and probably are) big differences between landline phone users and cellular phone users. The design in question is a stratified sample.

8.46: (a) The wording is clear, but will almost certainly be slanted toward a high positive response. (Would anyone hear the phrase "brain cancer" and *not* be inclined to agree that a warning label is a good idea?) (b) The question makes the case for a national health care system, and so will slant responses toward "yes." (c) This survey question is most likely to produce a response similar to: "Uhh...yes? I mean, no? I'm sorry, could you repeat the question?" (And, if the person is able to understand the question, it is slanted in favor of day-care subsidies.)

8.47: Answers will vary considerably. See the textbook for several examples. (a) One example: "Should colleges do away with the 'tenure' system, which effectively allows lazy and incompetent faculty members to stay in highly-paid, easy, taxpayer-funded jobs?" (b) On example: "Do you regularly look at online pornography?"

8.48: In Canada, as in many places, elected officials aren't necessarily qualified. In this case, the Minister is terribly misguided. Critics of the proposal are worried that the sample will not be representative of the population — presumably because people that fill out the optional long-form questions will be systematically different from those that don't. Larger samples do not address such problems of bias.

8.49 and 8.50 are Web-based exercises.

Chapter 9 Solutions

9.1: This is an observational study: No treatment was assigned to the subjects; we merely observed cell phone usage (and presence/absence of cancer). The explanatory variable is cell phone usage, and the response variable is whether or not a subject has brain cancer.

9.2: This is an experiment: Each subject is (presumably randomly) assigned to a group, each with its own treatment (Arial or Brush font). The explanatory variable is the font, and the response variables are then perceived effort (in minutes) and willingness to make the exercise part of their daily routine.

9.3: This is an observational study, so it is not reasonable to conclude any cause-and-effect relationship. At best, we might advise smokers that they should be mindful of potential weight gain and its accompanying ailments.

9.4: Subjects: the "healthy people aged 18 to 40." Factor: the pill given to the subject. Treatments: ginkgo or placebo. Response variable: the number (or fraction) of e's identified by each subject.

9.5: Individuals: pine seedlings. Factor: amount of light. Treatments: full light, 25% light, or 5% light. Response variable: dry weight at the end of the study.

9.6: Subjects: the students. Factors: type of attack, and prime used. Treatments: for the prime: *love thy neighbor* prime, or *eye-for-an-eye* prime; for the type of attack: on military target, or on cultural/educational target. Response variable: rating of U.S. reaction to attack.

		Prime Used	
		Love thy Neighbor	Eye-for-an-Eye
Target	Military	1	2
	Cultural	3	4

9.7: Making a comparison between the treatment group and the percent finding work *last year* is not helpful. Over a year, many things can change: the state of the economy, hiring costs (due to an increasing minimum wage or the cost of employee benefits), etc. (In order to draw conclusions, we would need to make the $500 bonus offer to some people and not to others, and compare the two groups.)

9.8. (a) The diagram is provided. The response variable is weight loss. (b) Label the students from 01 to 50, and pick 25 to receive Treatment 1 (the rest will receive Treatment 2). If using Table B, line 130, the sample is 05, 16, 48, 17, 40, 20, 19, 45, 32, 41, 04, 25, 29, 43, 37, 39, 31, 50, 18, 07, 13, 33, 30, 21, 36.

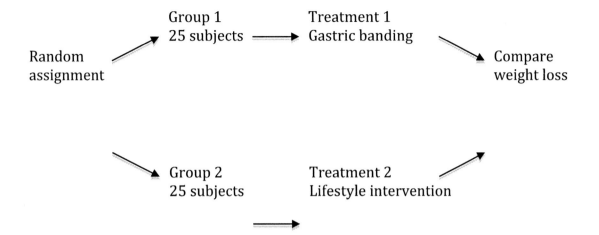

9.9. (a) Diagram below. (b) If using Table B, label 01 to 36 and take two digits at a time.

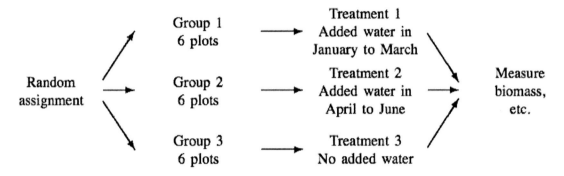

9.10. Assign 24/6 = 4 students to each treatment. The diagram is shown below. We assign labels 01 through 24, then use the first four 2-digit numbers in this range for Group 1, the next four for Group 2, etc. The table below shows the assignments. Note that with this many assignments, you will run through many lines of Table B. Once you've filled out members for 5 groups, the 6th group contains all the remaining, unassigned subjects.

Group 1: 20 Shi, 16 Kruger, 04 Baker, 18 Minor
Group 2: 07 Brower, 13 Greenberg, 02 Anthony, 05 Biery
Group 3: 19 Schwartz, 23 Truitt, 21 Stanley, 08 Carroll
Group 4: 10 Cote, 11 Delp, 15 Koster, 12 Disbro
Group 5: 14 Kessis, 09 Cohen, 24 Walsh, 22 Tory
Group 6: 01 Abramson, 03 Austen, 06 Blake, 17 Linder

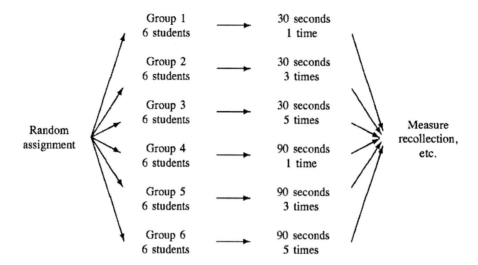

9.11. In a controlled scientific study, the effects of factors other than the nonphysical treatment (e.g., the placebo effect, differences in the prior health of the subjects) can be eliminated or accounted for, so that the differences in improvement observed between the subjects can be attributed to the differences in treatments.

9.12. If this year is considerably different in some way from last year, we cannot compare electricity consumption over the two years. For example, if this summer is warmer, the customers may run their air conditioners more. The possible differences between the two years would confound the effects of the treatments.

9.13. (a) The researchers simply observed the diets of subjects; they did not alter them. (That is, no treatments were assigned.) (b) Such language is reasonable because with observational studies, no "cause and effect" conclusion would be reasonable.

9.14. "Double-blind" means that the treatment (testosterone or placebo) assigned to a subject was unknown to both the subject and those responsible for assessing the effectiveness of that treatment. "Randomized" means that patients were randomly assigned to receive either the testosterone supplement or a placebo. "Placebo-controlled" means that some of the subjects were given placebos. Even though these possess no medical properties, some subjects may show improvement or benefits just as a result of participating in the experiment; the placebos allow those doing the study to observe this effect.

9.15. In this case, "lack of blindness" means that the experimenter knows which subjects were taught to meditate. He or she may have some expectation about whether or not meditation will lower anxiety; this could unconsciously influence the diagnosis.

9.16. (a) Each swimmer swims one time using each breathing technique (B2 and B4). A coin is tossed to determine the order in which these techniques are used. (b) In a completely randomized design, the 10 male collegiate swimmers would be assigned randomly to the two treatments, 5 swimmers using technique B2 and the other 5 using technique B4. (c) If swimmers select their own technique, it would be an observational study.

9.17. (a) *Completely randomized design:* Randomly assign 15 students to Group 1 (easy mazes) and the other 15 to Group 2 (hard mazes). Compare the time estimates of Group 1 with those of Group 2. (b) *Matched-pairs design:* Each student does the activity twice, once with the easy mazes, and once with the hard mazes. Randomly decide (for each student) which set of mazes is used first. Compare each student's "easy" and "hard" time estimate (for example, by looking at each "hard" minus "easy" difference). *Alternate matched-pairs design:* Again, all students do the activity twice. Randomly assign 15 students to Group 1 (easy first) and 15 to Group 2 (hard first).

9.18. For each block (pair of lecture sections), randomly assign one section to be taught using standard methods and the other to be taught with multimedia. Then (at the end of the term) compare final-exam scores and student attitudes. The diagram below is *part* of the whole block diagram; there would also be three other pieces like this (one for each of the other instructors). The randomization will vary with the starting line in Table B—or the randomization can be done by flipping a coin for each block.

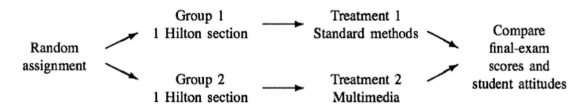

9.19. (a) This is an observational study: behavior (alcohol consumption) is observed, but no treatment is imposed.

9.20. (b) This is an experiment (a treatment is imposed), but there is no control group.

9.21. (c) two factors, each with two levels.

9.22. (b) completely randomized design.

9.23. (b) the score on the memory test of their recall of advertisements is the response.

9.24. (a) Each of the 36 subjects needs a label.

9.25. (b) The communities are paired up, then one is chosen to have the advertising campaign.

9.26. (a) The choice should be made randomly.

9.27. (b) This was a (matched-pairs) experiment, but in order to give useful information, the subjects should be chosen from those who might be expected to buy this car.

9.28. (a) This is an observational study; the subjects chose their own "treatments" (how much to drink). The explanatory variable is alcohol consumption, and the response variable is whether or not a subject dies. (There may have been other variables, but these were the only ones mentioned in the problem.) (b) Many answers are possible. For example, some nondrinkers might avoid drinking because of other health concerns. We do not know what kind of alcohol (beer? wine? whiskey?) the subjects were drinking.

9.29. This is an experiment, because the treatment is selected (randomly, we assume) by the interviewer. The explanatory variable (treatment) is the level of identification, and the response variable is whether or not the interview is completed.

9.31. (a) In an observational study, we simply observe subjects who have chosen to take supplements and compare them with others who do not take supplements. In an experiment, we *assign* some subjects to take supplements and assign the others to take no supplements (or better yet, assign the others to take a placebo). (b) "Randomized" means that the assignment to treatments is made randomly, rather than by some other method (e.g., asking for volunteers). "Controlled" means that some subjects were used as a "control" group—probably meaning that they received placebos—which gives a basis for comparison to observe the effects of the treatment. (c) Subjects who choose to take supplements have other characteristics that are confounded with the effect of the supplements; one of those characteristics is that people in this group are more likely to make healthy lifestyle choices (about smoking, drinking, eating, exercise, etc.). When we randomly assign subjects to a treatment, the effect of those characteristics is erased, because some of those subjects will take the supplement, and some will take the placebo.

9.32. In the diagram below, equal numbers of subjects are assigned to each treatment.

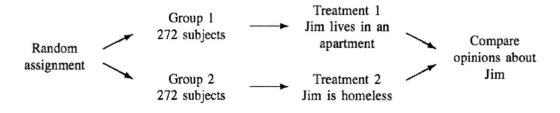

9.33. (a) Diagram below. (b) Assign labels 001 to 120. If using Table B, line 108 gives 090, 009, 067, 092, 041, 059, 040, 080, 029, 091

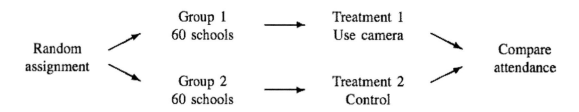

9.34. (a) A diagram is shown below. (b) Label the subjects from 01 through 30. From line 120, we choose subjects corresponding to the numbers 16, 04, 26, 21, 19, 07, 22, 10, 25, 13, 15, 05, 29, 09, 08 for the first group, and the rest for group 2. Hence, the marijuana group consists of Mattos, Bower, Williams, Sawant, Reichert, Deis, Scannell, Giriunas, Stout, Kennedy, Mani, Burke, Zaccai, Fritz, and Fleming. All other subjects are assigned to the non-marijuana group. (c) This could be a double-blind experiment, assuming that subjects can't distinguish between the types of marijuana smoked. Also, the persons measuring output and earnings of subjects don't know what kind of marijuana a subject smoked.

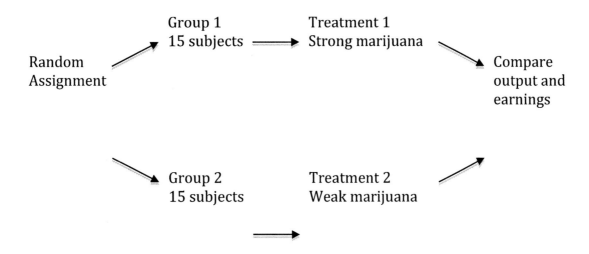

9.35. Use a completely randomized design; the diagram is provided. Labeling the men from 01 through 39, and starting on line 107 of Table B, we make the assignments shown in the table on the right.

Group 1:   20, 11, 38, 31, 07, 24, 17, 09, 06
Group 2:   36, 15, 23, 34, 16, 19, 18, 33, 39
Group 3:   08, 30, 27, 12, 04, 35
Group 4:   02, 32, 25, 14, 29, 03, 22, 26, 10
Group 5:   Everyone else

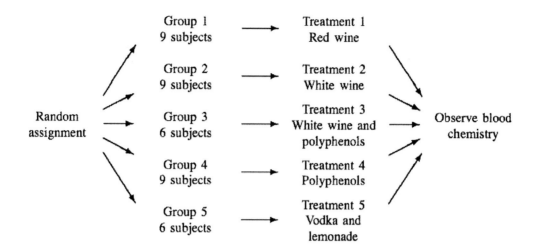

9.36. (a) There are 2 factors. The first factor is Type of granola, and has two levels (regular and low-fat). The second factor is Serving size label, and has three levels (2 servings, 1 serving, and no label). Hence, there are 6 treatment combinations (regular granola at 2 servings, regular granola at 1 serving, regular granola with no serving label, low-fat granola with 2 servings, low-fat granola with 1 serving, and low-fat granola with no serving label). At 20 subjects per treatment, there were 120 subjects in the experiment. (b) The outline looks as the one in Exercise 9.10, except that each of the 6 groups has 20 subjects, and the treatments are as described in (a).

9.37. (a) The outline is given below. There are 40 subjects, so we assign 10 subjects to each of the four treatments. The four treatments are outlined:

	Antidepressant	No drug
Stress management	1	2
None	3	4

(b) Assign labels 01 through 40 (in alphabetical order). The full randomization is easy with the Simple Random Sample applet: each successive sample leaves the population hopper, so that you need only click Sample three times to assign 30 subjects to three groups; the 10 subjects remaining in the hopper are the fourth group. Alternatively, line 125 of Table B gives the following subjects for Group 1: 21 Jiang, 37 Suarez, 18 Hersch, 23 Kim, 19 Hurwitz, 03 Alawi, 39 Wilson   24 Landers, 27 Morgan, and 13 Garrett.

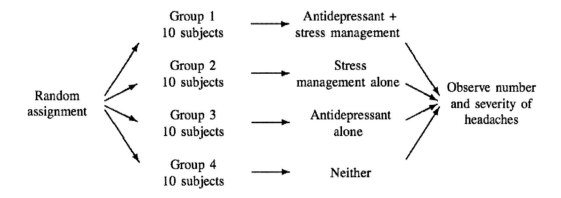

9.38. (a) Diagram below. (b) Assign labels from 001 to 240. (c) Randomly select 53 subjects for Treatment 1, then 64 for Treatment 2, then 60 for Treatment 3. The remaining 63 subjects belong to Treatment 4. If Table B is used, subjects chosen will vary with starting line.

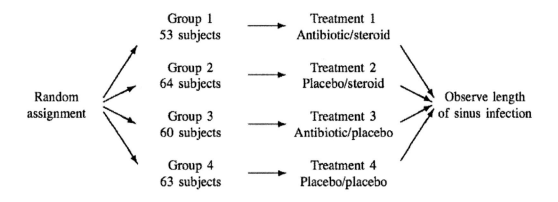

9.39. The factors are pill type and spray type. "Double-blind" means that the treatment assigned to a patient was unknown to both the patient and those responsible for assessing the effectiveness of that treatment. "Placebo-controlled" means that some of the subjects were given placebos. Even though these possess no medical properties, some subjects may show improvement or benefits just as a result of participating in the experiment; the placebos allow those doing the study to observe this effect.

9.40. "No significant difference" does *not* mean the groups are identical. While there almost certainly were *some* differences in these variables between the four groups, those differences were no bigger than we might expect from true random allocation. For example, the proportions of smokers in the four groups were sufficiently similar that the effect of smoking on sinus infections would be nearly the same in each group.

9.41. (a) The subjects are randomly chosen Starbucks customers. Each subject tastes two cups of coffee, in identical unlabeled cups. One contains regular mocha frappuccino, the other the new light version. The cups are presented in random order, half the subjects get regular then light, the other half light then regular. Each subject says which cup he or she prefers. (b) We must assign

10 customers to get regular coffee first. Label the subjects 01 to 20. Starting at line 141, the "regular first" group is: 12, 16, 02, 08, 17, 10, 05, 09, 19, 06.

9.42. The sketches requested in the problem are not shown here; random assignments will vary among students. (a) Label the circles 1 to 6, then randomly select three (using Table B, or simply by rolling a die) to receive the extra CO_2. Observe the growth in all six regions, and compare the mean growth within the three treated circles with the mean growth in the other three (control) circles. (b) Select pairs of circles in each of three different areas of the forest. For each pair, randomly select one circle to receive the extra CO_2 (using Table B or by flipping a coin). For each pair, compute the difference in growth (treated minus control).

9.43. Each player will be put through the sequence (100 yards, four times) twice—once with oxygen and once without. For each player, randomly determine whether to use oxygen on the first or second trial. Allow ample time (perhaps a day or two) between trials for full recovery.

9.44. (a) This is a block design. (b) The diagram might be similar to the one below (which assumes equal numbers of subjects in each group).

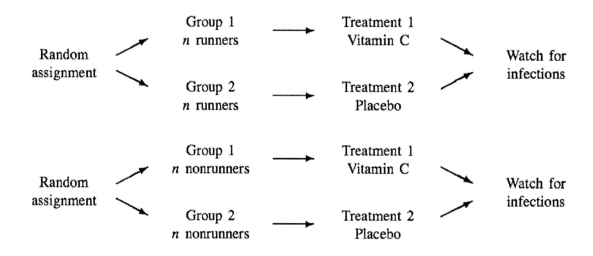

9.45. Diagram is shown below. The last stage ("Observe heart health") might be described in more detail.

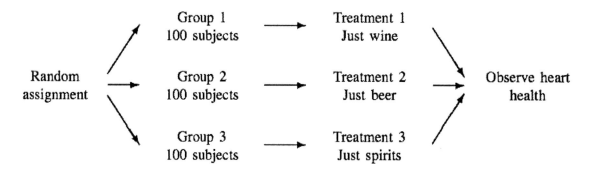

9.46. Divide the men and women into three groups of equal size. Diagram below.

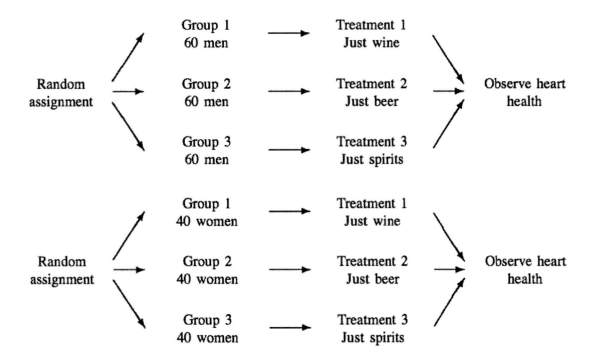

9.47. Any experiment randomized in this way assigns all the women to one treatment and all the men to the other. That is, sex is completely confounded with treatment. If women and men respond differently to the treatment, the experiment will be strongly biased. The direction of the bias is random, depending on the coin toss.

9.48. (a) The explanatory variable is the beta-carotene/vitamin(s) taken each day; the response variable is whether or not colon cancer develops. (b) Diagram is shown below; equal group sizes are convenient but not necessary. (c) Neither the subjects nor the researchers who examined them knew who was getting which treatment. (d) The observed differences were no more than what might reasonably occur by chance even if there is no effect due to the treatments. (e) Fruits and vegetables contain fiber; this could account for the benefits of those foods. Also, people who eat lots of fruits and vegetables may have healthier diets overall (e.g., less red meat).

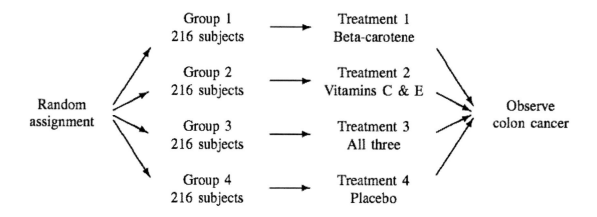

9.49. (a) "Randomized" means that patients were randomly assigned to receive either Saint-John's-wort or a placebo. "Double-blind" means that the treatment assigned to a patient was unknown to both the patient and those responsible for assessing the effectiveness of that treatment. "Placebo-controlled" means that some of the subjects were given placebos. Even though these possess no medical properties, some subjects may show improvement or benefits just as a result of participating in the experiment; the placebos allow those doing the study to observe this effect. (b) Diagram below.

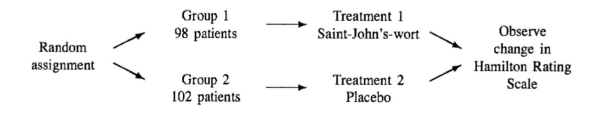

9.50. (a) We expect half of the sample to be made up of older students, so we expect 12.5 (half of 25) older students in the sample. (b) Results will vary, but probability computations reveal that more than 97.7% of samples will have 9 to 16 older employed subjects (and 99.6% of samples have 8 to 17 older employed subjects). Additionally, if students average their 20 samples, nearly all students (more than 99%) should find that the average number of older employed subjects is between 11.3 and 13.7.

Note: X, *the number of older employed subjects in the sample, has a hypergeometric distribution with parameters N = 50, r = 25, n = 25, so that P($9 \leq X \leq 16$) = 0.977. The theoretical average number of older employed subjects in the sample is 12.5.*

9.51 and 9.52 are Web-based exercises.

Chapter 10 Solutions

10.1: In the long run, of a large number of Texas Hold 'em games in which you hold a pair, the fraction in which you can make four of a kind will be about 2/245. It *does not* mean that exactly 2 out of 245 such hands would yield four of a kind. The probability of an event is the long-run frequency of times the event occurs if the experiment is repeated endlessly... not 245 times.

10.2: (a) An impossible event has probability 0. (b) A certain event has probability 1. (c) 0.99 would correspond to an even that is very likely but will not occur once in a while in a long sequence of trials. (d) An event with probability 0.45 will occur slightly less often than it occurs.

10.3: (a) There are 21 zeros among the first 200 digits of the table (rows 101–105), for a proportion of 0.105. (b) Answers will vary, but more than 99% of all students should get between 7 and 33 heads out of 200 flips.

10.4: (a) In almost 99% of all simulations, there will be between 5 and 15 heads, so the sample proportion will be between 0.25 and 0.75. (b) Shown is the theoretical histogram; a stemplot of 25 proportions will have roughly that shape.

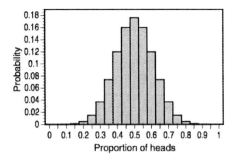

10.5: (a) S = {lives on campus, lives off campus}. (b) S = {All numbers between _____ and _____ years}. (Choices of upper and lower limits will vary.) (c) S = {all amounts greater than or equal to 0}, or S = {0, 0.01, 0.02, 0.03, . . .}. (d) S = {A, B, C, D, F} (students might also include "+" and "–").

10.6: (a) The accompanying table illustrates the 16 possible pair combinations in the sample space. (b)Each of the 16 outcomes has probability 1/16.

10.7: For the sample space, add 1 to each pair-total in the table shown in the previous solution: S = {3, 4, 5, 6, 7, 8, 9}. As all faces are equally likely and the dice are independent, each of the 16 possible pairings is equally likely, so (for example) the probability of a total of 5 is 3/16, because 3 pairings add to 4 (and then we add 1). The complete set of probabilities is shown in the table.

Total	Probability
3	1/16
4	2/16
5	3/16
6	4/16
7	3/16
8	2/16
9	1/16

10.8: (a) 23% (17% + 6%) majored in engineering or science. This makes use of Rule 3, because (assuming there are no double majors) "undergraduate students in engineering" and "undergraduate students in science" have no students in common. (b) 47% (100% − 53%) did not major in business or commerce. This makes use of Rule 4.

10.9: (a) Event B specifically rules out obese subjects, so there is no overlap with event A. (b) A or B is the event "The person chosen is overweight or obese." $P(A \text{ or } B) = P(A) + P(B) = 0.34 + 0.33 = 0.67$. (c) $P(C) = 1 − P(A \text{ or } B) = 1 − 0.67 = 0.33$.

10.10: (a) The given probabilities have sum 0.90, so P(other language) = 0.10. (b) P(not English) = $1 − 0.08 = 0.92$. (Or, add the other three probabilities.) (c) P (neither English nor French) = $0.02 + 0.10 = 0.12$. (Or, subtract $0.08 + 0.80$ from 1.)

10.11: Model 1: Not legitimate (probabilities have sum 6/7). Model 2: Legitimate. Model 3: Not legitimate (probabilities have sum 7/6). Model 4: Not legitimate (probabilities cannot be more than 1).

10.12: (a) A = {4, 5, 6, 7, 8, 9}, so $P(A) = 0.097 + 0.079 + 0.067 + 0.058 + 0.051 + 0.046 = 0.398$. (b) B = {2, 4, 6, 8}, so $P(B) = 0.176 + 0.097 + 0.067 + 0.051 = 0.391$. (c) A or B = {2, 4, 5, 6, 7, 8, 9}, so $P(A \text{ or } B) = 0.176 + 0.097 + 0.079 + 0.067 + 0.058 + 0.051 + 0.046 = 0.574$. This is different from $P(A) + P(B)$ because A and B are not disjoint.

10.13: (a) This is a legitimate probability model because the probabilities sum to 1. (b) The event {X < 4} is the event that somebody lifts weights 3 or fewer days per week. $P(X < 4) = 0.73 + 0.06 + 0.06 + 0.06 = 0.91$. (c) This is the event {X ≥ 1}. $P(X ≥ 1) = 1 − P(X = 0) = 1 − 0.73 = 0.27$.

10.14: (a) $P(Y ≤ 0.6) = 0.6$. (b) $P(Y < 0.6) = 0.6$. (c) $P(0.4 ≤ Y ≤ 0.8) = 0.4$.

10.15: (a) The area of a triangle is $\frac{1}{2}bh = \frac{1}{2}(2)(1) = 1$. (b) $P(X < 1) = 0.5$. (c) $P(X < 0.5) = 0.125$.

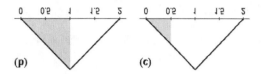

(p)   (c)

10.16: (a) This is $P(X \geq 35)$. (b) $P(X \geq 35) = P(Z \geq \frac{35-25}{6.4}) = P(Z \geq 1.56) = 1 - 0.9406 = 0.0594$ (using Table A).

10.17: (a) $X \geq 3$ means the student's grade is B or higher (B, B+, A- or A). $P(X \geq 3) = 0.14 + 0.10 + 0.08 + 0.09 = 0.41$. (b) "Poorer than B-" means any grade **lower** than B- (e.g. C+, C, C-, D+, D, or F). We want $P(X < 2.7) = P(X \leq 2.3) = 0.10 + 0.12 + 0.04 + 0.04 + 0.08 + 0.08 = 0.46$.

10.18: (a) $Y \geq 8$ means the student runs the mile in 8 minutes or more. $P(Y \geq 8) = P(Z \geq \frac{8-7.11}{0.74}) = P(Z \geq 1.20) = 1 - 0.8849 = 0.1151$ (using Table A). (b) "The student could run mile in less than 6 minutes" is the event $Y < 6$. $P(Y < 6) = P(Z < \frac{6-7.11}{0.74}) = P(Z < -1.50) = 0.0668$ (using Table A).

10.19: (a) Answers will vary (probably wildly). (b) A personal probability might take into account specific information about one's own driving habits, or about the kind of traffic one usually drives in. (c) Most people believe that they are better-than-average drivers (whether or not they have any evidence to support that belief).

10.20: (a) If Joe says P(Maryland wins) = 0.1, then he believes P(Duke wins) = 0.2 and P(North Carolina wins) = 0.3. (b) Joe's probabilities for Duke, Clemson, and North Carolina add up to 0.6, so that leaves probability 0.4 for all other teams.

10.21: (a) Probabilities express the *approximate* fraction of occurrences out of many trials.

10.22: (b) The set {0, 1, 2, 3, 4, 5} lists all possible counts.

10.23: (b) This is a discrete (but not equally likely) model.

10.24: (b) The other probabilities add to 0.98, so this must be 0.02.

10.25: (c) P(Republican or Democrat) = P(Republican) + P(Democrat) = 0.28 + 0.28 = 0.56.

10.26: (b) P(not Republican) = 1 − P(Republican) = 1 − 0.28 = 0.72.

10.27: (b) There are 10 equally likely possibilities, so P(seven) = 1/10.

10.28: (c) "7 or greater" means 7, 8, or 9—three of the ten possibilities.

10.29: (b) 24% (0.16 + 0.05 + 0.02 + 0.01 = 0.24, or 24%) have 3 or more cars.

10.30: (c) $Y > 1$ standardizes to $Z > 2.56$, for which Table A gives 0.0052.

10.31: (a) There are sixteen possible outcomes: { HHHH, HHHM, HHMH, HMHH, MHHH, HHMM, HMHM, HMMH,MHHM, MHMH, MMHH, HMMM, MHMM, MMHM, MMMH, MMMM }. (b) The sample space is {0,1,2,3,4}.

10.32: (a) Legitimate. (b) Legitimate (even if the deck of cards is not!). (c) Not legitimate (the total is more than 1).

10.33: (a) The given probabilities have sum 0.73, so this probability must be $1 - 0.73 = 0.27$. (b) P(at least a high school education) $= 1 - P$ (has not finished HS) $= 1 - 0.13 = 0.87$. (Or, add the other three probabilities.)

10.34: In computing the probabilities, we have dropped the trailing zeros from the land area figures. (a) P(area is forested) $= 4176/9094 = 0.4592$. (b) P(area is not forested) $= 1 - 0.4592 = 0.5408$.

10.35: (a) All probabilities are between 0 and 1, and they add to 1. (We must assume that no one takes more than one language.) (b) The probability that a student is studying a language other than English is $0.43 = 1 - 0.57$ (or add all the other probabilities). (c) This probability is $0.40 = 0.30 + 0.08 + 0.02$.

10.36: (a) The given probabilities add to 0.96, so other colors must account for the remaining 0.04. (b) P(silver or white) $= 0.26 + 0.16 = 0.42$, so P(neither silver nor white) $= 1 - 0.42 = 0.58$.

10.37: Of the seven cards, there are three 9's, two red 9's, and two 7's. (a) P(draw a 9) $= 3/7$. (b) P(draw a red 9)$=2/7$. (c) P(don't draw a 7) $= 1-P$(draw a 7)$= 1 - 2/7 = 5/7$.

10.38: The probabilities of 2, 3, 4, and 5 are unchanged (1/6), so P(1 or 6) must still be 1/3. If P(6)$=0.2$, then P(1)$= 1/3 - 0.2 = 0.1333$ (or 2/15).

Face	⚀	⚁	⚂	⚃	⚄	⚅
Probability	0.13	1/6	1/6	1/6	1/6	0.2

10.39: Each of the 90 guests has probability 1/90 of winning the prize. The probability that the winner is a woman is the sum of 1/90 42 times, one for each woman. The probability is $42/90 = 0.467$.

10.40: (a) It is legitimate because every person must fall into exactly one category, the probabilities are all between 0 and 1, and they add up to 1. (b) $0.156 = 0.001 + 0.006 + 0.144 + 0.005$ is the probability that a randomly chosen American is Hispanic. (c) $0.333 = 1 - 0.667$ is the probability that a randomly chosen American is not a non-Hispanic white.

10.41: (a) It is legitimate because every person must fall into exactly one category, the probabilities are all between 0 and 1, and they add up to 1. (b) P(15–19-year-old with others) $= 0.169$. (c) P(15–19-year-old) $= 0.171$—the sum of the numbers in the first column. (d) P(lives with others) $= 0.532$—the sum of the numbers in the third row.

10.42: (a) *A* corresponds to the outcomes in the first column and the third row. (b)_Adding up those 6 outcomes gives $P(A) = 0.534$. (Note that this is different from the sum of the probabilities in (c) and (d) of Exercise 10.41 because that sum counts the overlap (0.169) twice.)

10.43: (a) P(20 years old or older) $= 1 - 0.171 = 0.829$ (or sum the entries in the second, third and fourth columns). (b) P(does not live alone) $= 1 - P$(lives alone) $= 1 - 0.073 = 0.927$.

10.44: (a) *X* is discrete, because it has a finite sample space. (b) "At least one nonword error" is the event $\{X \geq 1\}$ (or $\{X > 0\}$). $P(X \geq 1) = 1 - P(X = 0) = 0.9$. (c) $\{X \leq 2\}$ is "no more than two nonword errors," or "fewer than three nonword errors." $P(X \leq 2) = P(X = 0) + P(X = 1) + P(X = 2) = 0.1 + 0.2 + 0.3 = 0.6$. $P(X < 2) = P(X = 0) + P(X = 1) = 0.1 + 0.2 = 0.3$.

10.45: (a) All 9 digits are equally likely, so each has probability 1/9:

Value of *W*	1	2	3	4	5	6	7	8	9
Probability	$\frac{1}{9}$	$\frac{1}{9}$	$\frac{1}{9}$	$\frac{1}{9}$	$\frac{1}{9}$	$\frac{1}{9}$	$\frac{1}{9}$	$\frac{1}{9}$	$\frac{1}{9}$

(b) $P(W \geq 6) = 4/9 = 0.444$, or twice as big as the Benford's law probability.

10.46: (a) There are 10 pairs. Just using initials: {(A, D), (A, M), (A, S), (A, R), (D, M), (D, S), (D, R), (M, S), (M, R), (S, R)}. (b) Each has probability 1/10 = 10%. (c) Mei-Ling is chosen in 4 of the 10 possible outcomes: 4/10 = 40%. (d) There are 3 pairs with neither Sam nor Roberto, so the probability is 3/10.

10.47: (a) BBB, BBG, BGB, GBB, GGB, GBG, BGG, GGG. Each has probability 1/8. (b) Three of the eight arrangements have two (and only two) girls, so $P(X = 2) = 3/8 = 0.375$. (c) See table.

Value of *X*	0	1	2	3
Probability	1/8	3/8	3/8	1/8

10.48: The possible values of *Y* are 1, 2, 3, . . . , 12, each with probability 1/12. Aside from drawing a diagram showing all the possible combinations, one can reason that the first (regular) die is equally likely to show any number from 1 through 6. Half of the time, the second roll shows 0, and the other half it shows 6. Each possible outcome therefore has probability $(1/6)(1/2) = 1/12$.

10.49: (a) This is a continuous random variable because the set of possible values is an interval. (b) The height should be 1/2 because the area under the curve must be 1. The density curve is illustrated. (c) $P(Y \leq 1) = 1/2$.

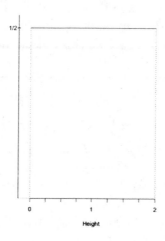

Height

10.50: For these probabilities, compute the areas of the appropriate rectangle under the density shown above (Exercise 10.49). (a) $P(0.5 < Y < 1.3) = 0.4$. (b) $P(Y \geq 0.8) = 0.6$.

10.51: (a) $P(0.51 \leq V \leq 0.55) = P(\frac{0.51-0.53}{0.009} \leq Z \leq \frac{0.55-0.53}{0.009}) = P(-2.22 \leq Z \leq 2.22) = 0.9868 - 0.0132 = 0.9736$. (b) $P(V \geq 0.55) = P(Z \geq \frac{0.55-0.53}{0.009}) = P(Z \geq 2.22) = 1 - 0.9868 = 0.0132$.

10.52: $P(8.9 \leq x \leq 9.1) = P(\frac{8.9-9}{0.075} \leq Z \leq \frac{9.1-9}{0.075}) = P(-1.33 \leq Z \leq 1.33) = 0.9082 - 0.0918 = 0.8164$.

10.53. (a) Because there are 10,000 equally likely four-digit numbers (0000 through 9999), the probability of an exact match is 1/10,000. (b) There is a total of $24 = 4 \times 3 \times 2 \times 1$ arrangements of the four digits 5, 9, 7, and 4 (there are four choices for the first digit, three for the second, two for the third), so the probability of a match in any order is 24/10,000.

10.54. Note that in this experiment, factors other than the nickel's characteristics might affect the outcome. For example, if the surface used is not quite level, there will be a tendency for the nickel to fall in the "downhill" direction.

10.55. (a)–(c) Results will vary, but after n tosses, the distribution of the proportion $\hat{p}$ is approximately Normal with mean 0.5 and standard deviation $1/(2\sqrt{n})$, while the distribution of the count of heads is approximately Normal with mean $0.5n$ and standard deviation $\sqrt{n}/2$, so using the 68–95–99.7 rule, we have the results shown in the table on the right. Note that the range for $\hat{p}$ gets narrower, while the range for the count gets wider.

n	99.7% Range for $\hat{p}$	99.7% Range for count
40	0.5 ± 0.237	20 ± 9.5
120	0.5 ± 0.137	60 ± 16.4
240	0.5 ± 0.097	120 ± 23.2
480	0.5 ± 0.068	240 ± 32.9

10.56. (a) Virtually all answers will be between 62% and 88%, and with about 95% of students' answers between 66% and 84%. (b) Answers will vary, of course. Many students should have longest runs longer than 6.

10.57. (a) With $n = 20$, the variability in $\hat{p}$ is larger. With $n = 80$, nearly all answers will be between 0.24 and 0.56. With $n = 320$, nearly all answers will be between 0.32 and 0.48.

10.58 is a Web-based exercise.

Chapter 11 Solutions

11.1: Both 3.8 and 160.2 active cells per 100,000 cells are statistics (related to one sample — the subjects before infusion and the same subjects after infusion).

11.2: Both 41% and 36% are parameters (related to the population of all registered voters in Florida); 34% is a statistic (related to the sample of registered voters among those called).

11.3: Both 12% and 23 are statistics, as they describe the sample of 230 American male weight lifters.

11.4: Sketches will vary; one result is shown below.

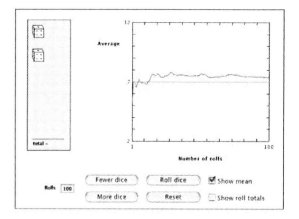

11.5: Although the probability of having to pay for a total loss for 1 or more of the 12 policies is very small, if this were to happen, it would be financially disastrous. On the other hand, for thousands of policies, the law of large numbers says that the average claim on many policies will be close to the mean, so the insurance company can be assured that the premiums they collect will (almost certainly) cover the claims.

11.6: (a) The population is the 12,000 students; the population distribution (Normal with mean 7.11 minutes and standard deviation 0.74 minute) describes the time it takes a randomly selected individual to run a mile. (b) The sampling distribution (Normal with mean 7.11 minutes and standard deviation 0.074 minute) describes the average mile-time for 100 randomly selected students.

11.7: (a) $\mu = 694/10 = 69.4$. (b) The table below shows the results for line 116. Note that we need to choose 5 digits because the digit 4 appears twice. (When choosing an SRS, no student should be chosen more than once.) (c) The results for the other lines are in the table; the histogram is shown next to the table. (Students might choose different intervals than those shown here.) The center of the histogram is a bit lower than 69.4 (it is 66.9), but for a small group of x-values, we should not expect the center to be in exactly the right place.

Note: *You might consider having students choose different samples from those prescribed in this exercise, and then pooling the results for the whole class. With more values of* x, *a better picture of the sampling distribution begins to develop.*

Line	Digits	Scores	*x*-bar
116	14459	63 + 72 + 72 + 59 = 266	66.5
117	3816	55 + 75 + 63 + 65 = 258	64.5
118	7319	66 + 55 + 63 + 59 = 243	60.75
119	95857	59 + 72 + 75 + 66 = 272	68
120	3547	55 + 72 + 72 + 66 = 265	66.25
121	7148	66 + 63 + 72 + 75 = 276	69
122	1387	63 + 55 + 75 + 66 = 259	64.75
123	54580	72 + 72 + 75 + 86 = 305	76.25
124	7103	66 + 63 + 86 + 55 = 270	67.5
125	9674	59 + 65 + 66 + 72 = 262	65.5

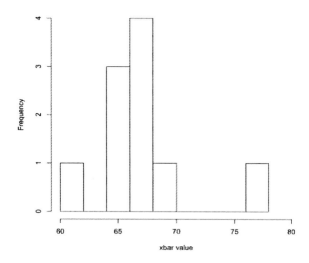

11.8: (a) $\bar{x}$ is not systematically higher than or lower than μ; that is, it has no particular tendency to underestimate or overestimate μ. (b) With large samples, $\bar{x}$ is more likely to be close to μ, because with a larger sample comes more information (and therefore less uncertainty).

11.9: (a) The sampling distribution of $\bar{x}$ is $N(186, 41/\sqrt{100}) = N(186$ mg/dl, 4.1 mg/dl). Therefore, $P(183 < x < 189) = P(-0.73 < Z < 0.73) = 0.5346$. (b) With $n = 1000$, the sample mean has the $N(186$ mg/dl, 1.2965 mg/dl) distribution, so $P(183 < x < 189) = P(-2.31 < Z < 2.31) = 0.9792$.

11.10: (a) $\sigma/\sqrt{n} = 10/\sqrt{4} = 5$ mg. (b) Solve $\sigma/\sqrt{n} = 2$, or $10/\sqrt{n} = 2$, so $\sqrt{n} = 5$, or $n = 25$. The average of several measurements is more likely than a single measurement to be close to the mean.

11.11: No: the histogram of the sample values will look like the population distribution, whatever it might happen to be. (For example, if we roll a fair die many times, the histogram of sample values should look relatively flat—probability close to 1/6 for each value 1, 2, 3, 4, 5, and 6.) The central limit theorem says that the histogram of *sample means* (from many large samples) will look more and more Normal.

11.12: (a) $\mu_{\bar{x}} = 0.5$ and $\sigma_{\bar{x}} = \sigma/\sqrt{n} = 0.7/\sqrt{50} = 0.09899$. (b) Because this distribution is only approximately Normal, it would be quite reasonable to use the 68–95–99.7 rule to give a rough estimate: 0.6 is about one standard deviation above the mean, so the probability should be about 0.16 (half of the 32% that falls outside ±1 standard deviation). Alternatively, $P(\bar{x} > 0.6) = P(Z > \frac{0.6 - .5}{0.09899}) = P(Z > 1.01) = 0.1562$.

11.13: STATE: We ask what is the probability that the average loss for 10,000 such policies will be greater than $85, when the long-run average loss is $75? PLAN: Use the central limit theorem to approximate this probability. SOLVE: The central limit theorem says that, in spite of the skewness of the population distribution, the average loss among 10,000 policies will be approximately $N(\$75, \$300/\sqrt{10,000}) = N(\$75, \$3)$ Now $P(\bar{x} > \$85) = P(Z > \frac{85 - 75}{3}) = P(Z > 3.33) = 1 - 0.9996 = 0.0004$. CONCLUDE: We can be about 99.96% certain that average losses will not exceed $85 per policy.

11.14: (b) statistic. This is a proportion of the people interviewed in the sample of 60,000 households.

11.15: (c) parameter. 58.8% is a proportion of all registered voters (the population).

11.16: (b) The law of large numbers says that the mean from a large sample is close to the population mean. Statement (c) is also true, but is based on the central limit theorem, not on the law of large numbers.

11.17: (a) The mean of the sample means ($\bar{x}$'s) is the same as the population mean (μ).

11.18: (c) The standard deviation of the distribution of $\bar{x}$ is $\sigma/\sqrt{n}$.

11.19: (a) "Unbiased" means that the estimator is right "on the average."

11.20: (c) The central limit theorem says that the mean from a large sample has (approximately) a Normal distribution. Statement (a) is also true, but is based on the law of large numbers, not on the central limit theorem.

11.21: (b) For $n = 6$ women, $\bar{x}$ has a $N(266, 16/\sqrt{6}) = N(266, 6.5320)$ distribution, so $P(\bar{x} > 270) = P(Z > 0.61) = 0.2709$.

11.22: 1 is a parameter (the mean of the population of all conductivity measurements); 1.07 is a statistic (the mean of the 10 measurements in the sample).

11.23: Both 25.40 and 20.41 are statistics (related, respectively, to the two samples).

11.24: In the long run, the gambler earns an average of 94.7 cents per bet. In other words, the gambler loses (and the house gains) an average of 5.3 cents for each $1 bet.

11.25: $\bar{x}$ has mean $\mu = 852$ mm, and standard deviation $\sigma/\sqrt{n} = 82/\sqrt{10} = 25.93$ mm.

11.26: (a) $P(20 < X < 30) = P(\frac{20-25}{6.4} < Z < \frac{30-25}{6.4}) = P(-0.78 < Z < 0.78) = 0.7823 - 0.2177 = 0.5646$. (b) If $n = 25$ students, the sampling distribution of $\bar{x}$ is $N(25, 6.4/\sqrt{25}) = N(25, 1.28)$. (c) $P(20 < \bar{x} < 30) = P(\frac{20-25}{1.28} < Z < \frac{30-25}{1.28}) = P(-3.91 < Z < 3.91) \approx 1$.

11.27: Let X be Shelia's measured glucose level. (a) $P(X > 140) = P(Z > 1.5) = 0.0668$. (b) If $\bar{x}$ is the mean of four measurements (assumed to be independent), then $\bar{x}$ has a $N(122, 12/\sqrt{4}) = N(122$ mg/dl, 6 mg/dl) distribution, and $P(\bar{x} > 140) = P(Z > 3) = 0.0013$.

11.28: (a) Let $\bar{x}$ be the mean number of minutes per day that the 5 randomly selected mildly obese people spend walking. Then $\bar{x}$ has the $N(373, 67/\sqrt{5}) = N(373$ min., 29.96 min.) distribution. Now $P(\bar{x} > 420) = P(Z > \frac{420-373}{29.96}) = P(Z > 1.57) \approx 0.0582$. (b) Let $\bar{x}$ be the sample mean number of minutes per day for the 5 randomly selected lean people. $\bar{x}$ has the $N(526, 107/\sqrt{5}) = N(526$ min., 47.85 min.). $P(\bar{x} > 420) = P(Z > -2.22) = 0.9868$.

11.29: As shown in Exercise 11.27(b), the mean of four measurements has a $N(122$ mg/dl, 6 mg/dl) distribution, and $P(Z > 1.645) = 0.05$ if Z is $N(0,1)$, so $L = 122 + 1.645 \times 6 = 131.87$ mg/dl.

11.30: (a) For the emissions E of a single car, $P(E > 0.07) = P(Z > \frac{0.07-0.05}{0.01}) = P(Z > 2) = 0.0228$. (b) The average $\bar{x}$ is Normal with mean 0.05 g/mi and standard deviation $0.01/\sqrt{25} = 0.002$ g/mi. Therefore, $P(\bar{x} > 0.07) = P(Z > \frac{0.07-0.05}{0.002}) = P(Z > 10) \approx 0$.

11.31: (a) The central limit theorem gives that $\bar{x}$ will have a Normal distribution with mean 8.8 beats per five seconds, and standard deviation $1/\sqrt{12} = 0.288675$ beats per five seconds. (b) $P(\bar{x} < 8) = P(Z < -2.77) = 0.0028$. (c) If the total number of beats in one minute is less than 100, then the average over 12 5-second intervals needs to be less than $100/12 = 8.333$ beats per five seconds. $P(\bar{x} < 8.333) = P(Z < -1.62) = 0.0526$.

11.32: The mean NOX level for 25 cars has a $N(0.05$ g/mi, 0.002 g/mi) distribution, and $P(Z > 2.326) = 0.01$ if Z is $N(0,1)$, so $L = 0.05 + (2.326)(0.002) = 0.054652$ g/mi.

11.33: STATE: What are the probabilities of an average return over 10%, or less than 5%? PLAN: Use the central limit theorem to approximate this probability. SOLVE: The central limit theorem says that over 40 years, $\bar{x}$ (the mean return) is approximately Normal with mean $\mu = 10.8\%$ and standard deviation $17.1\%/\sqrt{40} = 2.704\%$. Therefore, $P(\bar{x} > 10\%) = P(Z > -0.30) = 0.6179$, and $P(\bar{x} < 5\%) = P(Z < -2.14) = 0.0162$. CONCLUDE: There is about a 62% chance of getting average returns over 10%, and a 1.6% chance of getting average returns less than 5%. Note: than 5%. **Note:** *We have to assume that returns in separate years are independent.*

11.34: STATE: What is the probability that the total weight of the 22 passengers exceeds 4500 lb? PLAN: Use the central limit theorem to approximate this probability. SOLVE: If W is total weight, then the sample mean weight is $\bar{x} = W/22$. The event that the total weight exceeds 4500 pounds is equivalent to the event that $\bar{x}$ exceeds $4500/22 = 204.55$ lb. The central limit theorem says that $\bar{x}$ is approximately Normal with mean 190 lb and standard deviation $35/\sqrt{22} = 7.462$ lb. Therefore, $P(W > 4500) = P(\bar{x} > 204.55) = P(Z > \frac{204.55 - 190}{7.462}) = P(Z > 1.95) = 0.0256$.

CONCLUDE: There is a small chance—about 2.56%—that the total weight exceeds 4500 lb.

11.35: We need to choose n so that $6.4/\sqrt{n} = 1$. That means $\sqrt{n} = 6.4$, so $n = 40.96$.

Because n must be a whole number, take $n = 41$.

11.36: (a) 99.7% of all observations fall within 3 standard deviations, so we want

$3\sigma/\sqrt{n} = 1$. The standard deviation of x must therefore be $1/3 = 0.33$ point. (b) We need to choose n so that $6.4/\sqrt{n} = 0.33$. This means $\sqrt{n} = 19.2$, so $n = 368.64$. Because n must be a whole number, take $n = 369$.

11.37: On the average, Joe loses 40 cents each time he plays (that is, he spends \$1 and gets back 60 cents).

11.38: (a) With $n = 14{,}000$, $\mu_{\bar{x}} = \$0.60$ and $\sigma_{\bar{x}} = \$18.96/\sqrt{14{,}000} = \$0.1602$.

(b) $P(\$0.50 < \bar{x} < \$0.70) = P(-0.62 < Z < 0.62) = 0.4648$.

11.39: (a) With $n = 150{,}000$, $\mu_{\bar{x}} = \$0.40$ and $\sigma_{\bar{x}} = \$18.96/\sqrt{150{,}000} = \$0.0490$.

(b) $P(\$0.30 < \bar{x} < \$0.50) = P(-2.04 < Z < 2.04) = 0.9586$.

11.40: (a) The estimate in Exercise 11.38 was 0.4648 (Table A) or 0.4674, so the Normal approximation slightly underestimates the exact answer. (b) With $n = 3500$, the Normal approximation gives $P(\$0.50 < \bar{x} < \$0.70) = P(-0.31 < Z < 0.31)$, which is 0.2434 (Table A). This is just a bit smaller than the exact answer. (c) The probability that their average winnings fall between \$0.50 and \$0.70 is the same as the probability found in part (b) of the previous exercise, for which the Normal approximation gives 0.9586 (Table A) or 0.9589 (software), so the approximation differs from the exact value by only about 0.0003.

11.41: The mean is 10.5 (= (3)(3.5) because a single die has a mean of 3.5). Sketches will vary, as will the number of rolls; one result is shown.

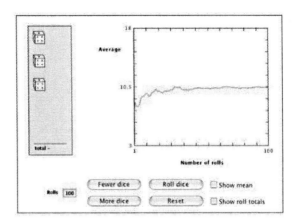

11.42 and 11.43 are Web-based exercises.

Chapter 12 Solutions

12.1: It is unlikely that these events are independent. In particular, it is reasonable to expect that younger adults are more likely than older adults to be college students. **Note**: *Using the notation of conditional probability introduced later in this chapter,* P(*college student | over 55*) < 0.08.

12.2: This would not be surprising: assuming that all the authors are independent (for example, none were written by siblings or married couples), we can view the nine names as being a random sample, and the probability that none of these are among the 10 most common names is $P(N = 0) = (1 - 0.096)^9 = 0.4032$.

12.3: If we assume that each site is independent of the others (and that they can be considered as a random sample from the collection of sites referenced in scientific journals), then P(all seven are still good) $= (0.87)^7 = 0.3773$.

12.4: A Venn diagram is provided. B is the event "the degree is a bachelor's degree," and W is the event "the degree was earned by a woman." The probability of the overlap is given. Subtracting this from the given probabilities for B and W gives the probabilities of the rest of those events. Those probabilities add to 0.80, so P(neither B nor W) = 0.20. (a) Because $P(W) = 0.59$, P(degree was earned by a man) $= P(\text{not } W) = 1 - 0.59 = 0.41$, or 41%. (b) $P(B \text{ and not } W) = 0.50 - 0.29 = 0.21$, or 21%. (c) Since $P(B \text{ and } W) = 0.29$, but $P(B) \times P(W) = (0.50)(0.59) = 0.295$, then $P(B \text{ and } W) \neq P(B) \times P(W)$. Hence, B and W are not independent.

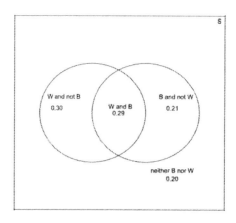

142

12.5: (a) A Venn diagram is provided. (b) The events are

{A and B}   = {student is at least 25 and local}

{A and not B}   = {student is at least 25 and not local}

{B and not A}   = {student is less than 25 and local}

{neither A nor B} = {student is less than 25 and not local}

(c) $P(A$ and $B)$ is given. Subtracting this from the given probabilities for A and B gives $P(A$ and not $B)$ and $P(B$ and not $A)$. Those probabilities add to 0.90, so P(neither B nor W) = 0.10.

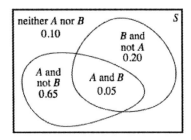

12.6: Refer to the Venn diagram in the solution of Exercise 12.4. Using the notation given in that solution, $P(W \mid B) = \dfrac{P(B \text{ and } W)}{P(B)} = 0.29/0.50 = 0.58$.

12.7: $P(B \mid \text{not } A) = \dfrac{P(B \text{ and not } A)}{P(\text{not } A)} = \dfrac{P(B) - P(B \text{ and } A)}{P(\text{not } A)} = \dfrac{0.2}{0.3} = 0.667$.

12.8: Let R be the event "game is a role playing game," while S is the event "game is a strategy game." Then $P(\text{not } S) = 1 - 0.354 = 0.646$, and $P(R \mid \text{not } S) = \dfrac{P(R \text{ and not } S)}{P(\text{not } S)} = \dfrac{0.139}{0.646} = 0.2152$. (Note that "$R$ and not S" is equivalent to R.)

12.9: Let H be the event that an adult belongs to a club, and T be the event that he/she goes at least twice a week. We have been given $P(H) = 0.15$ and $P(T \mid H) = 0.50$. Note also that $P(T$ and $H) = P(T)$, since one has to be a member of the club in order to attend. So $P(T) = P(H)P(T \mid H) = (0.15)(0.50) = 0.075$. About 7.5% of all adults go to health clubs at least twice a week.

12.10: PLAN: Express the information we are given in terms of events and their probabilities: let A = {the teen is online}, B = {the teen has a profile}, and C = {the teen has commented on a friend's blog}. Then $P(A) = 0.93$, $P(B \mid A) = 0.55$, and $P(C \mid A$ and $B) = 0.76$. We want to find $P(A$ and B and $C)$. SOLVE: Use the multiplication rule: $P(A$ and B and $C) = P(A)P(B \mid A)P(C \mid A$ and $B) = (0.93)(0.55)(0.76) = 0.3887$. CONCLUDE: About 39% of all teens are online, have a profile, and have placed comments on a friend's blog.

12.11: (a) and (b) These probabilities are provided in the table. (c) The product of these conditional probabilities gives the probability of a flush in spades by the general multiplication rule: we must draw a spade, and then another, and then a third, a fourth, and a fifth. The product of these probabilities is about 0.0004952. (d) Because there are four possible suits in which to have a flush, the probability of a flush is four times that found in (c), or about 0.001981.

$$P(\text{1st card} \spadesuit) = \tfrac{13}{52} = \tfrac{1}{4} = 0.25$$
$$P(\text{2nd card} \spadesuit \mid 1 \spadesuit \text{ picked}) = \tfrac{12}{51} = \tfrac{4}{17} \doteq 0.2353$$
$$P(\text{3rd card} \spadesuit \mid 2 \spadesuit\text{s picked}) = \tfrac{11}{50} = 0.22$$
$$P(\text{4th card} \spadesuit \mid 3 \spadesuit\text{s picked}) = \tfrac{10}{49} \doteq 0.2041$$
$$P(\text{5th card} \spadesuit \mid 4 \spadesuit\text{s picked}) = \tfrac{9}{48} = \tfrac{3}{16} = 0.1875$$

12.12: (a) There are a total of 976 professors, of which 272 are women, so $P(\text{woman}) = 272/976 = 0.2787$. (b) $P(\text{woman} \mid \text{full professor}) = 73/375 = 0.1947$. (c) Rank and sex are not independent; if they were, the probabilities in (a) and (b) would be equal.

12.13: PLAN: We construct a tree diagram showing the results (allergic or not) for each of the three individuals. SOLVE: In the tree diagram, each "up-step" represents an allergic individual (and has probability 0.01), and each "down-step" is a non-allergic individual (and has probability 0.99). At the end of each of the 8 complete branches are the value of X. Any branch with 2 up-steps and 1 down-step has probability $0.01^2 \times 0.99^1 = 0.000099$, and yields $X = 2$. Any branch with 1 up-step and 2 down-steps has probability $0.01^1 \times 0.99^2 = 0.009801$, and yields $X = 1$.

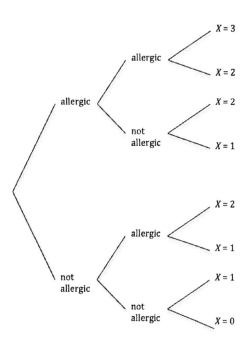

There are three branches each corresponding to $X = 2$ and $X = 1$, and only one branch each for $X = 3$ and $X = 0$. Because $X = 0$ and $X = 3$ appear on one branch each, $P(X = 0) = 0.99^3 = 0.970299$ and $P(X = 3) = 0.01^3 = 0.000001$. Meanwhile, $P(X = 1) = 3(0.01)^1(0.99)^2 = 0.029403$, and $P(X = 2) = 3(0.01)^2(0.99)^1 = 0.000297$. CONCLUDE: $P(X = 0) = 0.970299$, $P(X = 1) = 0.029403$, $P(X = 2) = 0.000297$, and $P(X = 3) = 0.000001$.

12.14: (a) The tree diagram follows. (b) $P(\text{positive}) = 0.009985 + 0.00594 = 0.015925$.

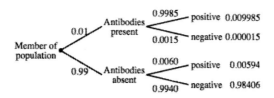

12.15: $P(X = 2 | X \geq 1) = \dfrac{P(X = 2 \text{ and } X \geq 1)}{P(X \geq 1)} = \dfrac{P(X = 2)}{P(X \geq 1)} = \dfrac{0.000297}{1 - 0.970299} = 0.010$.

12.16: $P \text{ (has antibody | positive)} = \dfrac{0.009985}{0.015925} = 0.627$.

12.17: (b) This probability is $(0.98)^3 = 0.9412$.

12.18: (b) This probability is $1 - (0.98)^3 = 0.0588$.

12.19: (a) $P(\text{at least one positive}) = 1 - P(\text{both negative}) = 1 - P(\text{first negative})P(\text{second negative}) = 1 - (0.1)(0.2) = 0.98$.

12.20: (b) There were 23,190 female recipients out of a total of $26,338 + 23,190 = 49,528$ doctorates. Hence, P(female) = 23,190/49,528 = 0.4682, or 0.47.

12.21: (c) Of $6,006 + 1,623 = 7,629$ Engineering doctorates, 1,623 were awarded to females. Then P(female | engineering) = 1,623/7,629 = 02127, or 0.21.

12.22: (b) Of 23,190 female doctorates, 1,623 were awarded in Engineering. Hence, P(engineering | female) = 1,623/23,190 = 0.0699, or 0.07.

12.23: (c) We want the fraction of engineering doctorates conferred to women. Hence, A (engineering degree) is what has been given. Hence, $P(B | A)$.

12.24: (b) $P(W \text{ or } S) = P(W) + P(S) - P(W \text{ and } S) = 0.52 + 0.25 - 0.11 = 0.66$.

12.25: (c) $P(W \text{ and } D) = P(W)P(D | W) = (0.86)(0.028) = 0.024$.

12.26: (b) $P(D) = P(W \text{ and } D) + P(B \text{ and } D) + P(A \text{ and } D) = (0.86)(0.028) + (0.12)(0.044) + (0.02)(0.035) = 0.030$.

12.27: $P(8 \text{ losses}) = (0.75)^8 = 0.1001$.

12.28: P(none are O-negative) = $(1 - 0.072)^{10}$ = 0.4737, so P(at least one is O-negative) = 1 − 0.4737 = 0.5263.

12.29: (a) P(win the jackpot) = $\left(\frac{1}{20}\right)\left(\frac{9}{20}\right)\left(\frac{1}{20}\right)$ = 0.001125. (b) The other (non-cherry) symbol can show up on the middle wheel, with probability $\left(\frac{1}{20}\right)\left(\frac{11}{20}\right)\left(\frac{1}{20}\right)$ = 0.001375, or on either of the outside wheels, with probability = $\left(\frac{19}{20}\right)\left(\frac{9}{20}\right)\left(\frac{1}{20}\right)$ (each). (c) Combining all three cases from part (b), we have P(exactly two cherries) = 0.001375 + 2 · 0.021375 = 0.044125.

12.30: (a) $(0.80)^2$ = 0.64. (b) P(sighting on at least one day) = 1 − P(sighting on neither day) = 1 − $(0.20)^2$ = 0.96. (c) We want the number of trips, k, such that $1 - (0.20)^k \geq 0.99$. You can solve this algebraically for k, yielding $k \geq 2.86$, which must be rounded up to 3. Details follow:

$$1 - (0.20)^k \geq 0.99$$
$$(0.20)^k \leq 1 - 0.99 = 0.01$$
$$k\ln(0.20) \leq \ln(0.01)$$
$$k(-1.609) \leq -4.605$$
$$k \geq \frac{-4.605}{-1.609} = 2.862$$

Alternatively, we can solve this by trial and error: If we try k =2, for example, $1 - (0.20)^2$ = 0.96, which fails. However, with k = 3, $1 - (0.20)^3$ = 0.992, which satisfies the requirement. Hence, at least three trips are needed to assure at least 0.99 probability of at least one sighting.

12.31: PLAN: Let I be the event "infection occurs" and let F be "the repair fails." We have been given $P(I)$ = 0.03, $P(F)$ = 0.14, and $P(I \text{ and } F)$ = 0.01. We want to find P(not I and not F). SOLVE: First use the general addition rule: $P(I \text{ or } F) = P(I) + P(F) - P(I \text{ and } F)$ = 0.03 + 0.14 − 0.01 = 0.16. This is the shaded region in the Venn diagram provided. Now observe that the desired probability is the complement of "I or F" (the *unshaded* region): P(not I and not F) = 1 − $P(I \text{ or } F)$ = 0.84. CONCLUDE: 84% of operations succeed and are free from infection.

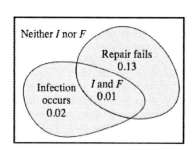

12.32: Let W be the event that a whale is seen. Let D be the event that a dolphin is seen. The Venn diagram is provided below. (a) $P(W) = 0.05 + 0.15 = 0.20$. (b) $P(W$ and not $D) = 0.05$. (c) Yes, since $P(W$ and $D) = 0.15 = P(W)P(D) = (0.20)(0.75) = 0.15$.

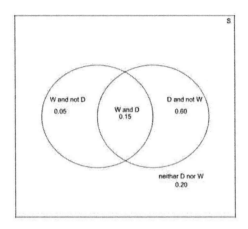

12.33: PLAN: Let I be the event "infection occurs" and let F be "the repair fails." Refer to the Venn diagram in Exercise 12.31 (ignoring the shading). We want to find $P(I \mid \text{not } F)$. SOLVE: We have $P(I \mid \text{not } F) = \dfrac{P(I \text{ and not } F)}{P(\text{not } F)} = \dfrac{0.02}{0.86} = 0.0233$. CONCLUDE: The probability of

infection given that the repair is successful is 0.0233. That is, in 2.33% of all successful operation cases, the patient develops infection.

12.34: Note that in this diagram, events A, B, and C should not overlap and should account for all possibilities (that is, those three events fill the entire diagram). Meanwhile, D intersects all three of the others. The probabilities $P(A$ and $D)$, $P(B$ and $D)$, and $P(C$ and $D)$ give the probability of each overlapping region, and the portion of each event A, B, and C outside of D must account for the rest of that event's probability. As can be seen from the diagram, $P(D) = 0.4 = 0.1 + 0.1 + 0.2$.

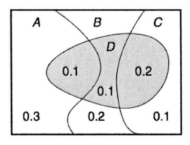

12.35: Let H be the event student was home schooled. Let R be the event student attended a regular public school. We want $P(H \mid \text{not } R)$. Note that the event "H and not R" = "H" since the events are disjoint. Then $P(H \mid \text{not } R) = \dfrac{P(H)}{P(\text{not } R)} = \dfrac{0.006}{1 - 0.781} = 0.0274$.

12.36: (a) P (income $\geq \$30,000) = 0.315 + 0.180 + 0.031 = 0.526$. (b) P (income $\geq \$75,000 \mid$

$$\text{income} \geq \$30,000) = \frac{P(\text{income} \geq \$75,000)}{P(\text{income} \geq \$30,000)} = \frac{0.211}{0.526} = 0.4011.$$

12.37: (a) These events are not independent, because P(pizza with mushrooms) = 4/7, but P(mushrooms | thick crust) = 2/3 (if the events were independent, these probabilities would be equal). Alternatively, note that P(thick crust with mushrooms) = 2/7, which is not equal to the product of P(mushrooms) = 4/7 and P(thick crust pizza) = 3/7. (b) With the eighth pizza, P(mushrooms) = 4/8 = 1/2, and P (mushrooms | thick crust) = 2/4 = 1/2 , so these events are independent.

12.38: (a) P(two boys | at least one boy) = $\dfrac{P(\text{two boys})}{P(\text{at least one boy})} = \dfrac{0.25}{0.75} = \dfrac{1}{3}$. (b) P(two boys |older

child is a boy) = $\dfrac{P(\text{two boys})}{P(\text{older child is boy})} = \dfrac{0.25}{0.50} = \dfrac{1}{2}$. Note that we can also find this by reasoning that P(two boys | older child is a boy) = P (younger child is a boy | older child is a boy). Because the two children's genders are independent, this probability is the same as the unconditional probability P(younger child is a boy) = 0.5.

12.39: Let W be the event "the person is a woman" and M be "the person earned a Master's degree." (a) P(not W) = 1421/3560 = 0.3992. (b) P(not W | M) = 282/732 = 0.3852. (c) The events "choose a man" and "choose a Master's degree recipient" are not independent. If they were, the two probabilities in (a) and (b) would be equal.

12.40. Let W be the event "the person is a woman" and A be "the person earned a Associate's degree." (a) $P(W)$ = 2139/3560 = 0.6008. (b) $P(A \mid W)$ = 556/2139 = 0.2599. (c) $P(W$ and $A)$ = $P(W)P(A \mid W)$ = (0.6008)(0.2599) = 0.1561. Except for rounding, this agrees with the directly computed probability: $P(W$ and A) = 556/3560 = 0.1562.

12.41: Let D be the event "a seedling was damaged by a deer." (a) $P(D)$ = 209/871 = 0.2400. (b) The conditional probabilities are:

$P(D|$ no cover) = 60/211 = 0.2844

$P(D|$ cover < 1/3) = 76/234 = 0.3248

$P(D \mid$ 1/3 to 2/3 cover) = 44/221 = 0.1991

$P(D \mid$ cover > 2/3) = 29/205 = 0.1415

(c) Cover and damage are not independent; $P(D)$ decreases noticeably when thorny cover is 1/3 or more.

12.42: This conditional probability is P(cover > 2/3 | not D) = 176/(151 + 158 + 177 + 176) = 176/662 = 0.2659, or 26.59%.

12.43. This conditional probability is P(cover < 1/3 | D) = 76/(60 + 76 + 44 + 29) = 76/209 = 0.3636, or 36.36%.

12.44: We first construct the Venn diagram for this set of exercises. To find the probabilities in this Venn diagram, begin with $P(A \text{ and } B \text{ and } C) = 0$ in the center of the diagram. Then the two-way intersections $P(A \text{ and } B)$, $P(A \text{ and } C)$, and $P(B \text{ and } C)$ go in the remainder of the overlapping areas; if $P(A \text{ and } B \text{ and } C)$ had been something other than 0, we would have subtracted this from each of the two-way intersection probabilities to find, for example, $P(A \text{ and } B \text{ and not } C)$. Next, determine $P(A \text{ only})$ so that the total probability of the regions that make up the event A is 0.50. Finally, $P(\text{none}) = P(\text{not } A \text{ and not } B \text{ and not } C) = 0.10$ because the total probability inside the three sets A, B, and C is 0.90. The completed Venn diagram is shown.

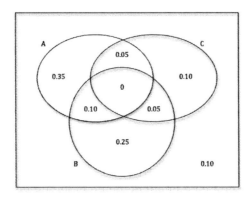

We seek $P(\text{no offer}) = P(\text{not } A \text{ and not } B \text{ and not } C) = 0.10$.

12.45: This is $P(A \text{ and not } B \text{ and not } C) = 0.35$.

12.46: $P(B \mid C) = 0.05/0.20 = 0.25$. $P(C \mid B) = 0.05/0.40 = 0.125$.

12.47: (a) $P(\text{doubles on first toss}) = 1/6$, since 6 of the 36 equally likely outcomes enumerated in Figure 10.2 involve rolling doubles. (b) We need no doubles on the first roll (which happens with probability 5/6), then doubles on the second toss. $P(\text{first doubles appears on toss 2}) = (5/6)(1/6) = 5/36$. (c) Similarly, $P(\text{first doubles appears on toss 3}) = (5/6)^2(1/6) = 25/216$. (d) $P(\text{first doubles appears on toss 4}) = (5/6)^3(1/6)$, etc. In general, $P(\text{first doubles appears on toss } k) = (5/6)^{k-1}(1/6)$. (e) $P(\text{go again within 3 turns}) = P(\text{roll doubles in 3 or fewer rolls}) = P(\text{roll doubles on 1st, 2nd, or 3rd try}) = (1/6) + (5/6)(1/6) + (5/6)^2(1/6) = 0.4213$.

12.48: The tree diagram provided organizes this information; the probability of each outcome is the product of the individual branch probabilities leading to it. The total probability of the serving player winning a point is $0.4307 + 0.208034 = 0.6387$.

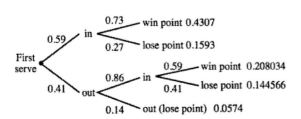

12.49: PLAN: Let W, B, and H be the events that a randomly selected voter is (respectively) white, black, and Hispanic. We have been given $P(W) = 0.4$, $P(B) = 0.4$, $P(H) = 0.2$. If $F =$ "a voter votes for the candidate," then $P(F \mid W) = 0.3$, $P(F \mid B) = 0.9$, $P(F \mid H) = 0.5$. We want to find $P(F)$. SOLVE: The tree diagram provided organizes the information. The numbers on the right side of the tree are found by the general multiplication rule; for example, $P(\text{"white" and "for"}) = P(W \text{ and } F) = P(W)P(F \mid W) = (0.4)(0.3) = 0.12$. We find $P(F)$ by adding all the numbers next to the branches ending in "for": $P(F) = 0.12 + 0.36 + 0.10 = 0.58$. CONCLUDE: The black candidate expects to get 58% of the vote.

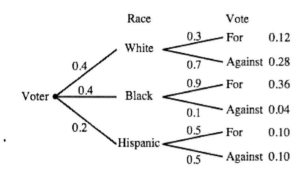

12.50: $P(\text{first serve in} \mid \text{server won point}) = \dfrac{P(\text{first serve in and server won point})}{P(\text{server won point})} = \dfrac{0.4307}{0.6387} =$ 0.6743, or 67.43%.

12.51: $P(B \mid F) = \dfrac{P(B \text{ and } F)}{P(F)} = \dfrac{0.36}{0.58} = 0.6207$, or about 62%.

12.52 (a) Let $C = \{\text{teen owns a cell phone}\}$ and $T = \{\text{texts}\}$. We are given: $P(C) = 0.75$ and $P(T|C) = 0.87$. So, $P(C \text{ and } T) = P(C)*P(T|C) = (0.75)(0.87) = 0.6525$. (b) Let $M = \{\text{more than 6,000 texts a month}\}$. We want $P(C \text{ and } T \text{ and } M) = P(C)*P(T|C)*P(M|C \text{ and } T) = (0.75)(0.87)(0.15) = 0.0979$.

12.53: For a randomly selected resident of the United States, let W, B, A, and L be (respectively) the events that this person is white, black, Asian, and lactose intolerant. We have been given

$P(W) = 0.82 \qquad P(B) = 0.14 \qquad P(A) = 0.04$

$P(L|W) = 0.15 \qquad P(L|B) = 0.70 \qquad P(L|A) = 0.90$

(a) $P(L) = (0.82)(0.15) + (0.14)(0.70) + (0.04)(0.90) = 0.257$, or 25.7%.

(b) $P(A \mid L) = P(A \text{ and } L)/P(L) = (0.04)(0.90)/0.257 = 0.1401$, or 14%.

12.54: Let R = {recent donor}, P = {pledged}, and C = {contributed}. (We could also give names to the "past donor" and "new prospect" events, but we do not need these for this explanation.) (a) The percent of calls resulting in a contribution can be found by considering all the branches of the tree that end in a contribution, meaning that we compute, for example, $P(C$ and $R) = P(R) \cdot P(P \mid R) \cdot P(C \mid R$ and $P)$. This gives

$P(C) = (0.5)(0.4)(0.8) + (0.3)(0.3)(0.6) + (0.2)(0.1)(0.5) = 0.224$, or 22.4%. (b) $P(R|C) =$
$\dfrac{P(C \text{ and } R)}{P(C)} = \dfrac{(0.5)(0.4)(0.8)}{0.224} = 0.7143$, or 71.4%.

12.55: In this problem, allele 29 is playing the role of A, and 0.181 is the proportion with this allele ($a = 0.181$). Similarly, allele 31 is playing the role of B, and the proportion having this allele is $b = 0.071$. The labels aren't important – you can reverse assignments of A and B. The proportion of the population with combination (29,31) is therefore $2(0.181)(0.071) = 0.025702$. The proportion with combination (29,29) is $(0.181)(0.181) = 0.032761$. Of course under these assignments, there are other alleles possible for this locus.

12.56: The proportion having combination (16,17) is $2(0.232)(0.212) = 0.098368$.

12.57: In Exercise 12.55, we found that the proportion of the population with allele (29,31) at loci D21S11 is 0.025702. In Exercise 12.56, we found that the proportion with allele (16,17) at loci D3S1358 is 0.098368. Assuming independence between loci, the proportion with allele (29,31) at D21S11 and (16,17) at D3S1358 is $(0.098368)(0.025702) = 0.002529$.

12.58: If the DNA profile found on the hair is possessed by 1 in 1.6 million individuals, then we would expect about 3 individuals in the database of 4.5 million convicted felons to demonstrate a match. This comes from (4.5 million)/(1.6 million) = 2.8125, which was rounded up to 3.

12.59 and 12.60 are Web-based exercises.

Chapter 13 Solutions

13.1: Binomial. (1) We have a fixed number of observations ($n = 15$). (2) It is reasonable to believe that each call is independent of the others. (3) "Success" means reaching a live person, "failure" is any other outcome. (4) Each randomly dialed number has chance $p = 0.2$ of reaching a live person.

13.2: Not binomial. We do not have a fixed number of observations.

13.3: Not binomial. The trials aren't independent. If one tile in a box is cracked, there are likely more tiles cracked.

13.4: We have a fixed number of independent trials, each leading to success (used the Internet for personal reasons) or failure, with the probability of success constant from trial to trial. We're counting the number of successes in our sample. Hence, the number in the sample who used the Internet is binomial in distribution with $n = 1500$ and $p = 0.80$.

13.5: (a) C, the number caught, is binomial with $n = 10$ and $p = 0.7$. M, the number missed, is binomial with $n = 10$ and $p = 0.3$. (b) We find $P(M = 3) = \binom{10}{3}(0.3)^3(0.7)^7 =$ $120(0.027)(0.08235) = 0.2668$. With software, we find $P(M \geq 3) = 0.6172$.

13.6: Let N be the number of live persons contacted among the 15 calls observed. Then N has the binomial distribution with $n = 15$ and $p = 0.2$.

(a) $P(N = 3) = \binom{15}{3}(0.2)^3(0.8)^{12} = 0.2501$.

(b) $P(N \leq 3) = P(N = 0) + \cdots + P(N = 3) = 0.6482$.
(c) $P(N \geq 3) = P(N = 3) + \cdots + P(N = 15) = 0.6020$.
(d) $P(N < 3) = P(N = 0) + \cdots + P(N = 2) = 0.3980$.
(e) $P(N > 3) = P(N = 4) + \cdots + P(N = 15) = 0.3518$.

The TI-83/84 screen shown illustrates the use of that calculator's binompdf and binomcdf functions (found in the DISTR menu) to compute the first two probabilities. The first of these finds individual binomial probabilities, and the second finds cumulative probabilities (that is, it sums the probability from 0 up to a given number). Excel offers similar features with its BINOMDIST function. Calculators that do not have binomial probabilities may have a built-in function to compute the factorial, for example, $\binom{15}{3}$, which can then be multiplied by the appropriate probabilities.

```
binompdf(15,.2,3
         .2501388953
binomcdf(15,.2,3
         .6481621047
■
```

152

13.7: The screenshots below show Google's answers at the time these solutions were prepared. (a) 5 choose 2 returns 10. (b) 500 choose 2 returns 124,750, and 500 choose 100 returns $2.04169424 \times 10^{107}$. (c) (10 choose 1)*0.1*0.9^9 returns 0.387420489.

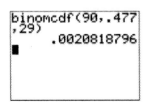

13.8: (a) With $n = 15$ and $p = 0.2$, we have $\mu = np = 3$ calls. (b) $\sigma = \sqrt{np(1-p)} = \sqrt{2.4} = 1.5492$ calls. (c) With $p = 0.08$, $\sigma = \sqrt{1.104} = 1.0507$ calls; with $p = 0.01$, $\sigma = \sqrt{0.1485} = 0.3854$ calls. As p approaches 0, the standard deviation decreases (that is, it also approaches 0).

13.9: (a) X is binomial with $n = 10$ and $p = 0.3$; Y is binomial with $n = 10$ and $p = 0.7$ (b) The mean of Y is $(10)(0.7) = 7$ errors caught, and for X the mean is $(10)(0.3) = 3$ errors missed. (c) The standard deviation of Y (or X) is $\sigma = \sqrt{10(0.7)(0.3)} = 1.4491$ errors.

13.10: Let X be the number of 1's and 2's; then X has a binomial distribution with $n = 90$ and $p = 0.477$ (in the absence of fraud). This should have a mean of 42.93 and standard deviation $\sigma = \sqrt{22.4524} = 4.7384$. Therefore, $P(X \leq 29) = P\left(Z \leq \dfrac{29 - 42.93}{4.7384}\right) = P(Z \leq -2.94) = 0.0016$. (Using software, we find that the exact value is 0.0021.) This probability is quite small, so we have reason to be suspicious.

```
binomcdf(90,.477
,29)
        .0020818796
■
```

13.11: (a) $\mu = (1520)(0.31) = 471.2$ and $\sigma = \sqrt{1520(0.31)(1-0.31)} = \sqrt{325.128} = 18.0313$ students. (b) Note that $np = (1520)(0.31) = 471.2 \geq 10$ and $n(1-p) = (1520)(0.69) = 1048.8 \geq 10$, so n is large enough for the Normal approximation to be reasonable. The college wants 475 students, so $P(X \geq 476) = P\left(Z \geq \dfrac{476 - 471.2}{18.0313}\right) = P(Z \geq 0.27) = 0.3936$. (c) The exact probability is 0.4045 (obtained from software), so the Normal approximation is 0.0109 too low. For a better approximation, consider using the continuity correction, described in Exercise 13.43.

13.12: (a) $\mu = (1000)(0.24) = 240$ and $\sigma = \sqrt{1000(0.24)(1-0.24)} = 13.5056$ first generation Canadians. (b) To check whether the Normal approximation can be applied, note that $np = 240$ and $n(1-p) = 760$ are both more than 10. We compute $P(210 \leq X \leq 270) =$
$$P\left(\frac{210-240}{13.5056} \leq Z \leq \frac{270-240}{13.5056}\right) = P(-2.22 \leq Z \leq 2.22) = 0.9736.$$

13.13: (b) He has 3 independent eggs, each with probability 1/4 of containing salmonella.

13.14: (b) $P(S \geq 1) = P(S > 0) = 1 - P(S = 0) = 1 - 0.4219 = 0.5781$.

13.15: (c) The selections are not independent; once we choose one student, it changes the probability that the next student is a business major.

13.16: (c) We must choose 3 of the 5 shots to be "made"; $\binom{5}{3} = 10$. Note that answer (b) is only wrong for its computation… in fact, a correct answer to this problem would also be $\binom{5}{2} = 10$ (not 20), since the act of deciding which 3 shots are made is equivalent to choosing which 2 shots are missed.

13.17: (a) This probability is $(0.60)^2(0.40)^3 = 0.02304$.

13.18: (a) Missing 3 shots means making 2 shots, so this probability is $\binom{5}{2}(0.4)^2(0.6)^3 = 0.2304$.

13.19: (b) This is the event that a single digit is 8 or 9, so the probability is 0.20.

13.20: (a) Two lines of the table means that we have $2(40) = 80$ digits. This is the number of "successes" (8 or 9) in $n = 80$ independent trials with $p = 0.20$.

13.21: (a) The mean is $np = (80)(0.20) = 16$.

13.22: (a) No: There is no fixed number of observations. (b) A binomial distribution is reasonable here; a "large city" will have a population much larger than 100 (the sample size), and each randomly selected juror has the same (unknown) probability p of opposing the death penalty. (c) In a Pick 3 game, Joe's chance of winning the lottery is the same every week, so assuming that a year consists of 52 weeks (observations), this would be binomial.

13.23: (a) A binomial distribution is *not* an appropriate choice for field goals made, because given the different situations the kicker faces, his probability of success is likely to change from one attempt to another. (b) It would be reasonable to use a binomial distribution for free throws made because we have $n = 150$ attempts, presumably independent (or at least approximately so), with chance of success $p = 0.8$ each time.

13.24: (a) $n = 20$ and $p = 0.25$. (b) $\mu = np = 5$ correct guesses. (c) $P(X = 5) =$

$$\binom{20}{5}(0.25)^5(0.75)^{15} = 0.2023.$$

13.25: (a) $n = 5$ and $p = 0.65$. (b) The possible values of X are the integers 0, 1, 2, 3, 4, 5. (c) All cases are computed:

$$P(X = 0) = \binom{5}{0}(0.65)^0(0.35)^5 = 0.00525 \qquad P(X = 1) = \binom{5}{1}(0.65)^1(0.35)^4 = 0.04877$$

$$P(X = 2) = \binom{5}{2}(0.65)^2(0.35)^3 = 0.18115 \qquad P(X = 3) = \binom{5}{3}(0.65)^3(0.35)^2 = 0.33642$$

$$P(X = 4) = \binom{5}{4}(0.65)^4(0.35)^1 = 0.31239 \qquad P(X = 5) = \binom{5}{5}(0.65)^5(0.35)^0 = 0.11603.$$

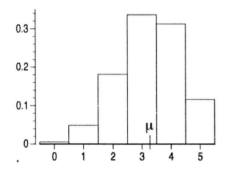

(d) $\mu = np = (5)(0.65) = 3.25$ and $\sigma = \sqrt{5(0.65)(1 - 0.65)} = 1.0665$ years. The mean μ is indicated on the probability histogram.

13.26: (a) This probability is $18/38 = 0.47368$. (b) X has the binomial ($n = 4$, $p = 0.47368$) distribution. (c) $P(\text{break even}) = P(X = 2) = \binom{4}{2}(0.47368)^2(1 - 0.47368)^2 = 0.37292$. (d) $P(\text{lose money}) = P(X < 2) = P(X = 0) + P(X = 1) = \binom{4}{0}(0.47368)^0(1 - 0.47368)^4 +$

$$\binom{4}{1}(0.47368)^1(1 - 0.47368)^3 = 0.07674 + 0.27625 = 0.35299.$$

13.27: (a) All women are independent, and each has the same probability of getting pregnant. (b) Under ideal conditions, the number who get pregnant is binomial with $n = 20$ and $p = 0.01$; $P(N \geq 1) = 1 - P(N = 0) = 1 - 0.8179 = 0.1821$. In typical use, $p = 0.03$, and $P(N \geq 1) = 1 - 0.5438 = 0.4562$.

13.28: X, the number of wins betting on "red" 200 times, is binomial with $n = 200$ and $p =$ 0.47368, using the information from Exercise 13.26. The Normal approximation is quite safe: np = 94.736 > 10 and $n(1 - p) = 105.264 > 10$. The mean is $\mu = np = 94.736$ and the standard deviation is $\sigma = \sqrt{200(0.47368)(1-0.47368)} = 7.06126$, so $P(X < 100) = P(X \le 99)$

$= P\left(Z \le \dfrac{99 - 94.736}{7.06126}\right) = P(Z \le 0.60) = 0.7257$. The exact binomial probability is 0.7502. As the

number of plays (n) increases, the probability of losing money will increase. For example, if $n =$ 400, $P(X < 200)$ = standardize = $P(Z \le 0.95) = 0.8289$. The exact binomial probability is 0.8424.

13.29: (a) X, the number of women who get pregnant in typical use, is binomial with $n = 600$ and $p = 0.03$. The Normal approximation is safe: $np = 18$ and $n(1 - p) = 582$ are both larger than 10.

The mean is 18 and the standard deviation is 4.1785, so $P(X \ge 20) = P\left(Z \ge \dfrac{20-18}{4.1785}\right) = P(Z \ge 0.48)$

= 0.3156. The exact binomial probability is 0.3477. (b) Under ideal conditions, $p = 0.01$, so $np =$ 6 is too small.

13.30: (a) We must assume that each drive is independent, and that he has a 52% chance of hitting the fairway each time. Both of these assumptions are suspect, and student opinions about which is less realistic may vary. (Hitting the fairway is not like, say, shooting a free throw; some fairways are harder to hit than others. Having an *average* success rate of 52% does not necessarily mean that Phil has a 52% chance of hitting *any* fairway.) (b) For a binomial distribution with $n = 14$ and $p = 0.52$, the average number of fairways hit is $np = (14)(0.52) =$ 7.28 fairways hit. In fact, 7 hit fairways is the most likely outcome, with $P(7$ hit fairways$) =$ 0.2071.

13.31: (a) If R is the number of red-blossomed plants out of a sample of 4, then $P(R = 3) =$ $\binom{4}{3}(0.75)^3(0.25)^1 = 0.4219$, using a binomial distribution with $n = 4$ and $p = 0.75$. (b) With $n =$ 60, the mean number of red-blossomed plants is $np = 45$. (c) If R is the number of red-blossomed plants out of a sample of 60, then $P(R \ge 45) =$ $P(Z \ge 0) = 0.5000$ (software gives 0.5688 using the binomial distribution).

13.32: (a) X, the number of positive tests, has a binomial distribution with $n = 1000$ and $p =$ 0.004. (b) $\mu = np = (1000)(0.004) = 4$ positive tests. (c) To use the Normal approximation, we need np and $n(1 - p)$ both bigger than 10, and as we saw in (b), $np = 4$.

13.33: (a) Of 1,498,000 total vehicles in these top 5 nameplates, Impalas accounted for proportion $184,000/1,498,000 = 0.12283$. (b) If I is the number of Impala buyers in the 1000 surveyed buyers, then I has the binomial distribution with $n = 1000$, and $p = 0.12283$. Hence, μ = $np = (1000)(0.12283) = 122.83$ and $\sigma = \sqrt{np(1-p)} = \sqrt{1000(0.12283)(1-0.12283)} = 10.38$ Impala buyers. (c) $P(I > 100) = P(I \ge 101) = P(Z \ge -2.10) = 0.9821$.

13.34: Let D be the number of members that drop out in the first 4 weeks. Then D has the binomial distribution with $n = 300$ and $p = 0.25$, assuming customer results are independent. Let $S = 300 - D$ be the number still enrolled after 4 weeks. Then S has the binomial distribution with $n = 300$ and $p = 0.75$. (a) For D, $\mu = np = (300)(0.25) = 75$ and $\sigma = \sqrt{np(1-p)} = \sqrt{300(0.25)(1-0.25)} = 7.5$ customers. (b) We use the Normal approximation to the distribution of S, since $np = 225$ and $n(1-p) = 75$ are both larger than 10. Now, $P(S \geq 210) = P(Z \geq -2) = 0.9772$.

13.35: (a) With $n = 100$, the mean and standard deviation are $\mu = 75$ and $\sigma = 4.3301$ questions, so $P(70 \leq X \leq 80) = P(-1.15 \leq Z \leq 1.15) = 0.7498$ (software gives 0.7967). (b) With $n = 250$, we have $\mu = 187.5$ and $\sigma = 6.8465$ questions, and a score between 70% and 80% means 175 to 200 correct answers, so $P(175 \leq X \leq 200) = P(-1.83 \leq Z \leq 1.83) = 0.9328$ (software gives 0.9428).

13.36: We have $\mu = 5000$ and $\sigma = 50$ heads, so using the Normal approximation, we compute $P(X \geq 5067$ or $X \leq 4933) = 2P(Z \geq 1.34) = 0.1802$. If Kerrich's coin were "fair," we would see results at least as far from 5000 as what he observed in about 18% of all repetitions of the experiment of flipping the coin 10,000 times. This is not unreasonable behavior for a fair coin.

13.37: (a) Answers will vary, but over 99.8% of samples should have 0 to 4 bad CDs. (b) Each time we choose a sample of size 10, the probability that we have exactly 1 bad CD is 0.3874; therefore, out of 20 samples, the number of times that we have exactly 1 bad CD has a binomial distribution with parameters $n = 20$ and $p = 0.3874$. This means that most students—99.8% of them—will find that between 2 and 14 of their 20 samples have exactly 1 bad CD, giving a proportion between 0.10 and 0.70. (If anyone has an answer outside of that range, which would be significant evidence that he or she did the exercise incorrectly.)

13.38: The number N of new infections is binomial with $n = 20$ and $p = 0.80$ (for unvaccinated children) or 0.05 (for vaccinated children). (a) For vaccinated children, the mean is $(20)(0.05) = 1$ new infection, and $P(N \leq 2) = 0.9245$. (b) For unvaccinated children, the mean is $(20)(0.80) = 16$ new infections, and $P(N \geq 18) = 0.2061$.

13.39: The number N of infections among untreated BJU students is binomial with $n = 1400$ and $p = 0.80$, so the mean is 1120 and the standard deviation is 14.9666 students. 75% of that group is 1050, and the Normal approximation is safe:

$$P(N \geq 1050) = P\left(Z \geq \frac{1050-1120}{14.9666}\right) = P(Z \geq -4.68),$$ which is very near to 1. (Exact

computation gives 0.999998.)

13.40: Let V and U be (respectively) the number of new infections among the vaccinated and unvaccinated children. (a) V is binomial with $n = 17$ and $p = 0.05$, with mean 0.85 infections. (b) U is binomial with $n = 3$ and $p = 0.80$, with mean 2.4 infections. (c) The overall mean is 3.25 infections $(2.4 + 0.85)$.

13.41: Define V and U as in the previous exercise. (a) $P(V=1) = 0.3741$ and

$P(U=1) = 0.0960$. Because these events are independent, $P(V=1$ and $U=1) =$ $P(V=1)P(U=1) = 0.0359$. (b) Considering all the possible ways to have a total of 2 infections, we have $P(2$ infections$) = P(V=0$ and $U=2) + P(V=1$ and $U=1) + P(V=2$ and $U=0) = P(V=0)P(U=2) + P(V=1)P(U=1) + P(V=2)P(U=0) = (0.4181)(0.3840) + (0.3741)(0.0960) + (0.1575)(0.0080) = 0.1977$.

13.42: (a) and (b) The unit square and circle are shown; the intersection A is shaded. (c) The circle has area π, and A is a quarter of the circle, so the area of A is $\pi/4$. This is the probability that a randomly selected point (X, Y) falls in A, so T is binomial with $n = 2000$ and $p = \pi/4 = 0.7854$. (d) The mean of T is $np = 2000(\pi/4) = 500\pi = 1570.7963$ and the standard deviation is

$$\sqrt{np(1-p)} = \sqrt{2000\frac{\pi}{4}\left(1-\frac{\pi}{4}\right)} = 18.3602.$$ (e) Because the mean of T is 500π, $T/500$ is an estimate

of π.

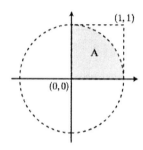

13.43: The number X of fairways Phil hits is binomial with $n = 24$ and $p = 0.52$. (a) $np = 12.48$ and $n(1-p) = 11.52$, so the Normal approximation is (barely) safe. (b) The mean is $np = 12.48$ and the standard deviation is $\sqrt{24(0.52)(0.48)} = 2.447529$. Using the Normal approximation, $P(X \geq 17) = P(Z \geq 1.85) = 0.0322$. (c) With the continuity correction, $P(X \geq 17) = P(X \geq 16.5) = P(Z \geq 1.64) = 0.0505$ (using Table A). Indeed, the answer using the continuity correction is closer to the exact answer (0.0487).

13.44 and 13.45 are Web-based exercises.

Chapter 14 Solutions

14.1: (a) The sampling distribution of $\bar{x}$ has mean μ (unknown) and standard deviation $\frac{\sigma}{\sqrt{n}} = \frac{34}{\sqrt{51000}} = 0.1506$. (b) According to this rule, 95% of all values of $\bar{x}$ fall within 2 standard deviations of the sampling distribution of μ. That is, within $2(0.1506) = 0.3012$. (c) 153 ± 0.3012, or between 152.7 and 153.3.

14.2 The sampling distribution of $\bar{x}$ has mean μ (unknown) and standard deviation $\frac{\sigma}{\sqrt{n}} = \frac{50}{\sqrt{400}} = 2.5$. A 95% confidence interval is $22 \pm 2(2.5) = 22 \pm 5$, or between 17 and 27.

14.3: Shown below are sample output screens for (a) 10 and (b) 1000 SRS's. In 99.4% of all repetitions of part (a), students should see between 5 and 10 hits (that is, at least 5 of the 10 SRS's capture the true mean μ). Out of 1000 80% confidence intervals, nearly all students will observe between 76% and 84% capturing the mean.

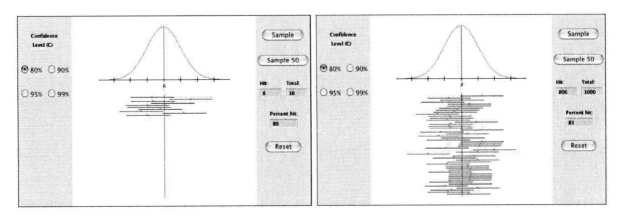

14.4: (a) 54 ± 4, or 50 to 58. (b) 95% confidence means that this interval was produced using a process for which, in the long run, 95% of all samples of the same size give an interval that contains the population mean percent of adults who want to lose weight.

14.5: Search Table A for 0.075 (half of the 15% that is not included in the middle, shaded area corresponding to 85% confidence). This area corresponds to $-z^* = -1.44$, or $z^* = 1.44$.

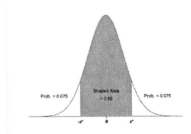

14.6: STATE: What is the true conductivity of this iron rod? PLAN: We will estimate the true conductivity, μ (the mean of all measurements of its conductivity), by giving a 90% confidence interval. SOLVE: The statement of the problem in the text suggests that the conditions for inference should be satisfied. The mean of the sample is $\bar{x}$ = 10.08333 microsiemens per centimeter. For 90% confidence, the critical value is z^* = 1.645. Hence, a 90% confidence interval for μ is

$$\bar{x} \pm z^* \frac{\sigma}{\sqrt{n}} = 10.08333 \pm 1.645 \frac{0.1}{\sqrt{6}} = 10.08333 \pm 0.06716 = 10.01617 \text{ to } 10.15049$$

microsiemens per centimeter. CONCLUDE: We are 90% confident that the iron rod's true connectivity is between 10.0162 and 10.1505 microsiemens per centimeter.

14.7: (a) A stemplot is provided. The two low scores (72 and 74) are both possible outliers, but there are no other apparent deviations from Normality.

```
 7 | 24
 7 |
 8 |
 8 | 69
 9 | 13
 9 | 68
10 | 023334
10 | 578
11 | 11222444
11 | 89
12 | 0
12 | 8
13 | 02
```

(b) STATE: What is the mean IQ μ of all seventh-grade girls in this school district? PLAN: We will estimate μ by giving a 99% confidence interval. SOLVE: The problem states that these girls are an SRS of the population, which is very large, so conditions for inference are met. In part (a), we saw that the scores are consistent with having come from a Normal population. With $\bar{x}$ = 105.84, and z^* = 2.576, our 99% confidence interval for μ is given by

$$105.84 \pm 2.576 \frac{15}{\sqrt{31}} = 105.84 \pm 6.94 = 98.90 \text{ to } 112.78 \text{ IQ points.} \text{ CONCLUDE: We are 99\%}$$

confident that the mean IQ of seventh-grade girls in this district is between 98.90 and 112.78 points.

14.8: (a) The three confidence intervals are given in the table below. In all three cases, $\bar{x}$ = 26.8 and $\frac{\sigma}{\sqrt{n}}$ = 0.2933, so the confidence interval is computed as 26.8 $\pm$ z^*(0.2933), where z^* changes with the confidence level. (b) The margins of error, given in the "m.e." column of the table, increase as confidence level increases.

Conf. Level	z^*	m.e.	Interval
90%	1.645	0.4824	26.32 to 27.28
95%	1.960	0.5748	26.23 to 27.37
99%	2.576	0.7555	26.04 to 27.56

14.9: With $z^* = 1.96$ and $\sigma = 7.5$, the margin of error is $z^* \dfrac{\sigma}{\sqrt{n}} = \dfrac{14.7}{\sqrt{n}}$. (a) and (b) The margins of error are given in the table. (c) Margin of error decreases as n increases. (Specifically, every time the sample size n is quadrupled, the margin of error is halved.)

n	m.e.
100	1.47
400	0.735
1600	0.3675

14.10: (a) With $\bar{x} = 22$, and $z^* = 1.645$, our 90% confidence interval for μ is given by

$22 \pm 1.645 \dfrac{50}{\sqrt{400}} = 22 \pm 4.11 = 17.89$ to 26.11 points. (b) The margin of error is $1.645 \dfrac{50}{\sqrt{400}} =$

4.11, which is smaller than the 5 we have in Exercise 14.2. (c) $1.960 \dfrac{50}{\sqrt{100}} = 9.8$. (d) Decreasing

the sample size increases the margin of error, provided the confidence level and population standard deviation remain the same.

14.11: (c) $z = 3.291$. Using Table A, search for 0.9995.

14.12: (a) The standard deviation of $\bar{x}$ is $\dfrac{\sigma}{\sqrt{n}} = \dfrac{0.001}{\sqrt{3}} = 0.000577$ gram, so the margin of error

is $1.96 \dfrac{\sigma}{\sqrt{n}} = 1.96(0.000577) = 0.00113$ gram.

14.13: (b) As the confidence level increases, z^* increases. This makes the margin of error larger.

14.14: (c) The margin of error is now $\dfrac{(2.576)(0.001)}{\sqrt{8}} = 0.00091$.

14.15: (b) The standard deviation of $\bar{x}$ is $\dfrac{\sigma}{\sqrt{n}} = \dfrac{35}{\sqrt{900}} = 1.167$.

14.16: (c) The margin of error is $1.960(1.167) = 2.29$, so the confidence interval is 150 ± 2.29.

14.17: (b) As the confidence level increases, z^* increases. This makes the margin of error larger.

14.18: (a) The larger the sample size, the smaller the margin of error, provided that the confidence level and population standard deviation remain the same.

14.19: (a) We use $\bar{x} \pm z^* \dfrac{\sigma}{\sqrt{n}}$, or $118 \pm 2.576 \dfrac{65}{\sqrt{463}} = 118 \pm 7.78 = 110.22$ to 125.78 minutes.
(b) The 463 students in this class must be a random sample of all of the first-year students at this university to satisfy conditions for inference.

14.20: The margin of error for 90% confidence is $1.645 \dfrac{2.5}{\sqrt{200}} = 0.2908$ kg/m^2, so the interval is $2.35 \pm 0.2908 = 2.0592$ to 2.6408 kg/m^2.

14.21: The margin of error is now $2.576 \dfrac{65}{\sqrt{464}} = 7.77$, so the extra observation has minimal impact on the margin of error (the sample was large to begin with). If $\bar{x} = 247$, then the 99% confidence interval for average amount of time spent studying becomes $247 \pm 7.77 = 239.23$ to 254.77 minutes. The outlier had a huge impact on $\bar{x}$, which shifts the interval a lot.

14.22: The student is incorrect. A 95% confidence interval does *not* contain 95% of population values. Instead, all we can say is that if we repeatedly sampled the same number of women, each determining a 95% confidence interval for their average perceived ideal weight, then in the long run 95% of these confidence intervals would capture the true, unknown average ideal weight as perceived by all American women.

14.23: This student is also confused. If we repeated the sample over and over, 95% of all future sample means would be within 1.96 standard deviations of μ (that is, within $1.96 \dfrac{\sigma}{\sqrt{n}}$) of the true, unknown value of μ. Future samples will have no memory of our sample.

14.24: The mistake is in saying that 95% of other polls would have results close to the results of this poll. Other surveys should be close to the truth — not necessarily close to the results of this survey. (Additionally, there is the suggestion that 95% means "exactly 19 out of 20," when really 95% refers to repeating the survey infinitely often.)

14.25: (a) A stemplot of the data is provided. Notice that the distribution is noticeably skewed to the left. The data do not appear to follow a Normal distribution.

```
23 | 0
24 | 0
25 |
26 | 5
27 |
28 | 7
29 |
30 | 149
31 | 389
32 | 033577
33 | 0126
```

(b) STATE: What is the mean load μ required to pull apart pieces of Douglas fir? PLAN: We will estimate μ by giving a 95% confidence interval. SOLVE: The problem states that we are willing to take this sample to be an SRS of the population. In spite of the shape of the stemplot, we are told to assume that this distribution is Normal with standard deviation $\sigma = 3000$ lb. We find $\bar{x} = 30{,}841$ lb, so the 95% confidence interval for μ is given by $30{,}841 \pm 1.96\dfrac{3000}{\sqrt{20}} = 30{,}841 \pm 1314.81 = 29{,}526.19$ to $32{,}155.81$ pounds. CONCLUDE: With 95% confidence, the mean load μ required to break apart pieces of Douglas fir is between 29,526.2 and 32,155.8 pounds.

4.26: (a) The stemplot (below) does look reasonably Normal.

-8	3
-7	80
-6	88552
-5	97633221
-4	9977430
-3	86310
-2	755322110
-1	800
-0	83
0	234
1	7
2	2

(b) STATE: What is the mean percent change μ in spinal mineral content of nursing mothers? PLAN: We will estimate μ by giving a 99% confidence interval. SOLVE: The problem states that we may consider these women to be an SRS of the population. In part (a), we concluded that the data appear as though they may have come from a Normal distribution. We find $\bar{x} = -3.587\%$, so the 99% confidence interval for μ is given by $-3.587\% \pm 2.576\dfrac{2.5\%}{\sqrt{47}} = -3.587\% \pm 0.939\% = -4.526\%$ to -2.648%. CONCLUDE: We are 99% confident that the mean percent change in spinal mineral content of nursing mothers is between -4.526% and -2.648%. That is, the mean spinal mineral content in nursing mothers decrease by between 2.65% and 4.53% with 99% confidence.

14.27: (a) A stemplot is given. There is little evidence that the sample does not come from a Normal distribution. For inference, we must assume that the 10 untrained students were selected randomly from the population of all untrained people.

1 9

2 2 3 9

3 0 0 1 3 5

4 2

(b) STATE: What is the average (mean) DMS odor threshold, μ, for all untrained people? PLAN: We will estimate μ with a 95% confidence interval. SOLVE: We have assumed that we have a random sample, and that the population we're sampling from is Normal. We obtain

$\bar{x} = 29.4$ $\mu g/l$. Our 95% confidence interval for μ is given by $29.4 \pm 1.96 \dfrac{7}{\sqrt{10}} = 29.4 \pm 4.34 = $ 25.06 to 33.74 $\mu g/l$. CONCLUDE: With 95% confidence, the mean sensitivity for all untrained people is between 25.06 and 33.74 $\mu g/l$.

14.28: Regardless of the level of confidence (the 95% confidence level has nothing to do with it), larger samples reduce margins of error, providing greater precision in estimating μ.

14.29 and 14.30 are Web-based exercises.

Chapter 15 Solutions

15.1: If $\mu = 115$, the distribution is approximately Normal with mean $\mu = 115$ and standard deviation $\frac{\sigma}{\sqrt{n}} = 6$. (b) The actual result lies out toward the high tail of the curve, while 118.6 is fairly close to the middle. If $\mu = 115$, observing a value similar to 118.6 would not be too surprising, but 125.8 is less likely, and it therefore provides some evidence that $\mu > 115$.

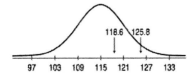

15.2: (a) If $\mu = 10.1$, then the sampling distribution of $\bar{x}$ is approximately Normal with mean $\mu = 10.1$ and standard deviation $\frac{\sigma}{\sqrt{n}} = 0.041$. (b) The plot provided shows sampling distribution described in (a). On the plot are the two indicated values of $\bar{x} = 10.09$ and $\bar{x} = 9.95$. We see that a value of $\bar{x} = 10.09$ would not be unusual if, in fact, $\mu = 10.1$, while a value of $\bar{x} = 9.95$ would be very unusual (more than 3 standard deviations away from 10.1). Hence, a value of $\bar{x} = 9.95$ would provide reason to doubt that $\mu = 10.1$, while $\bar{x} = 10.09$ would not.

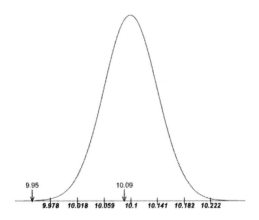

15.3: $H_0 : \mu = 115$ vs. $H_a : \mu > 115$. Because the teacher suspects that older students have a higher mean, we have a one-sided alternative.

15.4: $H_0 : \mu = 10.1$ vs. $H_a : \mu \neq 10.1$. This is a two-sided test because we wonder if the conductivity differs from 10.1.

15.5: $H_0 : \mu = 75$ vs. $H_a : \mu < 75$. The professor suspects this TA's students perform worse than the population of all students in the class on average.

15.6: $H_0 : \mu = \$31,666$ vs. $H_a : \mu \neq \$31,666$. This is a two-sided test because the researcher wonders if the income for women high school graduates in this school differs from the national average.

15.7: Hypotheses are statements about parameters, not statistics. The research question is not about the sample mean ($\bar{x}$), but should be about the population mean, μ.

15.8: With $\sigma = 1$ and $n = 10$, the standard deviation is $\dfrac{\sigma}{\sqrt{10}} = 0.3162$, so when $\mu = 0$, the distribution of $\bar{x}$ is $N(0, 0.3162)$. (b) The P-value is $P = 2P(\bar{x} \geq 0.3) = 2P\left(Z \geq \dfrac{0.3-0}{0.3162}\right) = 0.1711$.

15.9: With $\sigma = 60$ and $n = 18$, the standard deviation is $\dfrac{\sigma}{\sqrt{18}} = 14.1421$, so when $\mu = 0$, the distribution of $\bar{x}$ is $N(0, 14.1421)$. (b) The P-value is $P = 2P(\bar{x} \geq 17) = 2P\left(Z \geq \dfrac{17-0}{14.1421}\right) = 0.2302$.

15.10: If the drug lorcaserin had no effect, then we would expect the average weight loss for the treatment group (on lorcaserin) to be the same as the average weight loss for the control group (on placebo). Of course, by random chance alone, there will be some difference in these average weight losses. The P-value $P < 0.001$ says that if lorcaserin is ineffective, then the chance of observing as large an increased weight loss as the difference observed (5.8 kg – 2.2 kg = 3.6 kg) would happen by chance alone less than 1 in 1000 times. That is, we have seen something that should not have occurred by random chance, and this causes us to doubt the original assumption that lorcaserin is ineffective. Random chance does not explain the additional weight loss in the lorcaserin group.

15.11: (a) The P-value for $\bar{x} = 118.6$ is 0.2743. This is not significant at either $\alpha = 0.05$ or $\alpha = 0.01$. (b) The P-value for $\bar{x} = 125.8$ is 0.0359. This is significant at $\alpha = 0.05$, but not at $\alpha = 0.01$. (c) If $\mu = 115$ (that is, if H_0 were true), observing a value similar to 118.6 would not be too surprising, but 125.8 is less likely, and it therefore provides some evidence that $\mu > 115$.

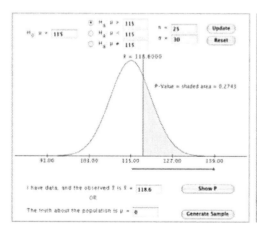
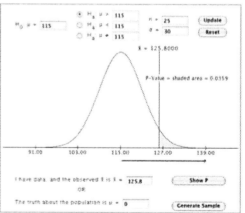

15.12: (a) The *P*-value for $\bar{x}$ = 10.09 is 0.8026. This is not significant at either α = 0.05 or α = 0.01. (b) The *P*-value for $\bar{x}$ = 9.95 is 0.0002. This is significant at both α = 0.05 and α = 0.01. (c) If μ = 10.1 (that is, if H_0 were true), observing a value similar to 10.09 would not be too surprising, but 9.95 is less likely, and it therefore provides strong evidence that μ is different from 10.1.

15.13: (a) $z = \dfrac{0.3-0}{1/\sqrt{10}} = \dfrac{0.3-0}{0.3162} = 0.9488$. (b) $z = \dfrac{1.02-0}{1/\sqrt{10}} = \dfrac{1.02-0}{0.3162} = 3.226$. (c) $z = \dfrac{17-0}{60/\sqrt{18}} = \dfrac{17-0}{14.1421} = 1.2021$. Note that in (c) the test is two-sided, while in (a) and (b) it is one-sided.

15.14: STATE: Is there evidence that the true conductivity of the iron rod is not 10.1? PLAN: Let μ be the rod's true conductivity (the mean of all measurements of its conductivity). We test H_0: μ = 10.1 against H_a: $\mu \neq$ 10.1; we are concerned with deviations in either direction, so this is a two-sided alternative. SOLVE: Assume we have a Normal distribution and an SRS. We have $\bar{x}$ = 10.0833, obtained from the data. The standard deviation of $\bar{x}$ is $\dfrac{0.1}{\sqrt{6}}$ = 0.048, so the test statistic is $z = \dfrac{10.0833-10.1}{0.048} = -0.35$ The *P*-value is $2P(Z \leq -0.35) = 0.728$. CONCLUDE: This sample gives little reason to doubt that the true conductivity is 10.1. That is, there is virtually no evidence that the true conductivity of the rod differs from 10.1. Random chance easily explains the observed sample mean.

15.15: STATE: Is there evidence that the average percent tip when bad news is received (a bad weather prediction) is less than 20%? PLAN: Let μ be the average percentage tip for all customers receiving bad news. We test H_0: μ = 20 against H_a: μ < 20 since we wonder if the value of μ is less than 20%. SOLVE: We have a sample of n = 20 customers, and observe $\bar{x}$ = 18.19%. The standard deviation of $\bar{x}$ is $\dfrac{2}{\sqrt{20}}$ = 0.4472, so the test statistic is $z = \dfrac{17.69-20}{0.4472} = -4.05$. The *P*-value is $P(Z \leq -5.1655) \approx 0$. CONCLUDE: There is overwhelming evidence that the average tip percentage when bad news is delivered is lower than the average tip percentage overall. Random chance does not explain the small value of $\bar{x}$ observed.

15.16: Using Table A, z = 1.876 is significant at the α = 0.05 level because it is larger than 1.645. It is not significant at the α = 0.01 level because it is smaller than 2.326.

15.17: This is not significant at the α = 0.05 level because z is not larger than 1.96 or less than –1.96. It is not (and therefore not) significant at the α = 0.01 level, since z is smaller than 2.576.

15.18: (a) $z = \dfrac{0.4365-0.5}{0.2887/\sqrt{100}} = -2.20$. (b) This result is significant at the 5% level, because $z < -$1.96. (c) It is not significant at the 1% level because $z \geq -2.576$. (d) This value of z is between 2.054 and 2.326, so the *P*-value is between 0.02 and 0.04 (because the alternative is two-sided).

15.19: (a) This is the definition of a *P*-value.

15.20: (b) To be significant at level α, we need $P < \alpha$.

15.21: (c) The *P*-value for $z = 2.433$ is 0.0075 (assuming that the difference is in the correct direction; that is, assuming that the alternative hypothesis was $H_a: \mu > \mu_0$).

15.22: (b) $z = \dfrac{29.667 - 30}{1/\sqrt{3}} = -0.5768$.

15.23: (a) The null hypothesis states that μ takes on the "default" value, 18 seconds.

15.24: (b) The researcher believes that loud noises will decrease the completion time, so the alternative is one-sided.

15.25: (c) The *P*-value refers to the probability of getting a sample as contrary to the null hypothesis as the sample observed, assuming H_0 is true.

15.26: (c) This is a two-sided alternative, so we have 0.0025 in each tail of the Normal distribution, leading to $|z| > 2.807$.

15.27: (b) This is a one-sided alternative, so we have 0.005 in the right tail of the Normal distribution, leading to $z > 2.807$.

15.28: (a) $H_0 : \mu = 120$ minutes vs. $H_a: \mu < 120$ minutes. (b) $z = \dfrac{118 - 120}{65/\sqrt{463}} = -0.662$. (c) *P*-value = $P(Z \le -0.662) = 0.2540$. There is little evidence that the average amount of time spent studying by all students is less than two hours.

15.29: (a) We test $H_0 : \mu = 0$ vs. $H_a: \mu > 0$. (b) $z = \dfrac{2.35 - 0}{2.5/\sqrt{200}} = 13.29$. (c) This value of *z* is far outside the range we would expect from the $N(0,1)$ distribution. Under H_0, it would be virtually impossible to observe a sample mean as large as 2.35 based on a sample of 200 men. Hence, the sample mean is not explained by random chance, and we would easily reject H_0.

15.30: We test $H_0: \mu = 5.19$ against $H_a: \mu \ne 5.19$. The alternative is two-sided because we had no prior belief about the direction of the difference. (That is, before looking at the data, we had no reason to expect that the mean for hotel managers would be higher or lower than 5.19.) (b) With $\bar{y} = 5.29$, the test statistic is $z = \dfrac{5.29 - 5.19}{0.78/\sqrt{148}} = 1.56$. (c) The *P*-value is $2P(Z \ge 1.56) = 0.1188$. There is only weak evidence that hotel managers have different mean femininity score than the general male population. Particularly when the large sample ($n = 148$) is taken into account, we suspect that male hotel managers don't differ much from males in general (in this respect).

15.31: "$P = 0.03$" *does* mean that H_0 is not likely to be correct... but only in the sense that it provides a poor explanation of the data observed. It means that if H_0 is true, a sample as contrary to H_0 as our sample would occur by chance alone only 3% of the time if the experiment was repeated over and over. However, it does *not* mean that there is a 3% chance that H_0 is true.

15.32: If the presence of pig skulls were not an indication of wealth, then differences similar to or bigger than those observed in this study would occur less than 1% of the time by chance.

15.33: The person making the objection is confusing practical significance with statistical significance. In fact, a 5% increase isn't a lot in a pragmatic sense. However, $P = 0.03$ means that random chance does not easily explain the difference observed. That is, there does seem to be an increase in mean improvement for those that expressed their anxieties... but the significance test does not address whether the difference is large enough to matter. Statistical significance is not practical significance.

15.34: With a *P*-value of 0.50, the sample difference between the two study groups was as likely to occur as not. In other words, the observed difference was no less likely than "heads" on the toss of a fair coin. The sample provides no evidence of a difference between pallidal stimulation and subthalamic stimulation.

15.35: In the sketch, the "significant at 1%" region includes only the dark shading ($z > 2.326$). The "significant at 5%" region of the sketch includes both the light and dark shading ($z > 1.645$). When a test is significant at the 1% level, it means that if the null hypothesis were true, outcomes similar to (or more extreme than) those seen are expected less than once in 100 repetitions of the experiment. When a test is significant at the 5% level, it means that if the null hypothesis were true, outcomes similar to (or more extreme than) those seen are expected less than five in 100 repetitions of the experiment. Hence, significance at the 1% level implies significance at the 5% level (or at any level higher than 1%). The converse is false: something that occurs "less than 5 times in 100 repetitions" is not necessarily as rare as something that happens "less than once in 100 repetitions," so a test that is significant at the 5% level is not necessarily significant at the 1% level.

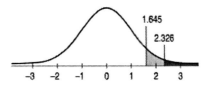

15.36: (a) The graduate student selected the alternative hypothesis after examining the data. The alternative hypothesis should be formulated before examining data, and especially should not be motivated by data. (b) The correct *P*-value is $2P(Z > 1.9) = 2(0.0287) = 0.0574$.

15.37: (a) Because a *P*-value is a probability, it can never be greater than 1. (b) The correct *P*-value is $P(Z \geq 1.33) = 0.0918$.

15.38: (a) STATE: Can we conclude that the mean strength μ of wood pieces differs from 32,500 pounds? PLAN: We test $H_0: \mu = 32,500$ against $H_a: \mu \neq 32,500$ at the $\alpha = 0.10$ level of significance. SOLVE: The sample mean is $\bar{x} = 30,841$ pounds. The test statistic is $z = \dfrac{30,841-32,500}{3,000/\sqrt{20}} = -2.473$. The P-value is $P = 2P(Z \leq -2.473) = 0.0134$. CONCLUDE: There is enough evidence (by far) at the $\alpha = 0.10$ level of significance to conclude that the wood's mean strength differs from 32,500 pounds. (b) STATE: Can we conclude that the mean strength μ of wood pieces differs from 31,500 pounds? PLAN: We test test $H_0: \mu = 31,500$ against $H_a: \mu \neq 31,500$ at the $\alpha = .10$ level of significance. SOLVE: The test statistic is $z = \dfrac{30,841-31,500}{3,000/\sqrt{20}} = -0.982$. The P-value is $P = 2P(Z \leq -0.982) = 0.3261$. CONCLUDE: There is not enough evidence at the $\alpha = 0.10$ level of significance to conclude that the wood's mean strength differs from 31,500 pounds. Random chance easily explains the sample mean's distance from 31,500 pounds, but not from 32,500 pounds.

15.39: STATE: What is the mean percent change μ in spinal mineral content of nursing mothers? PLAN: We will test the hypotheses $H_0: \mu = 0\%$ against $H_a: \mu < 0\%$. SOLVE: The sample mean is $\bar{x} = -3.587\%$. The test statistic is $z = \dfrac{-3.857-0}{2.5/\sqrt{47}} = -9.84$, and the P-value is $P(Z \leq -9.84) \approx 0$. CONCLUDE: There is overwhelming evidence that, on average, nursing mothers lose bone mineral.

15.40: STATE: Is there evidence that the mean DMS threshold for untrained tasters is greater than 25 µg/l? PLAN: We test $H_0 : \mu = 25$ µg/l vs. $H_a : \mu > 25$ µg/l.

SOLVE: We find that $\bar{x} = 29.4$ µg/l, and the test statistic is $z = \dfrac{29.4-25}{7/\sqrt{10}} = 1.99$, so the P-value is $P(Z > 1.99) = 0.0233$. CONCLUDE: This is strong evidence against H_0 (at the $\alpha = 0.05$ level); we conclude that the untrained student's mean threshold is greater than 25 µg/l.

15.41: (a) We test $H_0 : \mu = 0$ vs. $H_a : \mu > 0$, where μ is the mean sensitivity difference in the population. (b) STATE: Does eye grease have a significant impact on eye sensitivity? PLAN: We test the hypotheses stated in part (a). SOLVE: The mean of the 16 differences is $\bar{x} = 0.10125$, so the test statistic is $z = \dfrac{0.10125-0}{0.22/\sqrt{16}} = 1.84$. The one-sided P-value for this value of z is $P = 0.0329$. CONCLUDE: The sample gives significant evidence (at the $\alpha = 0.05$ level) that eye grease increases sensitivity.

15.42: (a) The margin of error for 90% confidence is $1.645\left(\dfrac{15}{\sqrt{72}}\right) = 2.9080$, so the interval is $126.07 \pm 2.9080 = 123.16$ to 128.98. (b) The test statistic is $z = \dfrac{126.07-128}{15/\sqrt{72}} = -1.09$, for which the two-sided P-value is $P = 0.2757$, which is greater than 0.10. (c) The test statistic is z

$$= \frac{126.07 - 129}{15/\sqrt{72}} = -1.66,$$ for which the two-sided *P*-value is $P = 0.0969$, which is (barely) less than 0.10.

15.43: (a) No, because 33 falls in the 95% confidence interval, which is (27.5, 33.9). (b) Yes, because 34 does not fall in the 95% confidence interval.

15.44 and 15.45 are Web-based exercises.

Chapter 16 Solutions

16.1: The most important reason is (c); this is a convenience sample consisting of the first 20 students on a list. This is not an SRS. Anything we learn from this sample will not extend to the larger population. The other two reasons are valid, but less important issues. Reason (a) — the size of the sample and large margin of error – would make the interval less informative, even if the sample were representative of the population. Reason (b) – nonresponse — is a potential problem with every survey, but there is no particular reason to believe it is more likely in this situation.

16.2: (a) The 95% confidence interval is $\bar{x} \pm z^* \dfrac{\sigma}{\sqrt{n}} = 1.92 \pm 1.96 \dfrac{1.83}{\sqrt{880}} = 1.92 \pm 0.1209 =$ 1.80 to 2.04 motorists. (b) The large sample size means that, because of the central limit theorem, the sampling distribution of $\bar{x}$ is roughly Normal even if the distribution of responses is not. (c) Only people with listed telephone numbers were represented in the sample, and the low response rate (10.9% = 5,029/45,956) means that even that group may not be well represented by this sample.

16.3: Any number of things could go wrong with this convenience sample. The day after Thanksgiving is widely regarded (rightly or wrongly) as a day on which retailers offer great deals — and the kinds of shoppers found that day probably don't represent shoppers generally. Also, the sample isn't random.

16.4: (a) The 95% confidence interval is $159 \pm 1.96 \dfrac{35}{\sqrt{501}} = 159 \pm 3.06 = 155.94$ pounds to 162.06 pounds. (b) The sample is an SRS, and it is certainly large enough so that the central limit theorem applies — we know that $\bar{x}$ has a sampling distribution that is approximately Normal. However, people are often inclined to misrepresent (lie or underestimate) their weights. Gallup did not weigh these women — they reported their own weights. If their responses are honest, then the confidence interval above can be relied upon. However, this may well not be the case.

16.5: No. The confidence interval does not describe the range of future values of $\bar{x}$. Instead, if we repeated the experiment over and over, each time computing a 95% confidence interval for the population mean μ, then 95% of these confidence intervals would capture the true population mean.

16.6: With $z^* = 1.96$ and $\sigma = 75$, the margin of error is $z^* \dfrac{\sigma}{\sqrt{n}} = \dfrac{14.7}{\sqrt{n}}$. (a) If $n = 100$, the margin of error is 1.47. (b) If $n = 400$, the margin of error is 0.735. If $n = 1600$, the margin of error is 0.3675. (c) As the sample size increases, the margin of error decreases. Notice that when the sample size quadruples, the margin of error is halved.

16.7: The margin of error only addresses chance variation in the random selection of a sample. Hence, the answer is (c). Sources of bias described in (a) and (b) are not accounted for in the margin of error, and are difficult to assess.

16.8: Computing by hand, we get results almost identical to those obtained using the Applet. The standard deviation of $\bar{x}$ is $\dfrac{\sigma}{\sqrt{n}} = \dfrac{116}{\sqrt{50}} = 16.405$. The test statistic is $\dfrac{\bar{x} - 515}{16.405}$. (a) If $\bar{x} = 541$, the test statistic is $z = 1.58$. The P-value is $P = P(Z \geq 1.58) = 0.057$. Hence, this is (barely) not significant at the 5% level. (b) If $\bar{x} = 542$, the test statistic is $z = 1.65$. The P-value is $P = P(Z \geq 1.65) = 0.049$. Hence, this is (barely) significant at the 5% level. Notice that there's no practical difference between $\bar{x} = 541$ and $\bar{x} = 542$, yet the decision we would make changes, strictly applying the 5% significance level.

16.9: The full applet output for $n = 5$ is below on the left. Next to this are the Normal curves drawn for $n = 15$ and $n = 40$. The reported P-values agree with the "hand-computed" values $z = \dfrac{4.8 - 5}{0.5/\sqrt{n}}$, and $P = P(Z \leq z)$, given in the table.

n	z	P
5	−0.89	0.1867
15	−1.55	0.0606
40	−2.53	0.0057

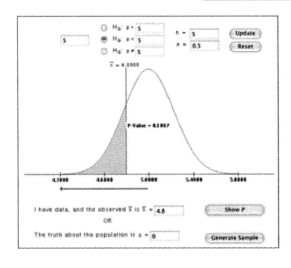
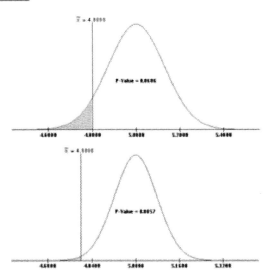

16.10: The confidence intervals are given in the table to the right.

In each case, the interval is $4.8 \pm 1.96\left(\dfrac{0.5}{\sqrt{n}}\right)$.

n	Interval
5	4.362 to 5.238
15	4.547 to 5.053
40	4.645 to 4.955

16.11: (a) In a sample of size $n = 500$, we expect to see about 5 people who have a *P*-value of 0.01 or less [$5 = (500)(0.01)$]. These 4 might have ESP, or they may simply be among the "lucky" ones that occurred by random chance, as expected. (b) The researcher should repeat the procedure on these 4 subjects to see whether they again perform well.

16.12: $n = \left(\dfrac{(1.96)(7.5)}{1} \right)^2 = 216.09.$ Take $n = 217$.

16.13: $n = \left(\dfrac{(1.645)(30)}{10} \right)^2 = 24.354.$ Take $n = 25$.

16.14: (a) "Power = 0.24" means that if really (unknown to the researcher) $\mu = 10.15$, then if we repeatedly sample $n = 6$ measurements, each time conducting the significance test described, we will correctly reject H_0 24% of the time. (b) This means that if $\mu = 10.15$, fully 76% of the time $(100\% - 24\% = 76\%)$ under repeated sampling, we will not reject H_0, even though we should.

16.15: (a) Increase power by taking more measurements. (b) If you increase α, you make it easier to reject H_0, and hence increase power. (c) A value of $\mu = 10.2$ is even further from the stated value of $\mu = 10.1$ under H_0, so power increases.

16.16: The powers (obtained using the applet) are summarized in the table:

(a)			(b)			(c)	
n	Power		μ	Power		α	Power
6	0.232		10.15	0.232		0.05	0.232
12	0.410		10.20	0.688		0.10	0.339
24	0.688		10.25	0.957		0.25	0.538

(a) As sample size increases (keeping everything else constant), power increases. (b) Keeping everything else constant, power is greater when the alternative considered is further away from 10.1. (c) Power increases when α increases, keeping everything else constant.

16.17: The table below summarizes power as σ changes. As σ decreases, power increases. More precise measurements increase the researcher's ability to recognize a false null hypothesis.

σ	0.10	0.05	0.025
Power	0.232	0.688	0.998

16.18: (a) H_0: The patient is healthy (or "the patient should not see a doctor"); H_a: The patient is ill (or "the patient should see a doctor"). A Type I error is a false positive— sending a healthy patient to the doctor. A Type II error means a false negative—clearing a patient who should be referred to a doctor. (b) One might wish to lower the probability of a false negative so that most ill patients are treated, especially for serious diseases that require fast treatment. On the other hand, if resources (for example, money or medical personnel) are limited, or for less serious health problems, lowering the probability of false positives might be desirable.

16.19: (a) All statistical methods are based on probability samples. We must have a random sample in order to apply them.

16.20: (c) Especially with respect to heart rates, male athletes can't be considered to be representative of all male students.

16.21: (b) Inference from a voluntary response sample is never reasonable. Online web surveys are voluntary response surveys.

16.22: (c) Well-designed surveys incur error due to random chance. This random variation is the only source of error accounted for in the margin of error. All forms of bias are not accounted for, and are errors in addition to those due to chance.

16.23: (a) There is no control group. Any observed improvement may be due to the treatment, or may be due to another cause.

16.24: (a) The power of the test increases with sample size. That is, with a larger sample size the small increase in life expectancy due to mild activity is more likely to be recognized.

16.25: (a) The significance level (α) is the probability of rejecting H_0 when H_0 is true.

16.26: (b) The power of the test is the probability of rejecting H_0 when H_0 is false. In this case, if $\mu = 3$, then H_0 is false, and power if the probability of rejecting.

16.27: (c) Power describes the test's ability to reject a false H_0.

16.28: We need to know that the 148 respondents were chosen at random from all general managers of three-star and four-star hotels. We also consider the possible presence of bias due to a low response rate, so we consider the response rate.

16.29: We need to know that the samples taken from both populations (hunter-gatherers, agricultural) are random. Are the samples large? Recall that if the samples are very large, then even a small, practically insignificant difference in prevalence of color blindness in the two samples will be deemed statistically significant.

16.30: (a) The sample described is a random sample, but women shopping at a suburban shopping mall don't represent the population of all women. (b) Since the sample is random, the sample is likely to represent the population of all women that shop at suburban malls.

16.31: Many people might be reluctant to relate details of their sex lives, or perhaps some will be inclined to exaggerate. It would not be surprising that such an estimate would be biased, but this author cannot guess the direction of bias (will the estimate be too high or too low on average?).

16.32: Because we have the percentages for each of the 13 Canadian provinces, we know the exact value of μ. This assumes that the percentages listed at the web site are not estimates (though they probably are).

16.33: The effect is greater if the sample is small. With a larger sample, the impact of any one value is small.

16.34: (a) A stemplot is shown. The distribution has a low outlier, which makes confidence interval methods unreliable. (b) The timeplot shows a decreasing trend over time, so we should not treat these 29 observations as a sample coming from a single population.

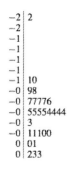
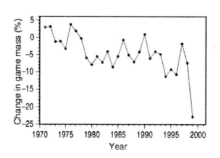

16.35: Opinion—even expert opinion—unsupported by data is the weakest type of evidence, so the third description is level C. The second description refers to experiments (clinical trials) and large samples; that is the strongest evidence (level A). The first description is level B: stronger than opinion, but not as strong as experiments with large numbers of subjects.

16.36: A significance test answers only question (b). The *P*-value states how likely the observed effect (or a stronger one) is if chance alone is operating. The observed effect may be significant (very unlikely to be due to chance) and yet not be of practical importance. And the calculation leading to significance *assumes* a properly designed study.

16.37: (a) The *P*-value decreases (the evidence against H_0 becomes stronger). (b) The power increases (the test becomes better at distinguishing between the null and alternative hypotheses).

16.38: It would not be reasonable to use this variable as a predictor for divorce rate. As the problem explains, the researcher tested for significance among "dozens" of candidate predictor variables. By chance alone, some of them will test as significant.

16.39: (a) The sample mean is $\bar{x} = 7.524$. The test statistic is $z = \dfrac{7.524 - 6}{2/\sqrt{5}} = 1.704$. The *P*-value is $P = 2P(Z \geq 1.704) = 0.0884$ (using software). This is not significant at the 5% level of significance.   (b) We would not reject 6 as a plausible value of μ, even though (unknown to the researcher) $\mu = 5$. This isn't surprising since $\bar{x} = 7.524$. In fact, we would not reject H_0: $\mu = 7$, either (and the *P*-value would be larger, suggesting less evidence against H_0).

16.40: (a) This means that if the "affirmation training" had no effect, the chance of observing a difference in the sample performances between the two groups of women (those with and those without affirmation training) as great as that observed would occur by chance alone less than 1 in 1000 times. In other words, random chance does not really explain the observed difference in the two groups of women. (b) If we repeated this study, each time constructing a 95% confidence interval for the average difference in scores between women with training and women without, then in the long run 95% of these intervals would capture the real, unknown average difference. (c) No. The estimated average "improvement" is 13 points (with margin of error 8 points). We have no sense for whether 13 is a meaningful or practically important improvement. What if the gender gap is 1000 points? What if it is 15 points? In the former case, an improvement of 13 points would be meaningless, while in the latter case it would be profound.

16.41: (a) "Statistically insignificant" means that the differences observed were no more than might have been expected to occur by chance even if SES had no effect on LSAT results. (b) If the results are based on a small sample, then even if the null hypothesis were not true, the test might not be sensitive enough to detect the effect. Knowing the effects were small tells us that the test was not insignificant merely because of a small sample size.

16.42: $n = \left(\dfrac{(2.576)(7)}{0.1} \right)^2 = 32{,}515.3$. Take $n = 32{,}516$. This would be an unreasonable sample size, of course, and this suggests that a sample of size n = 10 used in previous exercises would be far from adequate to estimate a mean DMS threshold to within 0.1.

16.43: $n = \left(\dfrac{(1.96)(3000)}{600} \right)^2 = 96.04$. Take $n = 97$.

16.44: A low-power test may do a good job of *not* incorrectly rejecting the null hypothesis (that is, avoiding a Type I error), but it will often accept H_0, even when it is false, simply because it is difficult to distinguish between H_0 and "nearby" alternatives.

16.45: (a) This test has a 20% chance of rejecting H_0 when the alternative is true. (b) If the test has 20% power, then when the alternative is true, it will fail to reject H_0 80% of the time. (c) The sample sizes are very small, which typically leads to low-power tests.

16.46: (a) The researchers conducted a two-sided test of hypotheses at the $\alpha = 0.05$ level of significance. (b) If there is, in fact a clinically significant difference (a difference of at least 10 percentage points) in risk of death between the early and late intervention groups, then this test would detect that difference (reject the hypothesis of no difference) 80% of the time, if the experiment was conducted repeatedly.

16.47: From the applet, against the alternative $\mu = 8$, power = 0.609. Against the alternative $\mu = 10$, power = 0.994.

16.48: (a) Because the alternative is $\mu > 0$, we reject H_0 at the 5% level when $z \geq 1.645$. (b) We reject H_0 when $(3.162)(\bar{x}) \geq 1.645$, or $\bar{x} \geq 0.5202$. (c) When $\mu = 0.8$, the power is

$$P(\bar{x} \geq 0.5202) = P\left(\frac{\bar{x} - 0.8}{1/\sqrt{10}} \geq \frac{0.5202 - 0.8}{1/\sqrt{10}}\right) = P(Z \geq -0.88) = 0.8106.$$

16.49: (a) Because the alternative is $\mu \neq 10.1$, we reject H_0 at the 5% level when $z \geq 1.96$ or $z \leq -1.96$. (b) Here, $z = \dfrac{\bar{x} - 10.1}{0.1/\sqrt{6}} = 24.4949(\bar{x} - 10.1)$. Hence, we reject H_0 if $24.4949(\bar{x} - 10.1) \leq -1.96$ or if $24.4949(\bar{x} - 10.1) \geq 1.96$. Equivalently (solving for $\bar{x}$), we reject H_0 if $\bar{x} \leq 10.02$ or $\bar{x} \geq 10.18$. (c) When $\mu = 10.15$, the power is

$$P(\bar{x} \leq 10.02) + P(\bar{x} \geq 10.18) = P\left(Z \leq \frac{10.02 - 10.15}{0.1/\sqrt{6}}\right) + P\left(Z \geq \frac{10.18 - 10.15}{0.1/\sqrt{6}}\right)$$

$$= P(Z \leq -3.18) + P(Z \geq 0.74) = 0.0007 + 0.2297 = 0.2304.$$

16.50: The probability of committing a Type I error is $\alpha = 0.01$. The probability of a Type II error is $1 - \text{Power} = 1 - 0.78 = 0.22$.

16.51: Power $= 1 - P(\text{Type II error}) = 1 - 0.14 = 0.86$.

16.52: (a) $P(\text{Type I error}) = P(\text{reject } H_0 \text{ when } H_0 \text{ is true}) = P(\bar{x} > 0 \text{ given that } \mu = 0) = 0.5$, since $\bar{x}$ has the Normal distribution with mean 0. (b) If $\mu = 0.2$, then $\bar{x}$ has the Normal distribution with mean 0.2 and standard deviation $1/\sqrt{16} = 0.25$. Hence, $P(\bar{x} \leq 0) = P\left(Z \leq \dfrac{0 - 0.2}{0.25}\right)$

$= P(Z \leq -0.80) = 0.2119$. (c) If $\mu = 0.5$, then $\bar{x}$ has the Normal distribution with mean 0.5 and standard deviation 0.25. Hence, $P(\bar{x} \leq 0) = P\left(Z \leq \dfrac{0 - 0.5}{0.25}\right) = P(Z \leq -2.00) = 0.0228$.

16.53: (a) In the long run, this probability should be 0.05. Out of 100 simulated tests, the number of false rejections will have a binomial distribution with $n = 100$ and $p = 0.05$. Most students will see between 0 and 10 rejections. (b) If the power is 0.808, the probability of a Type II error is 0.192, so in the long run, this probability should be 0.192. Out of 100 simulated tests, the number of false non-rejections will have a binomial distribution with $n = 100$ and $p = 0.192$. Most students will see between 10 and 29 non-rejections.

16.54 and **16.55** are Web-based Exercises.

Chapter 17 Solutions

Test Yourself Exercise Answers are answers or sketches. All of these problems are similar to ones found in Chapters 8–16, for which the solutions in this manual provide more detail.

17.1: (c) Hives with bees; Hives with no bees; No hives

17.2: (d)

17.3: (b)

17.4: (d)

17.5: (a) The subjects were not assigned to exercise type.

17.6: (a) Label the students 0001 through 3478. (b) Using Table B, starting with line 105, the first 5 students selected are 2940, 0769 (that is, 769), 1481, 2975, and 1315. (c) The response variable is summer income earned.

17.7: Many answers are possible. One possible lurking variable is "student attitude about purpose of college" (students with a view that college is about partying, rather than studying may be more likely to binge drink and more likely to have lower grades). Remember that a correct example of a lurking variable *must* be a variable that simultaneously drives both "GPA" and "binge drinking" together.

17.8: (a) Randomly select 32 of the 64 women, and assign these to the chocolate group. The other 32 women will be assigned to the carob group. Women, as well as the people evaluating them for impact of carob or chocolate, will not know which group they belong to. (b.) The first 5 women assigned to the chocolate group are 38, 44, 18, 33, and 46.

17.9: No doubt, Question A had 60% favoring a tax cut, while Question B had 22% favoring a tax cut. Question wording in A packages all government spending into an impersonal block that people don't relate to, or even strongly oppose. Question wording in B describes government spending with greater detail, and mentions government spending priorities most people care about (education, defense, etc.).

17.10: (d) the time each movie was shown is a confounding variable.

17.11: (b) the different types of movies.

17.12: People that visit the *NOVA Science Now* Web site don't represent American adults broadly. Those people taking the survey went out of the way to participate in this online poll, and they read pro and con arguments after watching a program about the issue. It seems reasonable to believe that these people understand the issues better than most American adults.

17.13: (a) a matched-pairs experiment.

17.14: (c) the 15 students interviewed.

17.15: (d) probably biased. It's not a random sample, and those walking at night probably have a different view of campus safety than those than the campus community broadly defined.

17.16: (a) S = {Male, Female} (b) S = {6, 7, 8, …, 19, 20} (c) S = {All values $2.5 \leq$ VOP ≤ 6.1 liters per minute} (d) S = {All heart rates such that heart rate > 0}.

17.17: (a) $1 - 0.66 - 0.21 - 0.07 - 0.04 = 0.02$.

17.18: (b) $1 - 0.66 = 0.34$.

17.19: $Y > 1$, or $Y \geq 2$. $P(Y \geq 2) = 1 - 0.26 = 0.74$.

17.20: $P(2 < Y \leq 4) = P(3 \leq Y \leq 4) = 0.16 + 0.15 = 0.31$.

17.21: (d) $1 - 0.33 = 0.67$.

17.22: All of the probabilities are between 0 and 1 (inclusive), and they sum to 1. Hence, this is a legitimate discrete probability model.

17.23: $P(X \leq 2)$ is the probability of women giving birth to 2 or fewer children during their childbearing years. $P(X \leq 2) = 0.193 + 0.174 + 0.344 = 0.711$. 71.1% of women give birth to 2 or fewer children during their childbearing years.

17.24: (c) $P(X < 2) = P(X \leq 1) = 0.193 + 0.174 = 0.367$.

17.25: $P(X \geq 3) = 0.181 + 0.074 + 0.034 = 0.289$.

17.26: (b) Continuous, but not Normal.

17.27: (a) The height of the density curve is $1/5 = 0.2$, since the area under the density function must be 1.

17.28: $P(1 \leq Y \leq 3) = 2/5 = 0.4$.

17.29: (b) This is a personal probability.

17.30: (b) 0.3707, since this is $P(Z \geq 1/3)$, or $P(Z \geq 0.33)$.

17.31: (c) mean = 100, standard deviation = $15/\sqrt{60} = 1.94$ (rounded).

17.32: (a) 0.0049, since this is $P(Z \geq 2.58)$.

17.33: The answer in 17.30 would change, since this refers to the population distribution, which is now non-Normal. The answer in 17.31 would not change — the mean of $\bar{x}$ is 100, and the standard deviation of $\bar{x}$ is 1.94, regardless of the population distribution. The answer in 17.32 would, essentially, not change. The central limit theorem tells us that the sampling distribution of $\bar{x}$ is approximately Normal when n is large enough (and 60 should be large enough), no matter what the population distribution.

17.34: Whether $n = 15$ or $n = 150$, the mean of $\bar{x}$ is 445 *ms*. If $n = 15$, the standard deviation of $\bar{x}$ is $82/\sqrt{15} = 21.17$ *ms*. If $n = 150$, the standard deviation of $\bar{x}$ is $82/\sqrt{150} = 6.70$ *ms*.

17.35: If the population we're sampling from is heavily skewed, then a larger sample is required for the Central Limit Theorem to apply. Hence, if $n = 15$, the sampling distribution of $\bar{x}$ may not be approximately Normal, but if $n = 150$, it will surely be approximately Normal.

17.36: $P(\bar{x} > 450) = P(Z > 0.75) = 0.2266$.

17.37: (a) $11{,}479/14{,}099 = 0.8142$. (b) $6457/(6457+1818) = 0.7803$.

17.38: (a) *F* and *G*.

17.39: (a) $1 - P(\text{failure}) = 1 - P(\text{both components fail}) = 1 - (0.20)(0.03) = 0.994$.

17.40: (b) $35\% - 15\% = 20\%$.

17.41: (c) the mean is $1000(0.63) = 630$; standard deviation is $\sqrt{1000(0.63)(1-0.63)} = 15.27$.

17.42: (a) This is a binomial distribution; $\binom{12}{8}(0.50)^8(1-0.50)^4 = 0.1208$. (b) If $n = 500$ and $p = 0.50$, then $np = 250$ and $n(1-p) = 250$, both of which are more than 10. Hence, the Normal approximation is reasonable. With mean $np = 250$ and standard deviation $\sqrt{np(1-p)} = 11.18$,
$$P(X \geq 235) = P\left(Z \geq \frac{235-250}{11.18}\right) = P(Z \geq -1.34) = 0.9099.$$

17.43: (c) $357 \pm 1.96\dfrac{50}{\sqrt{8}} = 322.35$ to 391.65.

17.44: (b) $357 \pm 1.645\dfrac{50}{\sqrt{8}}$ 327.92 to 386.08.

17.45: $357 \pm 1.282\dfrac{50}{\sqrt{8}}$ 334.37 to 379.63.

17.46: As the confidence level decreases, the margin of error decreases, resulting in a narrower confidence interval.

17.47: (b) 172 ± 18.03 mg/dl.

17.48: (d) 56. To cut the margin of error in half, we need to quadruple the sample size from 14 to 56.

17.49: (c) $n \geq \dfrac{(1.645)^2(41)^2}{5^2} = 181.95$, which rounds to 182.

17.50: (a) $H_0 : \mu = 48$, $H_a : \mu < 48$.

17.51: (c) $H_0 : \mu = 5$, $H_a : \mu \neq 5$.

17.52: (d) -1.46; $z = \dfrac{172 - 188}{41/\sqrt{14}} = -1.46$.

17.53: (c) $\alpha = 0.10$ but not at $\alpha = 0.05$. The *P*-value is 0.0721.

17.54: (a) $\alpha = 0.01$. Now $z = \dfrac{172 - 188}{41/\sqrt{56}} = -2.92$, so the *P*-value is 0.0018.

17.55: (d) No more than 0.01. In Exercise 17.54, $P = 0.0018$.

17.56: $87.6 \pm 1.96 \dfrac{15}{\sqrt{113}} = 87.6 \pm 2.77 = 84.83$ to 90.37.

17.57: We test $H_0 : \mu = 100$ vs. $H_a : \mu < 100$; $z = \dfrac{87.6 - 100}{15/\sqrt{113}} = -8.79$; *P*-value ≈ 0.

Overwhelming evidence that the mean IQ for the very-low-birth-weight population is less than 100.

17.58: The study above was an observational study, not an experiment because nobody assigned birth weights (the treatment) to the babies. In an observational study, a lurking variable may be driving both variables in the study (birth weight and IQ in this case).

17.59: (c) The statement "no differences were seen" means that the observed differences were not statistically significant at the significance level used by the researchers.

17.60: $P = 0.68$ means that the observed difference is easily explained by random chance. $P < 0.001$ means that the observed difference was exceedingly unlikely to have occurred by chance alone.

17.61: Here, $r^2 = 0.61$ means that 61% of the total variability in number of wildfires is explained by our model (by knowing the year). If there is really no relationship between number of fires and year (a surrogate for population here), then an observed linear relationship in our data as strong as that observed ($r^2 = 0.61$) would have been very unlikely to occur by chance alone. It seems reasonable to conclude that "year" and "wildfires" are positively associated — fires have increased over time, suggesting that population (or changing weather) increases wildfires. However, a cause-and-effect conclusion is not possible.

Supplementary Exercises

17.62: (a) One possible population: all full-time undergraduate students in the fall term on a list provided by the registrar. (b) A stratified sample with 125 students from each year is one possibility. (c) Mailed or emailed questionnaires might have high nonresponse rates. Telephone interviews exclude those without phones, and may mean repeated calling for those who are not home. Face-to-face interviews might be more costly than your funding will allow. Some students might be sensitive about responding to questions about sexual harassment.

17.63: Placebos do work with real pain, so the placebo response tells nothing about physical basis of the pain. In fact, placebos work poorly in hypochondriacs. The survey is described in the April 3, 1979, edition of the *New York Times*.

17.64: Parents who fail to return the consent form may be more likely to place less priority on education, and therefore may give their children less help with homework, and so forth. Including those children in the control group is likely to lower that group's score.

Note : *This is a generalization, to be sure: we are not saying that* every *such parent does not value education, only that the percent of this group that highly values education will almost certainly be lower than that same percent of the parents who return the form.*

17.65: (a) Increase. (b) Decrease. (c) Increase. (d) Decrease.

 Note: *The first and third statements make an argument in favor of a national health insurance system, while the second and fourth suggest reasons to oppose it.*

17.66: (a) The table shows the six treatments—three levels of Factor A (discount level) and two levels of Factor B (fraction of shoes on sale). (b) The diagram is shown. From line 111 of Table B, the first 10 subjects (group 1) are 48, 60, 51, 30, 41, 27, 12, 38, 50, and 59.

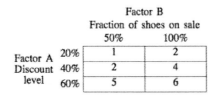

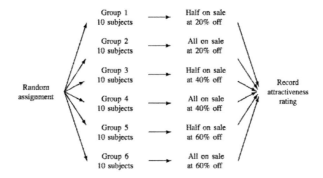

17.67: (a) The factors are storage method (three levels: fresh, room temperature for one month, refrigerated for one month) and preparation method (two levels: cooked immediately, or after one hour). There are therefore six treatments (summarized in the table). The response variables are the tasters' color and flavor ratings. (b) Randomly allocate n potatoes to each of the six groups, then compare ratings. (c) For each taster, randomly choose the order in which the fries are tasted.

	Cooked immediately	Wait one hour
Fresh	1	2
Stored	3	4
Refrigerated	5	6

17.68: There are many possible answers; the key is that the events A and B must be able to occur together.

17.69: (a) All probabilities are between 0 and 1, and their sum is 1. (b) Let R_1 be Taster 1's rating and R_2 be Taster 2's rating. Add the probabilities on the diagonal (upper left to lower right): $P(R_1 = R_2) = 0.03 + 0.08 + 0.25 + 0.20 + 0.06 = 0.62$. (c) $P(R_1 > R_2) = 0.19$. This is the sum of the ten numbers in the "lower left" part of the table; the bottom four numbers from the first column, the bottom three from the second column, the bottom two from the third column, and the last number in the fourth column. These entries correspond to, for example, "Taster 2 gives a rating of 1, and Taster 1 gives a rating more than 1." $P(R_2 > R_1) = 0.19$; this is the sum of the ten numbers in the "upper right" part of the table. We could also find this by noting that this probability and the other two in this exercise must add to 1 (because they account for all of the entries in the table). Alternatively, noting that the matrix is symmetric (relative to the main diagonal), we must have $P(R_1 > R_2) = P(R_2 > R_1)$.

17.70: $P(A) = P(B) = \cdots = P(F) = 0.72/6 = 0.12$ and $P(1) = P(2) = \cdots = P(8) = (1-0.72)/8 = 0.035$.

17.71: (a) Out of 100 BMIs, nearly all should be in the range $\mu \pm 3\sigma = 27 \pm 22.5 = 4.5$ to 49.5. (b) The sample mean $\bar{x}$ has a $N(\mu, \sigma/\sqrt{100}) = N(27, 0.75)$ distribution, so nearly all such means should be in the range $27 \pm 3(0.75) = 27 \pm 2.25$, or 24.75 to 29.25.

17.72: To cut the range of values of x in half, we need to halve the standard deviation of the distribution of $\bar{x}$, which requires increasing the sample size by a factor of 4, to $n = 400$. Those 400 individual BMIs will be as variable as the 100 individual BMIs (or more variable because there are now four times as many opportunities to observe extreme scores).

17.73: (a) This is an observational study: Behavior is observed, but no treatment is imposed. (b) "Significant" means unlikely to happen by chance. In this study, researchers determined that the fact that light-to-moderate drinkers had a lower death rate than the other groups is evidence of a real difference, rather than mere coincidence. (c) For example, some nondrinkers might avoid drinking because of other health concerns.

17.74: (a) A stemplot below confirms the description given in the text. (b) STATE: Does the presence of a lavender odor change the mean time spent in the restaurant? PLAN: Let μ be the mean time spent in the restaurant with the lavender odor. We test $H_0: \mu = 90$ min vs. $H_a: \mu \neq 90$ min; the alternative is two-sided because we do not know if the odor will increase or decrease the mean. SOLVE: A stemplot suggests that the distribution of customer times reasonably Normal; we also assume we have an SRS. We find that $\bar{x} = 105.7$, so the test statistic is $z = \dfrac{105.7 - 90}{15/\sqrt{30}} = 5.73$, and the P-value is extremely small ($P = 2P(Z > 5.73) \approx 0$).

CONCLUDE: This is overwhelming evidence that the mean time spent in the restaurant changes (increases) when the lavender odor is present.

```
 7 | 6
 8 |
 8 | 89
 9 | 234
 9 | 578
10 | 1234
10 | 5566788999
11 | 4
11 | 6
12 | 14
12 | 69
13 |
13 | 7
```

17.75: (a) The stemplot confirms the description given in the text. (Arguably, there are two "mild outliers" visible in the stemplot, although the $1.5 \times IQR$ criterion only flags the highest as an outlier.) (b) STATE: Is there evidence that the mean body temperature for all healthy adults is not equal to $98.6°$? PLAN: Let μ be the mean body temperature. We test $H_0: \mu = 98.6°$ vs. $H_a: \mu \neq 98.6°$; the alternative is two-sided because we had no suspicion (before looking at the data) that μ might be higher or lower than $98.6°$. SOLVE: Assume we have a Normal distribution and an SRS. The average body temperature in our sample is $\bar{x} = 98.203°$, so the test statistic is $z = \dfrac{98.203 - 98.6}{0.7/\sqrt{20}} = -2.54$. The two-sided P-value is $P = 2P(Z < -2.54) = 0.0110$. CONCLUDE: We have fairly strong evidence—significant at $\alpha = 0.05$, but not at $\alpha = 0.01$—that mean body temperature is not equal to $98.6°$. (Specifically, the data suggests that mean body temperature is lower.)

```
 96 | 8
 97 | 344
 97 | 888889
 98 | 0133
 98 | 5789
 99 |
 99 | 6
100 | 2
```

17.76: STATE: What is μ, the mean time spent in the restaurant on Saturday nights when a lavender odor is present? PLAN: We will estimate μ by giving a 95% confidence interval.

SOLVE: We assume that we have an SRS of the population, and that the distribution is roughly Normal with standard deviation 15 min. With $\bar{x}$ = 105.7, our 95% confidence interval for μ is

$$105.7 \pm 1.96 \left(\frac{15}{\sqrt{30}} \right) = 105.7 \pm 5.37, \text{ or } 100.33 \text{ to } 111.07 \text{ minutes. CONCLUDE: We are 95\%}$$

confident that the mean time spent in the restaurant is between 100.33 and 111.07 minutes.

17.77: STATE: What is the mean body temperature μ for healthy adults? PLAN: We will estimate μ by giving a 90% confidence interval. SOLVE: Assume we have a Normal distribution and an SRS. With $\bar{x}$ = 98.203, our 90% confidence interval for μ is

$$98.203 \pm 1.645 \left(\frac{0.7}{\sqrt{20}} \right) = 98.203 \pm 0.257, \text{ or } 97.95° \text{ to } 98.46°. \text{ CONCLUDE: We are 90\%}$$

confident that the mean body temperature for healthy adults is between 97.95° and 98.46°.

17.78: For the two-sided test $H_0: \mu = \$95{,}000$ vs. $H_a: \mu \neq \$95{,}000$ with significance level $\alpha = 0.01$, we can reject H_0 because \$95,000 falls outside the 99% confidence interval.

17.79: A low-power test has a small probability of rejecting the null hypothesis, at least for some alternatives. That is, we run a fairly high risk of making a Type II error (failing to reject H_0 when it is false) for such alternatives. Knowing that this can happen, we should not conclude that H_0 is "true" simply because we failed to reject it.

17.80: A Type I error means that we conclude the mean IQ is less than 100 when it really is 100 (or more). A Type II error means that we conclude the mean IQ is 100 (or more) when it really is less than 100.

Chapter 18 Solutions

18.1: The standard error of the mean is $s/\sqrt{n} = 63.9/\sqrt{1000} = 2.0207$ minutes.

18.2: The standard error of the mean is $s/\sqrt{n} = 15/\sqrt{10} = 4.743$ beats per minute.

18.3: (a) $t^* = 2.132$. (b) $t^* = 2.479$.

18.4: Here, df $= 30 - 1 = 29$. (a) $t^* = 2.045$. (b) $t^* = 0.683$.

18.5: (a) df $= 12 - 1 = 11$, so $t^* = 2.201$. (b) df $= 18 - 1 = 17$, so $t^* = 2.898$.
(c) df $= 6 - 1 = 5$, so $t^* = 2.015$.

18.6: (a) The stemplot provided shows a slight skew to the right, but not so strong that it would invalidate the t procedures. (b) With $\bar{x} = 18.66$, $s = 10.2768$, and $t^* = 2.093$ (df $= 19$), the 95% confidence interval for μ is $18.66 \pm 2.093 \dfrac{10.2768}{\sqrt{20}}$
$= 18.66 \pm 4.8096 = 13.8504$ to 23.4696.

```
0 | 67888
1 | 0004
1 | 67
2 | 012
2 | 57
3 | 00
3 | 78
```

18.7: STATE: What is the mean percent μ of nitrogen in ancient air? PLAN: We will estimate μ with a 90% confidence interval. SOLVE: We are told to view the observations as an SRS. A stemplot shows some left-skewness; however, for such a small sample, the data are not unreasonably skewed. There are no outliers. With $\bar{x} = 59.5889\%$ and $s = 6.2553\%$ nitrogen, and $t^* = 1.860$ (df $= 8$), the 90% confidence interval for μ is $59.5889 \pm 1.860 \dfrac{6.2553}{\sqrt{9}} = 59.5889 \pm$
$3.8783 = 55.71\%$ to 63.47%. CONCLUDE: We are 90% confident that the mean percent of nitrogen in ancient air is between 55.71% and 63.47%.

```
4 | 9
5 | 1
5 |
5 | 4
5 |
5 |
6 | 0
6 | 33
6 | 445
```

18.8: (a) df $= 20 - 1 = 19$. (b) $t = 1.84$ is bracketed by $t^* = 1.729$ (with right-tail probability 0.05) and $t^* = 2.093$ (with right-tail probability 0.025). Hence, since this is a one-sided significance test, $0.025 < P < 0.05$. (c) This test is significant at the 5% level since the $P < 0.05$. It is not significant at the 1% level since the $P > 0.01$. (d) From software, $P = 0.0407$.

18.9: (a) df = 15 − 1 = 14. (b) t = 2.12 is bracketed by t^* = 1.761 (with two-tail probability 0.10) and t^* = 2.145 (with two-tail probability 0.05). Hence, since this is a two-sided significance test, $0.05 < P < 0.10$. (c) This test is significant at the 10% level since the $P < 0.10$. It is not significant at the 5% level since the $P > 0.05$. (d) From software, $P = 0.0524$.

18.10: STATE: Is there evidence that the percent of nitrogen in ancient air was different from the present 78.1%? **PLAN:** We test $H_0: \mu = 78.1\%$ vs. $H_a: \mu \neq 78.1\%$. We use a two-sided alternative because, prior to seeing the data, we had no reason to believe that the percent of nitrogen in ancient air would be higher or lower. **SOLVE:** We addressed the conditions for inference in Exercise 18.7. In that solution, we found $\bar{x}$ = 59.5889% and s = 6.2553% nitrogen, so $t = \dfrac{59.5889 - 78.1}{6.2553/\sqrt{9}} = -8.88$. For df = 8, this is beyond anything shown in Table C, so $P < 0.001$ (software gives $P = 0.00002$). **CONCLUDE:** We have very strong evidence ($P < 0.001$) that Cretaceous air contained less nitrogen than modern air.

18.11: PLAN: Take μ to be the mean difference (monkey call minus pure tone) in firing rate. We test $H_0: \mu = 0$ vs. $H_a: \mu > 0$, using a one-sided alternative because the researchers suspect a stronger response to the monkey calls. **SOLVE:** We must assume that the monkeys can be regarded as an SRS. For each monkey, we compute the call minus pure tone differences; a stemplot of these differences (provided) shows no outliers or deviations from Normality. The mean and standard deviation are $\bar{x}$ = 70.378 and s = 88.447 spikes/second, so $t = \dfrac{70.378 - 0}{88.447/\sqrt{37}} =$ 4.84 with df = 36. This has a very small P-value: $P < 0.0001$. **CONCLUDE:** We have very strong evidence that macaque neural response to monkey calls is stronger than the response to pure tones.

```
−1 │ 10
−0 │ 8
−0 │ 110
 0 │ 011123333444
 0 │ 56667
 1 │ 0001244
 1 │ 6677
 2 │ 34
 2 │ 6
```

18.12: Using the information in Exercise 18.11, note that df = 36 is not contained in the table, so use df = 30 (round down in order to be conservative). Here, with t^* = 2.750, the 99% confidence interval is given by $70.378 \pm 2.750\dfrac{88.447}{\sqrt{37}} = 70.378 \pm 39.987 = 30.391$ to 110.365 spikes/second.

18.13: The stemplot suggests that the distribution of nitrogen contents is heavily skewed. Although *t* procedures are robust, they should not be used if the population being sampled from is this heavily skewed. In this case, *t* procedures are not reliable.

```
0 | 00000000000111
0 | 2222233
0 | 44
0 |
0 |
1 |
1 |
1 | 4
```

18.14: The provided stemplot of carbon-13 ratios suggests no strong skew, so use of *t* procedures is appropriate, assuming the sample is random. With $\bar{x} = -2.8825$, $s = 1.0360$, df = $24 - 1 = 23$, and $t^* = 1.714$, a 90% confidence interval for the mean carbon-13 ratio is given by $-2.8825 \pm 1.714 \dfrac{1.0360}{\sqrt{24}} = -2.8825 \pm 0.3625 = -3.2450$ to -2.5200.

```
-4 | 200
-3 | 9888765
-3 | 2
-2 | 8877
-2 | 4310
-1 | 85
-1 | 31
-0 | 8
```

18.15: (b) We virtually never know the value of σ.

18.16: (b) $t = \dfrac{8-10}{4/\sqrt{16}} = -2.$

18.17: (c) df = $25 - 1 = 24$.

18.18: (c) $P < 0.01$.

18.19: (a) 2.718. Here, df = 11.

18.20: (b) $t < -3.497$ or $t > 3.497$.

18.21: (c) 72.7 to 97.3. The interval is computed as $85 \pm 3.250 \dfrac{12}{\sqrt{10}}$.

18.22: (a) There is a clear outlier in the data. The *t* procedures are robust against mild skew, and they are used when σ is unknown.

18.23: (b) If you sample 64 unmarried male students, and then sample 64 unmarried female students, no matching is present.

18.24: (c) the data can be regarded as an SRS from the population.

18.25: For the student group: $t = \dfrac{0.08 - 0}{0.37/\sqrt{12}} = 0.749$ (not 0.49, as stated). For the non-student group: $t = \dfrac{0.35 - 0}{0.37/\sqrt{12}} = 3.277$ (rather than 3.25, a difference that might be due to rounding error). From Table C, the first P-value is between 0.4 and 0.5 (software gives 0.47), and the second P-value is between 0.005 and 0.01 (software gives 0.007).

18.26: With $\bar{x} = 26.8$ and $s = 7.42$, and using either $t^* = 1.984$ (using df $= 100$ from Table C) or $t^* = 1.9636$ (using df $= 653$ with software), the 95% confidence interval for mean BMI is $\bar{x} \pm t^* \left(\dfrac{s}{\sqrt{654}} \right)$, computed in both cases as

$$= 26.8 \pm 0.5756 = 26.2244 \text{ to } 27.3756 \text{ (using } t^* = 1.984\text{), or}$$

$$= 26.8 \pm 0.5697 = 26.2303 \text{ to } 27.3697 \text{ (using } t^* = 1.9636\text{).}$$

18.27: (a) The sample size is very large, so the only potential hazard is extreme skewness. Since scores range only from 0 to 500, there is a limit to how skewed the distribution could be. (b) From Table C, we take $t^* = 2.581$ (df $= 1000$), or using software take $t^* = 2.5775$. For either value of t^*, the 99% confidence interval is $250 \pm 2.581 = 247.4$ to 252.6. (c) Because the 99% confidence interval for μ does not contain 243 and is entirely above 243, we would fail to reject $H_0 : \mu = 243$ against the one-sided alternative hypothesis $H_a : \mu < 243$ at the 1% significance level.

18.28: (a) We have df $= 23 - 1 = 22$, so $t^* = 2.074$. A 95% confidence interval for the mean solution time is $11.58 \pm 2.074 \left(\dfrac{4.37}{\sqrt{23}} \right) = 11.58 \pm 1.89 = 9.69$ to 13.47 seconds. (b) We must assume that the 23 individuals in the neutral group can be regarded as an SRS from the population. Since the sample size is at least 15, we don't need to assume that the population is Normal. Indeed, t procedures can be used as long as the distribution of solution times for the neutral group is not heavily skewed, and as long as there are no outliers in the sample.

18.29: (a) A subject's responses to the two treatments would not be independent. (b) We have $t = \dfrac{-0.326 - 0}{0.181/\sqrt{6}} = -4.41$. With df $= 5$, $P = 0.0069$, significant evidence of a difference.

18.30: (a) A stemplot is provided below. A "0" in the row with stem of "333" corresponds to a data value of 0.03330. Since the sample size is less than 15, we look to see if the data appear close to Normal. The stemplot is roughly symmetric with one peak and no outliers. (b) With $\bar{x}$ = 0.03339, s = 0.00027, df = 8, and t^* = 2.30600 (using software to obtain t^* to 5 significant figures), a 95% confidence interval for the mean conductivity is $0.03339 \pm 2.30600\left(\dfrac{0.00027}{\sqrt{9}}\right)$ = 0.03318 to 0.03360 Watts. (c) Since 0.0330 is not contained in the 95% confidence interval computed in (b), we would reject $H_0 : \mu = 0.0330$ at the 5% significance level in favor of the two-sided alternative. There is strong evidence that the mean conductivity is different from 0.0330 watts.

```
330 | 0
331 |
332 | 0
333 | 0 0 0
334 | 0 0
335 |
336 |
337 | 0
338 |
339 | 0
```

18.31: (a) A stemplot is provided below, and suggests the presence of outliers. The sample is small and the stemplot is skewed, so use of t procedures is not appropriate. (b) We will compute two confidence intervals, as called for. In the first interval, using all 9 observations, we have df = 8 and t^* = 1.860. For the second interval, removing the two outliers (1.15 and 1.35), df = 6 and t^* = 1.943. The two 90% confidence intervals are:

$$0.549 \pm 1.860\left(\frac{0.403}{\sqrt{9}}\right) = 0.299 \text{ to } 0.799 \text{ grams, and}$$

$$0.349 \pm 1.943\left(\frac{0.053}{\sqrt{7}}\right) = 0.310 \text{ to } 0.388 \text{ grams.}$$

(c) The confidence interval computed without the two outliers is much narrower. Using fewer data values reduces degrees of freedom (yielding a larger value of t^*). Also, smaller sample sizes yield larger margins of error. However both of these effects are offset by removing two values far from the others — s reduces from 0.403 to 0.053 by removing them.

```
 2 | 5
 3 | 3 3 5 8
 4 | 0 0
 5 |
 6 |
 7 |
 8 |
 9 |
10 |
11 | 5
12 |
13 | 5
```

18.32: SOLVE: The mean is $\bar{x} = 25.42°$, and the standard deviation is $s = 7.47°$, and $t^* = 2.042$ (using df = 30 with Table C) or $t^* = 2.0262$ (using df = 37 with software). The confidence interval is nearly identical in both cases:

$$\bar{x} \pm t^* \left(\frac{s}{\sqrt{38}} \right) = 22.95° \text{ to } 27.89° \quad (t^* = 2.042), \text{ or}$$

$$= 22.96° \text{ to } 27.88° \quad (t^* = 2.0262).$$

CONCLUDE: We are 95% confident that the mean HAV angle among such patients is between $22.95°$ and $27.89°$.

18.33: (a) The stemplot provided clearly shows the high outlier mentioned in the text. (b) Let μ be the mean difference (control minus experimental) in healing rates. We test $H_0: \mu = 0$ vs. $H_a: \mu > 0$. The alternative hypothesis says that the control limb heals faster; that is, the healing rate is greater for the control limb than for the experimental limb. With all 12 differences: $\bar{x} = 6.417$ and $s = 10.7065$, so $t = \frac{6.417 - 0}{10.7065/\sqrt{12}} = 2.08$. With df = 11, $P = 0.0311$ (using software).

Omitting the outlier: $\bar{x} = 4.182$ and $s = 7.7565$, so $t = \frac{4.182 - 0}{7.7565/\sqrt{11}} = 1.79$. With df = 10, $P = 0.052$. Hence, with all 12 differences there is greater evidence that the mean healing time is greater for the control limb. When we omit the outlier, the evidence is weaker.

```
 -1 | 3
 -0 | 6
 -0 |
  0 | 12
  0 | 5789
  1 | 012
  1 |
  2 |
  2 |
  3 | 1
```

18.34: (a) Without the outlier, the mean is $\bar{x} = 24.76^\circ$, and the standard deviation decreases to s = 6.34°. Using df = 36 with software, $t^* = 2.0281$, so a 95% confidence interval for the population mean becomes $24.76 \pm 2.0281 \left(\dfrac{6.34}{\sqrt{37}} \right) = 22.64^\circ$ to 26.87°. (b) In Exercise 18.32, using all of the data, the 95% confidence interval was 22.96° to 27.88°. The confidence interval is wider because the presence of an outlier increases s.

18.35: (a) A histogram of the sample is provided. The sample has a significant outlier, and indicates skew. We might consider applying t procedures to the sample after removing the most extreme observation (37,786). (b) If we remove the largest observation, the remaining sample is not heavily skewed and has no outliers. Now we test $H_0 : \mu = 7000$ vs. $H_a : \mu \neq 7000$. With the outlier removed, $\bar{x} = 11{,}555.16$ and $s = 6{,}095.015$. Hence, $t = \dfrac{11555.16 - 7000}{6095.015/\sqrt{19}} = 3.258$. With df = 18 with software, $P = 0.0044$ (this is a two-sided test). There is overwhelming evidence that the mean number of words per day of men at this university differs from 7000.

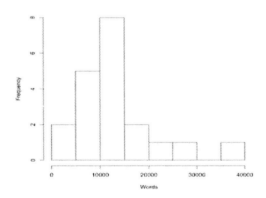

18.36: (a) The stemplot does not show any severe evidence of non-Normality, so t procedures should be safe. (b) With $\bar{x} = 1.1727$ days, $s = 0.4606$ days, and $t^* = 1.812$ (df = 10), the 90% confidence interval is $1.1727 \pm 1.812 \left(\dfrac{0.4606}{\sqrt{11}} \right) = 1.1727 \pm 0.2516 = 0.9211$ to 1.4243 days.

There is no indication that the sample represents an SRS of all patients whose melanoma has not responded to existing treatments, so inferring to the population of similar patients may not be reasonable.

```
0 | 6 7
0 | 8 9
1 | 0 0
1 | 3 3
1 | 4
1 |
1 | 9
2 | 0
```

18.37: (a) The stemplot of differences shows an extreme right skew, and one or two high outliers. The t procedures should not be used. (b) Some students might perform the test ($H_0: \mu = 0$ vs. $H_a: \mu > 0$) using t procedures, despite the presence of strong skew and outliers in the sample. If so, they should find $\bar{x} = 156.36$, $s = 234.2952$, and $t = 2.213$, yielding $P = 0.0256$.

```
0 | 0 0 1 2 2 3 8
1 | 0
2 | 1
3 |
4 |
5 | 1
6 |
7 | 0
```

18.38: The design described is matched pairs, and we are interested in the differences (helium filled – air filled) in punt distance. (a) A stemplot of the 39 differences is provided below. The plot suggests a roughly symmetric, single peak distribution for differences. Note that the randomization described means that we can treat the observations as a simple random sample from a population of all differences (for this kicker). Hence, t procedures seem to be appropriate here. (b) Let μ denote the mean difference (helium filled – air filled). We are interested in whether helium increases average distance traveled, so we test $H_0 : \mu = 0$ vs. $H_a : \mu > 0$. We have $\bar{x}$ = 0.462 feet and s = 6.867 feet. Hence, $t = \dfrac{0.462 - 0}{6.867/\sqrt{39}} = 0.420$. With df = 38, P = 0.3384, using software. There is virtually no evidence that the mean distance for helium-filled footballs is greater than that of air-filled footballs.

```
-1 | 4322
-0 | 975
-0 | 4322222111
 0 | 0012222233344
 0 | 6677889
 1 | 4
 1 | 7
```

18.39: (a) We test $H_0 : \mu = 0$ vs. $H_a : \mu > 0$, where μ is the mean difference (treated minus control). This is a one-sided test because the researchers have reason to believe that CO_2 will increase growth rate. (b) We have $\bar{x}$ = 1.916 and s = 1.050, so $t = \dfrac{1.916 - 0}{1.050/\sqrt{3}} = 3.16$ with df = 2. Hence, P = 0.044. This is significant at the 5% significance level. (c) For very small samples, t procedures should only be used when we can assume that the population is Normal. We have no way to assess the Normality of the population based on these four observations. Hence, the validity of the analysis in (b) is dubious.

18.40: (a) Weather conditions that change day to day can affect spore counts. So the two measurements made on the same day form a matched pair. (b) Take the differences (kill room counts – processing counts). For these differences, $\bar{x}$ = 1824.5 and s = 834.1 CFU/m^3. For the population mean difference, the 90% confidence interval for μ is $1824.5 \pm 2.353\left(\dfrac{834.1}{\sqrt{4}}\right) =$

$1824.5 \pm 981.3 = 843.2$ to 2805.8 CFU/m^3. The interval is so wide because the sample size is very small, but we are confident that the mean counts in the kill room are higher. (c) The data are counts, which are at best only approximately Normal, and we have only a small sample.

18.41: The stemplot (not asked for) reveals that these data contain two extreme high outliers (5973 and 8015). Hence, t procedures are not appropriate.

```
0 | 1123788
1 | 00115677899
2 | 01112458
3 |
4 |
5 | 9
6 |
7 |
8 | 0
```

18.42: (a) We test $H_0: \mu = 0$ vs. $H_a: \mu > 0$, where μ is the mean loss in sweetness (sweetness before storage minus sweetness after storage). This is a one-sided test because the researchers have reason to believe that storage reduces sweetness, and $\mu > 0$ represents this change. We have $\bar{x} = 1.02$ and $s = 1.196$, so $t = \dfrac{1.02 - 0}{1.196/\sqrt{10}} = 2.697$ with df $= 9$. Hence, $P = 0.012$. Hence, there is strong evidence that storage reduces sweetness for this cola. (b) We have only 10 observations, and it isn't possible to assess Normality of the distribution of score differences. Indeed, a stemplot of these data reveals possible skew in this distribution.

```
-1 | 3
-0 | 4
 0 | 47
 1 | 12
 2 | 0023
```

18.43: (a) The mean and standard deviation are $\bar{x} = 48.25$ and $s = 40.24$ thousand barrels. From Table C, $t^* = 2.000$ (df $= 60$). Using software, with df $= 63$, $t^* = 1.998$. The 95% confidence interval for μ is $48.25 \pm 2.000\left(\dfrac{40.24}{\sqrt{64}}\right) = 48.25 \pm 10.06 = 38.19$ to 58.31 thousand barrels.

(Using the software version of t^*, the confidence interval is almost identical: 38.20 to 58.30 thousand barrels.) (b) The stemplot confirms the skewness and outliers described in the exercise. The two intervals have similar widths, but the new interval (using a computer-intensive method) is shifted higher by about 2000 barrels. Although t procedures are fairly robust, we should be cautious about trusting the result in (a) because of the strong skew and outliers. The computer-intensive method may produce a more reliable interval.

```
0 | 00001111111111
0 | 2222222333333333333333
0 | 44444445555555
0 | 6666667
0 | 8899
1 | 01
1 |
1 | 5
1 |
1 | 9
2 | 0
```

18.44: (a) Let μ represent the mean *E. coli* counts for all possible 100 ml samples taken from all Central Ohio swimming areas. We test H_0 : $\mu = 130$ vs. H_a : $\mu > 130$ since the researchers are interested in whether these areas are unsafe on average. For our sample, $\bar{x} = 56.28125$ and $s = 77.28992$ bacteria. Of course, this will not lead to a rejection of H_0. We have $t = \dfrac{56.28125 - 130}{77.28992/\sqrt{16}} = -3.815$ on df $= 15$, so $P = 0.9991$. There is no evidence that swimming areas in Central Ohio have mean *E. coli* counts greater than 130 bacteria per 100ml. (b) A stemplot is provided. Note that stems are in units of 100 and data were rounded to the nearest 10. For example, "2 | 9" represents 290, which corresponds to the original sample value of 291, while "0 | 0" represents 0, which corresponds to the original sample value of 1. Due to extreme skew and the presence of outliers, t procedures should not be used here. Both tests provide similar P-values, and both tests reach the obvious conclusion, but this is not validation of the t-test.

```
0 | 01112223345559
1 | 9
2 | 9
```

18.45: PLAN: We will construct a 90% confidence interval for μ, the mean percent of beetle-infected seeds. SOLVE: A stemplot shows a single-peaked and roughly symmetric distribution. We assume that the 28 plants can be viewed as an SRS of the population, so t procedures are appropriate. We have $\bar{x} = 4.0786$ and $s = 2.0135$ percent. Using df = 27, the 90% confidence interval for μ is $4.0786 \pm 1.703\left(\dfrac{2.0135}{\sqrt{28}}\right) = 4.0786 \pm 0.648 = 3.43\%$ to 4.73%. CONCLUDE: The beetle infects less than 5% of seeds, so it is unlikely to be effective in controlling velvetleaf.

18.46: PLAN: We will test $H_0 : \mu = 0$ vs. $H_a : \mu > 0$, where μ represents the mean increase in T-cell counts after 20 days on blinatumomab. SOLVE: A stemplot suggests that t procedures are reasonable, with no evidence of non-Normality and no outliers. We have six subjects, with $\bar{x} = 0.5283$ and $s = 0.4574$ thousand cells. Hence, on df = 5 and $t = \dfrac{0.5283 - 0}{0.4574/\sqrt{6}} = 2.829, P = 0.0184$. We would reject H_0 at the 5% (or even 2%) significance level. CONCLUDE: The data give convincing evidence that the mean count of T cells is higher after 20 days on blinatumomab.

```
0 | 122
0 | 48
1 | 3
```

18.47: From Exercise 18.46, we have $\bar{x} = 0.5283$, $s = 0.4574$ and df = 5. Hence, a 95% confidence interval for the mean difference in T-cell counts after 20 days on blinatumomab is $0.5283 \pm 2.571\left(\dfrac{0.4574}{\sqrt{6}}\right) = 0.5283 \pm 0.4801 = 0.0482$ to 1.0084 thousand cells.

18.48: (a) Fund and index performances are certainly not independent; for

example, a good year for one is likely to be a good year for the other. (b) PLAN: Let μ be the mean difference (fund minus EAFE). We test $H_0 : \mu = 0$ vs. $H_a : \mu \neq 0$, taking a two-sided alternative because the VIG Fund could outperform or underperform the benchmark. (The case could be made for a one-sided alternative.) SOLVE: A stemplot shows no reason to doubt Normality. We must assume that the data we have can be viewed as an SRS. We find $\bar{x} = -0.0754\%$ and $s = 7.9979\%$, so $t = \dfrac{-0.0754 - 0}{7.9979/\sqrt{24}} = -0.05$, for which $P > 0.5$ (software gives 0.96). CONCLUDE: We have very little reason to doubt that $\mu = 0$; VIG Fund performance is not significantly different from its benchmark.

```
-1 | 6
-1 | 22
-0 | 877
-0 | 431100
 0 | 012234
 0 | 568
 1 | 124
```

18.49: (a) For each subject, randomly select which knob (right or left) that subject should use first. (b) PLAN: We test $H_0 : \mu = 0$ vs. $H_a : \mu < 0$, where μ denotes the mean difference in time (right-thread time – left-thread time), so that $\mu < 0$ means "right-hand time is less than left-hand time on average". SOLVE: A stemplot of the differences gives no reason that t procedures are not appropriate. We assume our sample can be viewed as an SRS. We have $\bar{x} = -13.32$

seconds and $s = 22.936$ seconds, so $t = \dfrac{-13.32 - 0}{22.936/\sqrt{25}} = -2.90$. With df = 24 we find $P = 0.0039$.

CONCLUDE: We have good evidence (significant at the 1% level) that the mean difference really is negative — that is, the mean time for right-hand-thread knobs is less than the mean time for left-hand-thread knobs.

```
-5 | 2
-4 | 853
-3 | 511
-2 | 94
-1 | 66621
-0 | 74331
 0 | 02
 1 | 1
 2 | 03
 3 | 8
```

18.50: PLAN: We test H_0 : $\mu = 0$ vs. H_a : $\mu \neq 0$, where μ denotes the mean difference in absorption (generic minus reference). The alternative is two-sided because we have no prior expectation of a direction for the difference. SOLVE: We assume that the subjects can be considered an SRS. A stemplot of the differences looks reasonably Normal with no outliers, so

the *t* procedures should be safe. We find $\bar{x} = 37$ and $s = 1070.6$, so $t = \dfrac{37 - 0}{1070.6/\sqrt{20}} = 0.15$.

With df = 19 we see that $P > 0.5$ (software gives $P = 0.88$). CONCLUDE: We cannot conclude that the two drugs differ in mean absorption level.

```
-2 | 3
-1 | 5
-1 | 31
-0 | 5
-0 | 321
 0 | 012334
 0 | 577
 1 | 1
 1 | 6
 2 | 0
```

18.51: Refer to the solution in Exercise 18.49. With df = 24, $t^* = 1.711$, so the confidence

interval for μ is given by $-13.32 \pm 1.711 \left(\dfrac{22.936}{\sqrt{25}} \right) = -13.32 \pm 7.85 =$

-21.2 to -5.5 seconds. Now $\bar{x}_{RH}/\bar{x}_{LH} = 104.12/117.44 = 0.887$. Hence, right-handers working with right-handed knobs can accomplish the task in about 89% of the time needed by those working with left-handed knobs.

18.52: PLAN: Let μ denote the average tip percentage for all patrons receiving a bad weather forecast. We test H_0 : $\mu = 20\%$ vs. H_a : $\mu < 20\%$. SOLVE: We assume we may consider the sample to be an SRS taken from the population of all patrons receiving such a weather report. A stemplot of these data reveal no reason to suspect that *t* procedures are not appropriate. There are no outliers, and the data are roughly symmetric with one peak. We find $\bar{x} = 18.19\%$ and $s = 2.105\%$, so $t = \dfrac{18.19 - 20}{2.105/\sqrt{20}} = -3.845$. With df = 19, $P = 0.0005$ (using software). CONCLUDE: There is overwhelming evidence that the mean tip percentage for patrons receiving a bad weather report is less than 20%. **Note**: *This does not imply that patrons receiving bad weather forecasts tip less than those that do not receive bad weather forecasts since we do not know that the mean percent tip in the control group is 20%. No comparison was made.*

```
13 | 6
14 | 0
15 |
16 | 1 8
17 | 0 5
18 | 0 0 2 4 5 8 8
19 | 0 1 2 4
20 | 0 2
21 |
22 |
23 | 2
```

18.53 – 18.55 are Web-based exercises.

Chapter 19 Solutions

19.1: This is a matched-pairs design. Each couple is a matched pair.

19.2: This involves two independent samples.

19.3: This involves a single sample.

19.4: This involves two independent samples (because the result of, for example, the first measurement using the new method is independent of the first measurement using the old method).

19.5: (a) If the loggers had known that a study would be done, they might have (consciously or subconsciously) cut down fewer trees than they typically would, in order to reduce the impact of logging. (b) STATE: Does logging significantly reduce the mean number of species in a plot after 8 years? PLAN: We test $H_0 : \mu_1 = \mu_2$ vs. $H_a : \mu_1 > \mu_2$, where μ_1 is the mean number of species in unlogged plots and μ_2 is the mean number of species in plots logged 8 years earlier. We use a one-sided alternative because we expect that logging reduces the number of tree species.

SOLVE: We assume that the data come from SRSs of the two populations. Stemplots suggest some deviation from Normality, and a possible low outlier for the logged-plot counts, but there is not strong evidence of non-Normality in either sample. We proceed with the t test for two samples. With $\bar{x}_1 = 17.50$, $\bar{x}_2 = 13.67$, $s_1 = 3.53$, $s_2 = 4.50$, $n_1 = 12$ and $n_2 = 9$: $\text{SE} = \sqrt{\dfrac{s_1^2}{n_1} + \dfrac{s_2^2}{n_2}}$ $= 1.813$ and $t = \dfrac{\bar{x}_1 - \bar{x}_2}{\text{SE}} = 2.11$. Using df as the smaller of $9 - 1$ and $12 - 1$, we have df $= 8$, and $0.025 < P < 0.05$. Using software, df $= 14.8$ and $P = 0.026$. CONCLUDE: There is strong evidence that the mean number of species in unlogged plots is greater than that for logged plots 8 years after logging.

```
Unlogged  Logged
   13| 000   0| 4
   14|       0|
   15| 00    0|
   16|       1| 0
   17|       1| 2
   18| 0     1| 455
   19| 00    1| 7
   20| 0     1| 88
   21| 0
   22| 00
```

19.6: STATE: Do obese people average more time lying down than lean people? PLAN: We test $H_0 : \mu_1 = \mu_2$ vs. $H_a : \mu_1 \neq \mu_2$, where μ_1 is the mean time spent lying down for the lean group, and μ_2 is the mean time for the obese group. SOLVE: We assume that the data come from SRSs of the two populations. See Example 19.2 for a discussion of conditions for inference applied to this problem. The stemplots do not indicate non-Normal data. We proceed with the t test for two samples. With $\bar{x}_1 = 501.6461$, $\bar{x}_2 = 491.7426$, $s_1 = 52.0449$, $s_2 = 46.5932$, $n_1 = 10$ and $n_2 = 10$: $SE = \sqrt{\dfrac{s_1^2}{n_1} + \dfrac{s_2^2}{n_2}} = 22.0898$ and $t = \dfrac{\bar{x}_1 - \bar{x}_2}{SE} = 0.448$. Using df as the smaller of 10–1 and 10–1, we have df = 9, and $P > 0.50$. Using software, df = 17.8 and $P = 0.6596$. CONCLUDE: There is no evidence to support a conclusion that lean people spend less time laying down (on average) than obese people.

```
Lean  |   | Obese
   9  | 3 |
      | 4 | 1
      | 4 |
  5   | 4 | 44
  6   | 4 | 6
  8   | 4 |
 10   | 5 | 001
 33   | 5 | 23
  5   | 5 |
  6   | 5 | 6
```

19.7: $\bar{x}_1 = 17.50$, $\bar{x}_2 = 13.67$, and $SE = 1.813$. Using df = 8, $t^* = 3.355$. Hence, a 99% confidence interval for the mean difference in number of species in unlogged and logged plots is $\bar{x}_1 - \bar{x}_2 \pm t^* SE = -2.253$ to 9.913 species.

19.8: In this study, men underestimated their average life expectancy by 19.50%, while women underestimated their average life expectancy by 12.71%. If these samples can be viewed as SRSs, then under $H_0 : \mu_1 = \mu_2$, a difference in sample means as great as the one observed (12.71% – 19.50%) is 2.177 standard errors below expected ($t = -2.177$), and a more extreme difference would have occurred by chance alone about 5.28% of the time under repeated sampling ($P = 0.05281$). There is somewhat strong evidence that men and women differ in their views on their own longevity.

19.9: (a) Back-to-back stemplots of the time data are shown below. They appear to be reasonably Normal, and the discussion in the exercise justifies our treating the data as independent SRSs, so we can use the t procedures. We wish to test $H_0 : \mu_1 = \mu_2$ vs. $H_a : \mu_1 < \mu_2$, where μ_1 is the is the population mean time in the restaurant with no scent, and μ_2 is the mean time in the restaurant with a lavender odor. Here, With $\bar{x}_1 = 91.27$, $\bar{x}_2 = 105.700$, $s_1 = 14.930$, $s_2 = 13.105$, $n_1 = 30$ and $n_2 = 30$: $SE = \sqrt{\dfrac{s_1^2}{n_1} + \dfrac{s_2^2}{n_2}} = 3.627$ and $t = \dfrac{\bar{x}_1 - \bar{x}_2}{SE} = -3.98$. Using software, df = 57.041 and $P = 0.0001$. Using the more conservative df = 29 (lesser of 30–1 and 30–1) and Table C, $P < 0.0005$. There is very strong evidence that customers spend more time on average in the restaurant when the lavender scent is present.

(b) Back-to-back stemplots of the spending data are below. The distributions are skewed and have many gaps. We wish to test $H_0 : \mu_1 = \mu_2$ vs. $H_a : \mu_1 < \mu_2$, where μ_1 is the the population mean amount spent in the restaurant with no scent, and μ_2 is the mean amount spent in the restaurant with lavender odor. Here, With $\bar{x}_1 = \$17.5133$, $\bar{x}_2 = \$21.1233$, $s_1 = \$2.3588$, $s_2 = \$2.3450$, $n_1 = 30$ and $n_2 = 30$: SE $= \sqrt{\dfrac{s_1^2}{n_1} + \dfrac{s_2^2}{n_2}} = \$0.6073$ and $t = \dfrac{\bar{x}_1 - \bar{x}_2}{\text{SE}} = -5.95$. Using software, df $= 57.041$ and $P < 0.0001$. Using the more conservative df $= 29$ and Table C, $P < 0.0005$. There is very strong evidence that customers spend more money on average when the lavender scent is present.

No scent		Lavender		No scent		Lavender
98	6			9	12	
322	7				13	
965	7	6			14	
44	8			99999999999999	15	
7765	8	89			16	
32221	9	234			17	
86	9	578		555555555555	18	5555555555
31	10	1234			19	
9776	10	5566788999		5	20	7
	11	4		9	21	5599999999
85	11	6			22	3558
1	12	14			23	
	12	69			24	99
	13			5	25	59
	13	7				

19.10: (a) The "compressed" stemplot shows no particular cause for concern. The "intermediate" stemplot shows slight skew and the outlier described in the problem statement.
(b) We wish to test $H_0 : \mu_1 = \mu_2$ vs. $H_a : \mu_1 < \mu_2$, where μ_1 is the population mean for the compressed soil, and μ_2 is the mean for the intermediate soil. Here, With $\bar{x}_1 = 2.9075$, $\bar{x}_2 = 3.2874$, $s_1 = 0.1390$, $s_2 = 0.2397$, $n_1 = 20$ and $n_2 = 19$: SE $= \sqrt{\dfrac{s_1^2}{n_1} + \dfrac{s_2^2}{n_2}} = 0.06317$ and $t = \dfrac{\bar{x}_1 - \bar{x}_2}{\text{SE}} = -6.013$. Using either version of df (software df $= 28.6$, more conservative df $= 18$), $P < 0.0001$. There is very significant evidence that the mean penetrability for compressed soil is lower than that for intermediate soil.

Compressed		Intermediate
26	8	2	99
27		3	0111111
27	6888	3	2333
28	122	3	4445
28	66	3	6
29	024	3	8
29	68	4	
30	0	4	2
30	88		
31			
31	68		

19.11: We have two small samples ($n_1 = n_2 = 4$), so the t procedures are not reliable unless both distributions are Normal.

19.12: Use the means in Exercise 19.10, and the corresponding SE = 0.06317. If we use software df = 28.6, then $t^* = 1.700$. If we use the more conservative df = 18, then $t^* = 1.734$. A 90% confidence interval for the mean difference in permeability between compressed and intermediate soils is $\bar{x}_1 - \bar{x}_2 \pm \ t^*$SE. Hence, −0.487 to −0.273 (if df = 28.6) or −0.489 to −0.270 (if df = 18).

19.13: Here are the details of the calculations:

$$SE_F = \frac{12.6961}{\sqrt{31}} \doteq 2.2803$$

$$SE_M = \frac{12.2649}{\sqrt{47}} \doteq 1.7890$$

$$SE = \sqrt{SE_F^2 + SE_M^2} \doteq 2.8983$$

$$df = \frac{SE^4}{\frac{1}{30}\left(\frac{12.6961^2}{31}\right)^2 + \frac{1}{46}\left(\frac{12.2649^2}{47}\right)^2} = \frac{70.565}{1.1239} \doteq 62.8$$

$$t = \frac{55.5161 - 57.9149}{SE} \doteq -0.8276$$

19.14: Let μ_1 denote the mean for men and μ_2 denote the mean for women. According to the output, $\bar{x}_1 = -19.50$, $\bar{x}_2 = -12.71$, $s_1 = 5.612$ and $s_2 = 5.589$. Hence, with $n_1 = 6$ and $n_2 = 7$:

$$t = \frac{\bar{x}_1 - \bar{x}_2}{\sqrt{\frac{s_1^2}{n_1} + \frac{s_2^2}{n_2}}} = \frac{-19.50 - (-12.71)}{\sqrt{\frac{5.612^2}{6} + \frac{5.589^2}{7}}} = -2.177.$$

Also,

$$df = \frac{\left(\frac{5.612^2}{6} + \frac{5.589^2}{7}\right)^2}{\frac{1}{6-1}\left(\frac{5.612^2}{6}\right)^2 + \frac{1}{7-1}\left(\frac{5.589^2}{7}\right)^2} = 10.68, \text{ rounded to two places.}$$

19.15: Reading from the software output shown in the statement of Exercise 19.13, we find that there was no significant difference in mean Self-Concept Scale scores for men and women ($t = -0.8276$, df = 62.8, $P = 0.4110$).

19.16: (c) the one-sample t interval. There is one sample, and only one score from each member of the sample.

19.17: (a) the two-sample t test. We have two independent populations: females and males.

19.18: (b) the matched-pairs t test. Two measurements (one for each test) are being taken on each mouse.

19.19: (b) confidence levels and *P*-values from the *t* procedures are quite accurate even if the population distributions are not exactly Normal.

19.20: (c) 20. Here, df is the lesser of (21–1 and 21–1).

19.21: (b) $\dfrac{15.84 - 9.64}{\sqrt{\dfrac{3.43^2}{21} + \dfrac{8.65^2}{21}}} = 3.05.$

19.22: (c) If random digit dialing produces an SRS, then our samples are SRSs from their respective populations. Also, the samples are large enough to overcome problems of potential non-Normality. **Note:** *Young people are less likely to have land-line-based telephones than older people. Random digit dialing only samples from land-line-based telephones.*

19.23: (a) We suspect that younger people use social networks more than older people, so this is a one-sided alternative.

19.24: (b) $0.0005 < P < 0.001$.

19.25: (a) To test the belief that women talk more than men, we use a one-sided alternative. $H_0 : \mu_M = \mu_F$ vs. $H_a : \mu_M < \mu_F$. (b)–(d) The small table below provides a summary of *t* statistics, degrees of freedom, and *P*-values for both studies. The two sample *t* statistic is computed as $t = \dfrac{\bar{x}_F - \bar{x}_M}{\sqrt{\dfrac{s_F^2}{n_F} + \dfrac{s_M^2}{n_M}}}$, and we the conservative approach for computing df as the smaller sample size, minus 1.

Study	t	df	Table C values	P-value
1	−0.248	55	$\lvert t \rvert < 0.679$	$P > 0.25$
2	1.507	19	$1.328 < t < 1.729$	$0.05 < P < 0.10$

Note that for Study 1 we reference df = 50 in Table C. (e) The first study gives no support to the belief that women talk more than men; the second study gives weak support, significant only at a relatively high significance level (say $\alpha = 0.10$).

19.26: (a) Call group 1 the Alcohol group, and group 2 the Placebo group. Then, since SEM = $s/\sqrt{n}$, we have $s = SEM\sqrt{n}$. Hence, $s_1 = 0.05\sqrt{25} = 0.25$ and $s_2 = 0.03\sqrt{25} = 0.15$. (b) Using the conservative Option 2, df = 24 (the lesser of 25 and 25, minus 1). (c) Here, with $n_1 = n_2 = 25$, SE = $\sqrt{\dfrac{s_1^2}{n_1} + \dfrac{s_2^2}{n_2}} = 0.0583$. With df = 24, we have $t^* = 1.711$, and a 90% confidence interval for the mean difference in proportions is given by $0.25 - 0.12 \pm 1.711(0.0583) = 0.13 \pm 0.10 = 0.03$ to 0.23.

19.27: (a) Call group 1 the Stress group, and group 2 the No stress group. Then, since SEM = $s/\sqrt{n}$, we have $s = SEM\sqrt{n}$. Hence, $s_1 = 3\sqrt{20} = 13.416$ and $s_2 = 2\sqrt{51} = 14.283$. (b) Using the conservative Option 2, df = 19 (the lesser of 20 and 51, minus 1). (c) We test $H_0 : \mu_1 = \mu_2$ vs. $H_a : \mu_1 \neq \mu_2$. With $n_1 = 20$ and $n_2 = 51$, SE = $\sqrt{\dfrac{s_1^2}{n_1} + \dfrac{s_2^2}{n_2}} = 3.605$, and $t = \dfrac{\bar{x}_1 - \bar{x}_2}{SE} = \dfrac{26 - 32}{3.605} = -$ 1.664. With df = 19, using Table C, $0.10 < P < 0.20$. There is little evidence in support of a conclusion that mean weights of rats in stressful environments differ from those of rats without stress.

19.28: (a) Parents who choose a Montessori school probably have different attitudes about education than other parents. (b) Over 55% of Montessori parents (30 out of 54) participated in the study, compared with about 22% of the other parents (25 out of 112) participated. (c) We test $H_0 : \mu_1 = \mu_2$ vs. $H_a : \mu_1 \neq \mu_2$, where μ_1 is the mean math score for Montessori children, and μ_2 is the mean score for non-Montessori children. With $\bar{x}_1 = 19$, $\bar{x}_2 = 17$, $s_1 = 3.11$, $s_2 = 4.19$, $n_1 = 30$ and $n_2 = 25$: SE = $\sqrt{\dfrac{s_1^2}{n_1} + \dfrac{s_2^2}{n_2}} = 1.0122$ and $t = \dfrac{\bar{x}_1 - \bar{x}_2}{SE} = 1.976$. Using df = 24 under Option 2, $0.05 < P < 0.10$. Using software, df = 43.5 and $P = 0.0545$. There is reasonably strong evidence of a difference in mean math scores between these two groups, but not quite enough evidence to reach such a conclusion at the 5% significance level.

19.29: (a) A placebo is an inert pill that allows researchers to account for any psychological benefit (or detriment) the subject might get from taking a pill. (b) Neither the subjects nor the researchers who worked with them knew who was getting ginkgo extract; this prevents expectations or prejudices from affecting the evaluation of the effectiveness of the treatment. (c) SE = $\sqrt{\dfrac{0.01462^2}{21} + \dfrac{0.01549^2}{18}} = 0.0048$, so the two-sample test statistic is $t = \dfrac{0.06383 - 0.05342}{SE}$ = 2.147. This is significant at the 5% level: $P = 0.0387$ (df = 35.35) or $0.04 < P < 0.05$ (df = 17). There is strong evidence that those who take gingko extract average more misses per line.

19.30: (a) Using the conservative two-sample procedures, df = 17 (the lesser of 18 and 18, minus 1). (b) Using the data summary provided in the problem description, $t = \dfrac{5.16 - 3.47}{\sqrt{\dfrac{3.5^2}{18} + \dfrac{2.0^2}{18}}} =$ 1.779. (c) We have $H_0 : \mu_1 = \mu_2$ vs. $H_a : \mu_1 \neq \mu_2$, where μ_1 is the mean for the lack-of-control group, and μ_2 is the mean for the in-control group. Using Table C, with df = 17, $0.05 < P < 0.10$. There is at best weak evidence of a difference in means between the in-control and lack-of-control groups.

19.31: Let μ_1 be mean for people with Asperger syndrome, and let and μ_2 be the mean for people without Asperger syndrome. We test $H_0 : \mu_1 = \mu_2$ vs. $H_a : \mu_1 \neq \mu_2$. This is a one-sided test, as the researchers suspect that people with Asperger syndrome have different mean score than people without Asperger syndrome. Here $\bar{x}_1 = -0.001$, $\bar{x}_2 = 0.42$, $n_1 = 19$, and $n_2 = 17$. We are given SEM (standard error for the mean) values for each group.

Since SEM $= s/\sqrt{n}$, we have $s = SEM\sqrt{n}$. Hence, $s_1 = 0.15\sqrt{19} = 0.6538$ and $s_2 = 0.17\sqrt{17} = 0.7009$. Hence, SE $= \sqrt{\dfrac{s_1^2}{n_1} + \dfrac{s_2^2}{n_2}} = 0.2267$ and $t = \dfrac{\bar{x}_1 - \bar{x}_2}{SE} = -1.857$. Using the conservative version for df (Option 2), df $= 16$ and $0.05 < P < 0.10$. Using software, df $= 32.89$ and $P = 0.0723$. There is strong evidence that the mean score for Asperger syndrome population is different than that of the non-Asperger population.

19.32: (a) The appropriate test is the matched-pairs test because a student's score on Try 1 is certainly correlated with his/her score on Try 2. Using the differences, we have $\bar{x} = 29$ and $s = 59$. (b) To test $H_0 : \mu = 0$ vs. $H_a : \mu > 0$, we compute $t = \dfrac{29 - 0}{59/\sqrt{427}} = 10.16$ with df $= 426$. This is certainly significant, with $P < 0.0005$. Coached students do improve their scores on average. (c) Table C gives $t^* = 2.626$ for df $= 100$, while software gives $t^* = 2.587$ for df $= 426$. The confidence interval is $\bar{x} \pm t^* s/\sqrt{n}$. Using the conservative value of t^*, this yields $29 \pm 2.626\dfrac{59}{\sqrt{427}} = 29 \pm 7.50 = 21.50$ to 36.50 points. Using software, the confidence interval is 21.61 to 36.39.

19.33: (a) The hypotheses are $H_0 : \mu_1 = \mu_2$ vs. $H_a : \mu_1 > \mu_2$, where μ_1 is the mean gain among all coached students, and μ_2 is the mean gain among uncoached students. We find SE $= \sqrt{\dfrac{59^2}{427} + \dfrac{52^2}{2733}} = 3.0235$ and $t = \dfrac{29 - 21}{3.0235} = 2.646$. Using the conservative approach, df $= 426$ is rounded down to df $= 100$ in Table C and we obtain $0.0025 < P < 0.005$. Using software, df $= 534.45$ and $P = 0.004$. There is evidence that

coached students had a greater average increase. (b) The 99% confidence interval is $8 \pm t^*(3.0235)$ where t^* equals 2.626 (using df $= 100$ with Table C) or 2.585 (df $= 534.45$ with software). This gives either 0.06 to 15.94 points, or 0.184 to 15.816 points, respectively. (c) Increasing one's score by 0 to 16 points is not likely to make a difference in being granted admission or scholarships from any colleges.

19.34: This was an observational study, not an experiment. The students (or their parents) chose whether or not to be coached; students who choose coaching might have other motivating factors that help them do better the second time. For example, perhaps students who choose coaching have some personality trait that also compels them to try harder the second time.

19.35: (a) Histograms for both data sets are provided below. Neither sample histogram suggests strong skew or presence of far outliers. Hence, t procedures are reasonable here. (b) Let μ_1 be the mean tip percentage when the forecast is good, and μ_2 be the mean tip percentage when the forecast is bad.

We have Here $\bar{x}_1 = 22.22$, $\bar{x}_2 = 18.19$, $s_1 = 1.955$, $s_2 = 2.105$, $n_1 = 20$, and $n_2 = 20$. We test $H_0 : \mu_1 = \mu_2$ vs. $H_a : \mu_1 \neq \mu_2$. Here, SE $= \sqrt{\dfrac{s_1^2}{n_1} + \dfrac{s_2^2}{n_2}} = 0.642$ and $t = \dfrac{\bar{x}_1 - \bar{x}_2}{\text{SE}} = 6.274$. Using df = 19 (the conservative Option 2) and Table C, we have $P < 0.001$. Using software, df = 37.8, and $P < 0.00001$. There is overwhelming evidence that the mean tip percentage differs between the two types of forecasts presented to patrons.

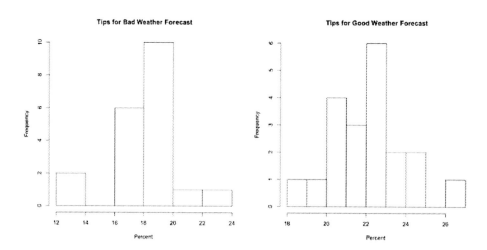

19.36: (a) Based on the stemplots, the *t* procedures should be safe. Both the stemplots and the means suggest that customers stayed (very slightly) longer when there was no odor. (b) Testing $H_0 : \mu_1 = \mu_2$ vs. $H_a : \mu_1 \neq \mu_2$, where μ_1 is the mean time in restaurant with no odor, and μ_2 is the mean time in restaurant with lemon odor. Now with $\bar{x}_1 = 91.2667$, $\bar{x}_2 = 89.7857$, $s_1 = 14.9296$, $s_2 = 15.4377$, $n_1 = 30$ and $n_2 = 28$ we find SE = 3.9927 and $t = 0.371$. This is not at all significant: $P > 0.5$ (df = 27, using Table C with Option 2 for conservative df) or $P = 0.7121$ (df = 55.4, using software). We cannot conclude that mean time in the restaurant is different when the lemon odor is present.

No odor		Lemon
	5	6
	6	03
98	6	
322	7	34
965	7	58
44	8	33
7765	8	8889
32221	9	0144
86	9	677
31	10	14
9776	10	5688
	11	23
85	11	
1	12	

19.37: Refer to results in Exercise 19.35. Using df = 19, $t^* = 2.093$ and the 95% confidence interval for the difference in mean tip percentages between these two populations is 22.22 − 18.19 $\pm$ 2.093(0.642) = 4.03 $\pm$ 1.34 = 2.69 to 5.37 percent. Using df = 37.8 with software, the corresponding 95% confidence interval is 2.73% to 5.33%.

19.38: (a) We provide some summary statistics describing the two samples. The second line for Permafresh, denoted with *, has the low outlier of interest omitted.

	n	$\bar{x}$	s
Permafresh	5	29.54	1.1675
Permafresh*	4	30.025	0.4992
Hylite	5	25.20	2.6693

(b) Stemplots are provided below for the two processes.

```
Permafresh |    | Hylite
           | 22 | 1
           | 23 | 9
           | 24 | 2
           | 25 |
           | 26 |
        6  | 27 | 0
           | 28 | 8
       95  | 29 |
       70  | 30 |
```

(c) With summary statistics listed in the table, we find the following test statistics and *P*-values:

		Conservative		Software	
	t	df	P	df	P
All points	3.33	4	$0.02 < P < 0.04$	5.48	0.0184
Outlier removed	3.96	3	$0.02 < P < 0.04$	4.35	0.0147

The mild outlier in the Permafresh sample had almost no effect on our conclusion. Despite the small sample sizes, there is good evidence that the mean breaking strengths of the two processes differ.

19.39: (a) The Hylite mean is greater than the Permafresh mean. (b) Shown are back-to-back stemplots for the two processes, which confirm that there are no extreme outliers. (c) We find SE = 1.334 and $t = -6.296$, for which the *P*-value is $0.002 < P < 0.005$ (using df = 4) or 0.0003 (using software, with df = 7.779). There is very strong evidence of a difference between the population means. As we might expect, the stronger process (Permafresh) is less resistant to wrinkles.

	n	$\bar{x}$	s
Permafresh	5	134.8	1.9235
Hylite	5	143.2	2.2804

```
Permafresh |    | Hylite
         2 | 13 |
        54 | 13 |
        76 | 13 |
           | 13 |
           | 14 | 1 1
           | 14 | 3
           | 14 | 5
           | 14 | 6
```

19.40: Summary statistics and background work is done in Exercise 19.38. The 90% confidence interval is $\bar{x}_1 - \bar{x}_2 \pm t^* SE$, where $t^* = 2.132$ (df = 4) or $t^* = 1.981$ (df = 5.476). This gives either

$$4.34 \pm 2.778 = 1.562 \text{ to } 7.118 \text{ pounds (with df = 4), or}$$

$$4.34 \pm 2.581 = 1.759 \text{ to } 6.921 \text{ pounds (with df = 5.476).}$$

19.41: Summary statistics and background work is done in Exercise 19.39. The 90% confidence interval is $\bar{x}_1 - \bar{x}_2 \pm t^* SE$, where $t^* = 2.132$ (df = 4) or $t^* = 1.867$ (df = 7.779). This gives either

$$-8.4 \pm 2.844 = -11.244 \text{ to } -5.556 \text{ degrees (with df = 4), or}$$

$$-8.4 \pm 2.491 = -10.891 \text{ to } -5.909 \text{ degrees (with df = 7.779).}$$

19.42: (a) A stemplot is provided. Each data value is rounded to the nearest thousand, and stems are in units of ten thousand. So, for example, the row "3 0 | 2 | 2 8" represents 4 people: 2 women that spoke about 23,000 and 20,000 words, and 2 men that spoke about 22,000 and 28,000 words. The stemplots suggest that there is some skew in both populations, but the sample sizes should be large enough to overcome this problem. (b) With subscripts as assigned in the statement of the problem (Group 1 = Women), we test $H_0 : \mu_1 = \mu_2$ vs. $H_a : \mu_1 > \mu_2$. We have $\bar{x}_1$ = 16,496.1, $\bar{x}_2$ = 12,866.7, s_1 = 7914.35, s_2 = 8342.47, n_1 = 27 and n_2= 20 we find SE = 2408.26 and t = 1.51. With df = 39.8 (software), P = 0.070. Using Table C with the more conservative df = 19, $0.05 < P < 0.10$. There is some evidence that on average, women say more words than men, but the evidence is not particularly strong.

```
        Women              Men
     9 8 8 7 6 | 0 | 4 4 5 6 7 8 9
 4 3 3 2 1 0 0 0 | 1 | 0 0 1 1 1 3 3 3
     9 9 8 7 6 5 | 1 | 6 8
             3 0 | 2 | 2
       7 6 5 5 5 | 2 | 8
                 | 3 |
                 | 3 | 8
             0   | 4 |
```

19.43: This is a two-sample t statistic, comparing two independent groups (supplemented and control). Using the conservative df = 5, $t = -1.05$ would have a P-value between 0.30 and 0.40, which (as the report said) is not significant. The test statistic $t = -1.05$ would not be significant for any value of df.

19.44: We test $H_0 : \mu_1 = \mu_2$ vs. $H_a : \mu_1 \neq \mu_2$, where μ_1 is the mean days behind caterpillar peak for the control group, and μ_2 is the mean days for the supplemented group. Now with $\bar{x}_1 = 4.0$, $\bar{x}_2 = 11.3$, $s_1 = 3.10934$, $s_2 = 3.92556$, $n_1 = 6$ and $n_2 = 7$ we find $SE = \sqrt{\dfrac{s_1^2}{n_1} + \dfrac{s_2^2}{n_2}} = 1.95263$ and $t = \dfrac{4.0 - 11.3}{SE} = -3.74$. The two-sided P-value is either $0.01 < P < 0.02$ (using df = 5) or 0.0033 (using df = 10.96 with software), agreeing with the stated conclusion (a significant difference).

19.45: These are paired t statistics: for each bird, the number of days behind the caterpillar peak was observed, and the t values were computed based on the pairwise differences between the first and second years. For the control group, df = 5, and for the supplemented group, df = 6. The control t is not significant (so the birds in that group did *not* "advance their laying date in the second year"), while the supplemented group t is significant with one-sided $P = 0.0195$ (so those birds did change their laying date).

19.46: PLAN: We test $H_0 : \mu_1 = \mu_2$ vs. $H_a : \mu_1 > \mu_2$, where μ_1 is the mean time for the treatment group, and μ_2 is the mean time for the control group. The alternative hypothesis is one-sided because the researcher suspects that the treatment group will wait longer before asking for help. **SOLVE:** We must assume that the data comes from an SRS of the intended population; we cannot check this with the data. The back-to-back stemplot shows some irregularity in the treatment times, and skewness in the control times. We hope that our equal and moderately large sample sizes will overcome any deviation from Normality. With $\bar{x}_1 = 314.0588$, $\bar{x}_2 = 186.1176$, $s_1 = 172.7898$, $s_2 = 118.0926$, $n_1 = 17$ and $n_2 = 17$ we find $SE = \sqrt{\dfrac{s_1^2}{n_1} + \dfrac{s_2^2}{n_2}} = 50.7602$ and $t = \dfrac{314.0588 - 186.1176}{SE} = 2.521$, for which $0.01 < P < 0.02$ (df = 16) or $P = 0.0088$ (df = 28.27). **CONCLUDE:** There is strong evidence that the treatment group waited longer to ask for help on average.

Treatment		Control
65	0	5689
3	1	012444
976	1	58
44	2	
5	2	79
	3	
6	3	7
44	4	01
876	4	
3	5	
	5	
0	6	

19.47: PLAN: We test $H_0 : \mu_1 = \mu_2$ vs. $H_a : \mu_1 > \mu_2$, where μ_1 is the mean weight loss for adolescents in the gastric banding group, and μ_2 is the mean time for the lifestyle intervention group. The alternative hypothesis is one-sided because the researcher suspects that gastric banding leads to greater average weight loss than lifestyle modification. SOLVE: We must assume that the data comes from an SRS of the intended population; we cannot check this with the data. The stemplots for each sample show no heavy skew and no outliers. With $\bar{x}_1 = 34.87$, $\bar{x}_2 = 3.01$, $s_1 = 18.12$, $s_2 = 13.22$, $n_1 = 24$ and $n_2 = 18$ (note that not all subjects completed the study). We find SE $= \sqrt{\dfrac{s_1^2}{n_1} + \dfrac{s_2^2}{n_2}} = 4.84$ and $t = \dfrac{314.0588 - 186.1176}{\text{SE}} = 6.59$, for which $P <$ 0.0005 (df = 17) or $P < 0.00001$ (df = 39.98 using software). CONCLUDE: There is strong evidence that adolescents using gastric banding lose more weight on average than those that use lifestyle modification.

Gastric Banding	Lifestyle Intervention
–0 | 5	–1 | 762
0 |	–0 |44331
1 | 359	0 |12466
2 | 02479	1 |155
3 | 12235679	2 | 0
4 | 139	3 | 4
5 | 37	
6 | 4	
7 |	
8 | 1	

19.48: PLAN: We test $H_0 : \mu_1 = \mu_2$ vs. $H_a : \mu_1 > \mu_2$, where μ_1 is the mean score for the Active group, and μ_2 is the mean score for the Traditional group. SOLVE: We must assume that the data comes from an SRS of the intended population. The stemplots for each sample show no heavy skew and no outliers. With $\bar{x}_1 = 3.6$, $\bar{x}_2 = 4.74$, $s_1 = 2.41$, $s_2 = 2.85$, $n_1 = 15$ and $n_2 = 23$. Of course, since $\bar{x}_1 < \bar{x}_2$, we will not conclude that $\mu_1 > \mu_2$. We find SE $= \sqrt{\dfrac{s_1^2}{n_1} + \dfrac{s_2^2}{n_2}} = 0.86$ and $t = \dfrac{3.6 - 4.74}{\text{SE}} = -1.32$, for which $P > 0.50$, regardless of df. If you use software, df = 33.42 and $P = 0.9026$. CONCLUDE: There is no support for a conclusion that active learning yields higher average score than traditional learning.

Active Group	Traditional Group
0 | 00	0 | 0
1 | 0	1 | 00
2 | 00	2 | 000
3 | 000	3 | 000
4 | 0	4 | 0
5 | 000	5 | 000
6 | 0	6 | 0000
7 | 0	7 | 000
8 | 0	8 | 00
	9 |
	10|
	11|
	12| 0

19.49: PLAN: Compare mean length by testing $H_0 : \mu_1 = \mu_2$ vs. $H_a : \mu_1 > \mu_2$, and by finding a 90% confidence interval for $\mu_1 - \mu_2$, where μ_1 is the mean for the treatment population and μ_2 is the mean for the control population. **SOLVE:** We must assume that we have two SRSs, and that the distributions of score improvements are Normal. The back-to-back stemplots of the differences ("after" minus "before") for the two groups; the samples are too small to assess Normality, but there are no outliers. With $\bar{x}_1 = 11.4$, $\bar{x}_2 = 8.25$, $s_1 = 3.1693$, $s_2 = 3.6936$, $n_1 = 10$ and $n_2 = 8$, we find SE $= \sqrt{\dfrac{3.1693^2}{10} + \dfrac{3.6936^2}{8}} = 1.646$ and $t = 1.914$. With either df = 7, $0.025 < P < 0.05$. With df = 13.92 (software), $P = 0.0382$. The 90% confidence interval is $(11.4 - 8.25) \pm t^* \text{SE}$, where $t^* = 1.895$ (df = 7) or $t^* = 1.762$ (df = 13.92): either 0.03 to 6.27 points, or 0.25 to 6.05 points. **CONCLUDE:** We have fairly strong evidence that the encouraging subliminal message led to a greater improvement in math scores, on average. We are 90% confident that this increase is between 0.03 and 6.27 points (or 0.25 and 6.05 points).

Treatment		Control
	0	455
76	0	7
	0	8
110	1	1
332	1	2
5	1	4
6	1	

19.50: (a) Refer to Exercise 19.48 for details. For 90% confidence, $t^* = 1.761$ (using df = 14) or $t^* = 1.692$ (using software). Hence, a 90% confidence interval for $\mu_1 - \mu_2$ is $3.6 - 4.74 \pm t^*(0.86)$, or –2.65 to 0.37 (using df = 14) or –2.60 to 0.32 (using df = 33.42). (b) Now we want a 90% confidence interval for the mean change in score for the active class. That is, we construct a 90% confidence interval for μ_1. With 15 observations, we have df = 14, and $t^* = 1.761$.

Hence, the confidence interval is given by $3.6 \pm 1.761 \dfrac{2.41}{\sqrt{15}} = 2.50$ to 4.70.

19.51: PLAN: Compare mean length by testing $H_0 : \mu_1 = \mu_2$ vs. $H_a : \mu_1 \neq \mu_2$, and by finding a 95% confidence interval for $\mu_1 - \mu_2$, where μ_1 is the mean for the Red population and μ_2 is the mean for the Yellow population. SOLVE: We must assume that the data comes from an SRS. We also assume that the data are close to Normal. The back-to-back stemplots show some skewness in the red lengths, but the t procedures should be reasonably safe. With $\bar{x}_1 = 39.7113$, $\bar{x}_2 = 36.1800$, $s_1 = 1.7988$, $s_2 = 0.9753$, $n_1 = 23$ and $n_2 = 15$, we find SE = 0.4518 and $t = 7.817$. With either df = 14 or df = 35.10, $P < 0.0001$. The 95% confidence interval is $(39.711 - 36.180) \pm t^*\text{SE}$, where $t^* = 2.145$ (df = 14) or $t^* = 2.030$ (df = 35.1): either 2.562 to 4.500 mm, or 2.614 to 4.448 mm. CONCLUDE: We have very strong evidence that the two varieties differ in mean length. We are 95% confident that the mean red length minus yellow length is between 2.562 and 4.500 mm (or 2.614 and 4.448 mm).

```
  Red   |    | Yellow
--------+----+---------
        | 34 | 56
        | 35 | 146
        | 36 | 0015678
   9874 | 37 | 01
8722100 | 38 | 1
    761 | 39 |
     65 | 40 |
   9964 | 41 |
     10 | 42 |
      0 | 43 |
```

19.52: Because this exercise asks for a "complete analysis," without suggesting hypotheses or confidence levels, student responses may vary. This solution gives 95% confidence intervals for the means in parts (a) and (b), and performs a hypothesis test and gives a 95% confidence interval for part (c). Note that the first two problems call for single-sample t procedures (Chapter 18), while the last uses the Chapter 19 procedures. Student answers should be formatted according to the "four-step process" of the text; these answers are not, but can be used to check student results. We begin with summary statistics.

	n	$\bar{x}$	s
Women	95	4.2737	2.1472
Men	81	6.5185	3.3471

Back-to-back stemplot of responses for men and women reveal that the distribution of claimed drinks per day for women is slightly skewed, but has no outliers. For men, the distribution is only slightly skewed, but contains four outliers. However, these outliers are not too extreme. In all problems, it seems use of t procedures is reasonable.

Women		Men
00000000	1	000
5555555500000	2	0000
555500000000000000000000	3	0000000
50000000000000000000	4	0000000000555
00000000000	5	000000005
50000000	6	00000005
00000000	7	000000005
000	8	000000000
000	9	0000
00	10	00000005
	11	0
	12	05
	13	
	14	
	15	000
	16	0

(a) We construct a 95% confidence interval for μ_w, the mean number of claimed drinks for women. Here, $t^* = 1.990$ (df = 80 in Table A) or $t^* = 1.9855$ (df = 94, software), and SE = $2.1472/\sqrt{95} = 0.2203$. Hence, a 95% confidence interval for μ_w is $4.2737 \pm 1.990(0.223) = 3.84$ to 4.71 drinks. The interval using software is virtually the same. With 95% confidence, the mean number of claimed drinks for women is between 3.84 and 4.71 drinks. (b) We construct a 95% confidence interval for μ_m, the mean number of claimed drinks for men. Here, $t^* = 1.990$ (df = 80 in Table A or software) and SE = $3.3471/\sqrt{81} = 0.3719$. Hence, a 95% confidence interval for μ_m is $6.5185 \pm 1.990(0.3719) = 5.78$ to 7.26 drinks. With 95% confidence, the mean number of claimed drinks for men is between 5.78 and 7.26 drinks. (c) We test $H_0 : \mu_m = \mu_w$ vs.

$H_a : \mu_m \neq \mu_w$. We have SE $= \sqrt{\dfrac{2.1472^2}{95} + \dfrac{3.3471^2}{81}} = 0.4322$ and $t = \dfrac{4.2737 - 6.5185}{\text{SE}} = -5.193$.

Regardless of the choice of df (80 or 132.15), this is highly significant ($P < 0.001$). We have very strong evidence that the claimed number of drinks is different for men and women. To construct a 95% confidence interval for $\mu_m - \mu_w$, we use $t^* = 1.990$ (df = 80) or $t^* = 1.9781$ (df =

132.15). Hence, using $\bar{x}_1 - \bar{x}_2 \pm t^* \sqrt{\dfrac{s_1^2}{n_1} + \dfrac{s_2^2}{n_2}}$, we obtain either 2.2448 ± 0.8601 or $2.2448 \pm$

0.8549. After rounding either interval, we report that with 95% confidence, on average, sophomore men who drink claim an additional 1.4 to 3.1 drinks per day compared with sophomore women who drink.

19.53 and 19.54 are Web-based exercises.

Chapter 20 Solutions

20.1: (a) The population consists of all persons between the ages of 18 and 30 living in the United States. The parameter p is the proportion of this population that prays at least once a week. (b) We estimate p by $\hat{p} = \dfrac{247}{385} = 0.6416$. We estimate that about 64% of people in this population pray at least once per week.

20.2: Under repeated sampling, about 95% of the time the sample proportion $\hat{p}$ would be within two standard deviations of the true value of p. Here, the standard deviation is $\sqrt{\dfrac{p(1-p)}{n}} =$ $\sqrt{\dfrac{0.68(1-0.68)}{1200}} = 0.0135$. Hence, about 95% of sample proportions would be between $0.68 - 2(0.0135) = 0.653$ and $0.68 + 2(0.0135) = 0.707$.

20.3: (a) The sampling distribution of $\hat{p}$ is approximately Normal with mean $p = 0.70$ and standard deviation $\sqrt{\dfrac{p(1-p)}{n}} = \sqrt{\dfrac{0.70(1-.070)}{1500}} = 0.0118$. (b) If $n = 6000$, the sampling distribution of $\hat{p}$ is approximately Normal with mean $p = 0.70$ and standard deviation $\sqrt{\dfrac{p(1-p)}{n}} = \sqrt{\dfrac{0.70(1-0.70)}{6000}} = 0.0059$. Notice that quadrupling the sample size (from 1500 to 6000) results in halving the standard deviation of $\hat{p}$ (0.0059 is one-half of 0.0118).

20.4: There were only 5 or 6 "successes" in the sample (because 5/2673 and 6/2673 both round to 0.2%).

20.5: The survey excludes residents of the northern territories, as well as those who have no phones or have only cell phone service. (b) $\hat{p} = \dfrac{1288}{1505} = 0.8558$ so $SE_{\hat{p}} = \sqrt{\dfrac{\hat{p}(1-\hat{p})}{n}} =$ 0.009055, and the 95% confidence interval is $0.8558 \pm (1.96)(0.009055) = 0.8381$ to 0.8736.

20.6: STATE: What proportion of weightlifting injuries in the 8 to 30 age group are accidental? PLAN: We will construct a 90% confidence interval for p. SOLVE: We are told that the sample is random and will assume that the sample is close to an SRS. Since both the number of successes (1552) and failures $(4111 - 1552 = 2559)$ are much greater than 15, we may assume that the sampling distribution of $\hat{p}$ is approximately Normal. Here, $\hat{p} = \dfrac{1552}{4111} = 0.3775$ and $SE_{\hat{p}} = \sqrt{\dfrac{\hat{p}(1-\hat{p})}{4111}} = 0.0076$. Hence, a 90% confidence interval for p is given by $0.3775 \pm 1.645(0.0076) = 0.365$ to 0.390. CONCLUDE: With 90% confidence, the proportion of all weightlifting injuries in this age group classified as accidental is between 0.365 and 0.390.

20.7: (a) Among the 14 observations, we have 11 successes and 3 failures. The number of successes and failures should both be at least 15 for the Normal approximation to be valid. (b) We add 4 observations: 2 successes and 2 failures. We now have 18 observations: 13 successes and 5 failures. Now $\tilde{p} = \dfrac{11+2}{14+4} = \dfrac{13}{18} = 0.7222$. (c) Using the plus four method,

$\text{SE}_{\tilde{p}} = \sqrt{\dfrac{\tilde{p}(1-\tilde{p})}{n+4}} = \sqrt{\dfrac{0.7222(1-0.7222)}{18}} = 0.1056$. Hence, a 90% confidence interval for p is $0.7222 \pm 1.645(0.1056) = 0.5485$ to 0.8959. The confidence interval is quite wide (even with only 90% confidence level used) because the sample size is so small.

20.8: As stated in the problem (see part (b)), conditions required for inference are satisfied for both intervals. (a) $\hat{p} = \dfrac{113}{1025} = 0.1102$, and $\text{SE}_{\hat{p}} = \sqrt{\dfrac{\hat{p}(1-\hat{p})}{1025}} = 0.0098$. A 95% confidence interval for p is given by $0.1102 \pm 1.96(0.0098) = 0.0910$ to 0.1294, or 9.1% to 13.0%. (b) Using the plus four method, $\tilde{p} = \dfrac{113+2}{1025+4} = 0.1118$, and $\text{SE}_{\tilde{p}} = \sqrt{\dfrac{\tilde{p}(1-\tilde{p})}{1029}} = 0.0098$. A 95% confidence interval for p is given by $0.1118 \pm 1.96(0.0098) = 0.0926$ to 0.1310, or 9.3% to 13.1%. These intervals are virtually identical, but the plus four confidence interval is very slightly shifted to the right. This shift is very small because adding 2 successes and 2 failures to an already large sample size (1025) has little impact.

20.9: (a) The sample proportion is $\hat{p} = \dfrac{20}{20} = 1$, so $\text{SE}_{\hat{p}} = \sqrt{\dfrac{\hat{p}(1-\hat{p})}{n}} = 0$. The margin of error would therefore be 0 (regardless of the confidence level), so large-sample methods give the useless interval 1 to 1. (b) The plus four estimate is $\tilde{p} = \dfrac{20}{20} = 0.9167$, and $\text{SE}_{\tilde{p}} = \sqrt{\dfrac{\tilde{p}(1-\tilde{p})}{24}} = 0.0564$. A 95% confidence interval for p is then $0.9167 \pm 1.96(0.0564) = 0.8062$ to 1.0272. Since proportions can't exceed 1, we say that a 95% confidence interval for p is 0.8061 to 1.

20.10: (a) We find that $\hat{p} = \dfrac{221}{270} = 0.8185$ and $\text{SE}_{\hat{p}} = \sqrt{\dfrac{\hat{p}(1-\hat{p})}{270}} = 0.02346$. Hence, the margin of error for 95% confidence is $(1.96)(0.02346) = 0.460$ (about 4.6%). (b) For a ± 0.03 margin of error, we need $n = \left(\dfrac{1.96}{0.03}\right)^2 p^*(1-p^*) = 4268.4\,p^*$. Now, to use the previous study as a pilot study, replace p^* with $\hat{p} = 0.8185$, yielding $n = 634.1$. Round this up in order to obtain a required sample size of at least 635.

20.11: $n = \left(\dfrac{z^*}{m}\right)^2 p^*(1-p^*) = \left(\dfrac{1.645}{0.04}\right)^2 (0.75)(1-0.75) = 317.1$, so use $n = 318$.

20.12: STATE: We wonder if the proportion of times the Belgian Euro coin spins heads is the same as the proportion of times is spins tails. SOLVE: Let p be the proportion of times a spun Belgian Euro coin lands heads. We test $H_0 : p = 0.50$ vs. $H_a : p \neq 0.50$. Since the sample consists of 250 trials, we expect 125 "successes" (heads) and 125 "failures" (tails). Hence, the sample is large enough to use the Normal approximation to describe the sampling distribution of $\hat{p}$. We assume the sample represents an SRS of all possible coin spins. Here, $\hat{p} = \dfrac{140}{250} = 0.56$

$$SE_{\hat{p}} = \sqrt{\frac{p_0(1-p_0)}{n}} = \sqrt{\frac{0.50(1-0.50)}{250}} = 0.0316. \text{ Hence, } z = \frac{\hat{p}-p_0}{SE} = \frac{0.57-0.50}{0.0316} = 2.22, \text{ and } P$$

$= 0.0264$. CONCLUDE: There is strong evidence that the proportion of times a Belgian Euro coin spins heads is not 0.50.

20.13: STATE: We wonder if the proportion of times the "best face" wins is more than 0.50. SOLVE: Let p be the proportion of times the "best face" wins. We test $H_0 : p = 0.50$ vs. $H_a : p > 0.50$. Since the sample consists of 32 trials, we expect 16 "successes" (best face wins) and 16 "failures" (best face does not win). Hence, the sample is large enough to use the Normal approximation to describe the sampling distribution of $\hat{p}$. We assume the sample is an SRS.

Here, $\hat{p} = \dfrac{22}{32} = 0.6875$ and $SE_{\hat{p}} = \sqrt{\dfrac{p_0(1-p_0)}{n}} = \sqrt{\dfrac{0.50(1-0.50)}{32}} = 0.0884.$ Hence, $z = \dfrac{\hat{p}-p_0}{SE}$

$= \dfrac{0.6875-0.50}{0.0884} = 2.12$, and $P = 0.0170$. CONCLUDE: There is strong evidence that the proportion of times the "best face" wins is more than 0.50.

20.14: (a) The number of trials is not large enough to apply the z test for a proportion. Here, the expected number of successes (heads) and the expected number of failures (tails) are both 5. These should be 15 or more. (b) As long as the sample can be viewed as an SRS, a z test for a proportion can be used. (c) Under the null hypothesis, we expect only $200(0.01) = 2$ failures. We should have at least 15 expected failures and at least 15 expected successes.

20.15: (b) The sampling distribution of $\hat{p}$ has mean $p = 0.60$.

20.16: (b) The standard deviation of $\hat{p}$ is $\sqrt{\dfrac{p(1-p)}{n}} = \sqrt{\dfrac{0.60(1-0.60)}{117}} = 0.0453.$

20.17: (c) $\hat{p} = \dfrac{1410}{3000} = 0.47.$

20.18: (c) The margin of error is $1.96\sqrt{\dfrac{\hat{p}(1-\hat{p})}{n}} = 1.96\sqrt{\dfrac{0.47(1-0.47)}{3000}} = 0.018.$

20.19: (c) $n = \left(\dfrac{z^*}{m}\right)^2 p^*\left(1-p^*\right) = \left(\dfrac{2.58}{0.02}\right)^2 (0.50)(1-0.50) = 4147.36$, round up to $n = 4148$.

20.20: (a) With $\tilde{p} = \dfrac{53+2}{100+4} = 0.5288$, the margin of error is $1.96\sqrt{\dfrac{\tilde{p}(1-\tilde{p})}{n+4}} =$

$1.96\sqrt{\dfrac{0.5288(1-0.5288)}{104}} = 0.096$.

20.21: (a) Sources of bias are not accounted for in a margin of error.

20.22: (a) The alternative hypothesis expresses the idea "more than half think their job prospects are good."

20.23: (c) $z = \dfrac{\hat{p} - p_0}{\sqrt{\dfrac{p_0(1-p_0)}{n}}} = \dfrac{0.53 - 0.50}{\sqrt{\dfrac{0.50(1-0.50)}{100}}} = 0.60$.

20.24: (a) The margin of error in (virtually all) publicly reported polls is associated with 95% confidence. This is done out of tradition.

20.25: (a) The survey excludes those who have no phones or have only cell-phone service. (b) Note that we have plenty of successes and plenty of failures, so conditions for large-sample confidence interval are met. With the sample proportion $\hat{p} = \dfrac{848}{1010} = 0.8396$, the large sample 95% confidence interval is

$$\hat{p} \pm z^* \sqrt{\dfrac{\hat{p}(1-\hat{p})}{n}} = 0.8396 \pm 1.96\sqrt{\dfrac{0.8396(1-0.8396)}{1010}} = 0.8170 \text{ to } 0.8622.$$

If we instead use the plus four method, $\tilde{p} = \dfrac{848+2}{1010+4} = 0.8383$, $SE_{\hat{p}} = 0.01156$, the margin of error is $1.96(0.01156) = 0.02266$, and the 95% confidence interval is 0.8156 to 0.8610.

20.26: We have 19 successes and $172 - 19 = 153$ failures. Both are large enough so that conditions for large-sample confidence interval use are met. We estimate that $\hat{p} = \dfrac{19}{172} = 0.1105$, $SE_{\hat{p}} = 0.02391$, the margin of error is $1.96\,SE_{\hat{p}} = 0.04685$, and the 95% confidence interval is 0.0636 to 0.1573. If we instead use the plus-four method, $\tilde{p} = \dfrac{19+2}{172+4} = 0.1193$, $SE_{\tilde{p}} = 0.02443$, the margin of error is $1.960\,SE_{\hat{p}} = 0.04789$, and the 95% confidence interval is 0.0714 to 0.1672.

20.27: (a) With $\hat{p} = \dfrac{848}{1010} = 0.8396$, $SE_{\hat{p}} = 0.01155$, so the margin of error is $1.96\,SE_{\hat{p}} = 0.02263 = 2.26\%$. (b) If instead $\hat{p} = 0.50$, then $SE_{\hat{p}} = 0.01573$ and the margin of error for 95% confidence would be $1.96\,SE_{\hat{p}} = 0.03084 = 3.08\%$. (c) For samples of about this size, the margin of error is no more than about $\pm 3\%$ no matter what $\hat{p}$ is.

20.28: (a) With 247 successes and 385–287 = 138 failures, conditions for large-sample inference are met. We have $\hat{p} = \frac{247}{385} = 0.6416$, $\text{SE}_{\hat{p}} = \sqrt{\frac{\hat{p}(1-\hat{p})}{385}} = 0.0244$. For a 99% confidence interval the margin of error is then $2.576\,\text{SE}_{\hat{p}} = 0.0630$. Hence, a 99% confidence interval for the proportion that pray at least once per week is 0.5786 to 0.7046, or 57.9% to 70.5%. (b) Using the plus four approach, $\tilde{p} = \frac{247+2}{385+4} = 0.6401$ and $\text{SE}_{\tilde{p}} = 0.0243$. The margin of error for 99% confidence is $2.576\,\text{SE}_{\tilde{p}} = 0.0627$, and the 99% confidence interval is 0.5774 to 0.7028, or 57.7% to 70.3%. The confidence intervals are very similar, with the plus four interval being slightly shifted closer toward 0.50 (shifted away from 1.0).

20.29: (a) The survey excludes residents of Alaska and Hawaii, and those who do not have cell-phone service. (b) We have 422 successes and 2063 failures, so the sample is large enough to use large-sample inference procedure. We have $\hat{p} = \frac{422}{2485} = 0.1698$, and $\text{SE}_{\hat{p}} = 0.0075$. For 90% confidence, the margin of error is $1.645\,\text{SE}_{\hat{p}} = 0.0124$ and the confidence interval is 0.1574 to 0.1822, or 15.7% to 18.2%. Using the plus four method, $\tilde{p} = \frac{422+2}{2485+4} = 0.1703$, $\text{SE}_{\tilde{p}} = 0.0075$, the margin of error is $1.645\,\text{SE}_{\tilde{p}} = 0.0124$, and the 90% confidence interval is 0.1579 to 0.1827, or 15.8% to 18.3%. (c) Perhaps people that use the cell phone to search for information online are younger, and more sexually related topics.

20.30: (a) For the large-sample interval, we would need at least 15 successes and failures; we have only 8 and 5 failures in the two samples. For plus-four intervals, we need only $n \geq 10$ (and confidence level 90% or more). (b) For the proportion preferring Times New Roman for Web use: $\tilde{p} = \frac{17+2}{25+4} = 0.6552$, $\text{SE}_{\tilde{p}} = 0.08826$, the margin of error is $1.96\,\text{SE}_{\tilde{p}} = 0.17299$, and the 95% confidence interval is 0.4822 to 0.8282. For the proportion who prefer Gigi: $\tilde{p} = \frac{20+2}{25+4} = 0.7586$, $\text{SE}_{\tilde{p}} = 0.07947$, the margin of error is $1.645\,\text{SE}_{\tilde{p}} = 0.13072$, and the 90% confidence interval is 0.6279 to 0.8893.

20.31: (a) In order to construct a large-sample confidence interval, we require at least 15 successes (swimming areas with unsafe levels of fecal coliform) and at least 15 failures (swimming areas with safe levels of fecal coliform). Here, we have 13 successes and 7 failures. In order to use the plus-four confidence intervals, we require at least 90% confidence and at least 10 trials. Hence, conditions for using the plus four method are satisfied. (b) Now $\tilde{p} = \frac{13+2}{20+4} = 0.625$, and $\text{SE}_{\tilde{p}} = \sqrt{\frac{\tilde{p}(1-\tilde{p})}{24}} = 0.0988$. Hence, the margin of error for 90% confidence is $1.645(0.0988) = 0.1626$, and the 90% confidence interval for the proportion of swimming areas with unsafe coliform levels is 0.4624 to 0.7879, or 46.2% to 78.8%.

20.32: (a) Both large-sample and plus four methods are safe because we have 880 trials, with 171 successes and $880 - 171 = 709$ failures. For the large-sample interval: $\hat{p} = \dfrac{171}{880} = 0.1943$, $SE_{\hat{p}}$ $= 0.01334$, the margin of error is $1.96\,SE_{\hat{p}} = 0.02614$, and the 95% confidence interval is 0.1682 to 0.2204. Using plus-four methods, $\tilde{p} = \dfrac{171+2}{880+4} = 0.1957$, $SE_{\tilde{p}} = \sqrt{\dfrac{\tilde{p}(1-\tilde{p})}{884}} = 0.01334$, the margin of error is $1.96\,SE_{\tilde{p}} = 0.02615$, and 95% confidence interval is 0.1695 to 0.2219. (b) More than 171 respondents have run red lights. We would not expect very many people to claim that they have run red lights when they have not, but some people will deny running red lights when they have.

20.33: (a) Because the smallest number of total tax returns (i.e., the smallest population) is still more than 100 times the sample size, the margin of error will be (approximately) same for all states. (b) Yes, it will change—the sample taken from Wyoming will be about the same size, but the sample from, for example, California will be considerably larger, and therefore the margin of error will decrease.

20.34: (a) $n = \left(\dfrac{z^*}{m}\right)^2 p^*(1-p^*) = \left(\dfrac{2.576}{0.015}\right)^2 (0.2)(1-0.2) = 4718.8$, so use $n = 4719$. (b)

$2.576\sqrt{\dfrac{(0.1)(0.9)}{4719}} = 0.01125.$

20.35: (a) The margins of error are $1.96\sqrt{\dfrac{\hat{p}(1-\hat{p})}{100}} = 0.196\sqrt{\hat{p}(1-\hat{p})}$ (below). (b) With $n = 500$,

the margins of error are $1.96\sqrt{\dfrac{\hat{p}(1-\hat{p})}{500}} = 0.088\sqrt{\hat{p}(1-\hat{p})}$. The new margins of error are less than half their former size.

	p	0.1	0.2	0.3	0.4	0.5	0.6	0.7	0.8	0.9
(a)	m.e.	.0588	.0784	.0898	.0960	.0980	.0960	.0898	.0784	.0588
(b)	m.e.	.0263	.0351	.0402	.0429	.0438	.0429	.0402	.0351	.0263

20.36: (a) PLAN: We construct a 99% confidence interval for the proportion of all 17-year-old students in 2008 who had at least one parent graduate from college. SOLVE: We are told to treat this sample as an SRS of 17-year-olds still in school. The sample size is very large, with n $= 9600$. We are told that $\hat{p} = 0.46$, so we have $9600(0.46) = 4416$ kids with a parent that graduated from college and 5184 kids that did not have a parent graduate from college. The number of successes and failures is very large (more than the required 15), so the large-sample confidence interval is appropriate. We have $SE_{\hat{p}} = \sqrt{\dfrac{\hat{p}(1-\hat{p})}{9600}} = 0.0051$, so a margin of error for 99% confidence is $2.576(0.0051) = 0.0131$, and a 99% confidence interval for the proportion is 0.4469 to 0.4731, or 44.69% to 47.31%.

CONCLUDE: With 99% confidence, the proportion of 17-year-old students still in school with at least one parent that graduated from college is between about 0.447 and 0.473. (b) It is difficult to guess, but perhaps parents that are college graduates are more likely to have children finish school. If so, then the proportion over the entire population is likely to be lower.

20.37: PLAN: We will give a 90% confidence interval for the proportion of all *Krameria cytisoides* shrubs that will resprout after fire. SOLVE: We assume that the 12 shrubs in the sample can be treated as an SRS. Because the number of resprouting shrubs is just 5, the conditions for a large sample interval are not met. Using the plus-four method: $\tilde{p} = \dfrac{5+2}{12+4} = 0.4375$, $\mathrm{SE}_{\tilde{p}} = 0.1240$, the margin of error is $1.645\,\mathrm{SE}_{\tilde{p}} = 0.2040$, and the 90% confidence interval is 0.2335 to 0.6415. CONCLUDE: We are 90% confident that the proportion of *Krameria cytisoides* shrubs that will resprout after fire is between about 0.23 and 0.64.

20.38: PLAN: With p representing the proportion of songs loaded by Suzanne, we test $H_0 : p = 0.50$ vs. $H_a : p \neq 0.50$. The test is two-sided because we wonder if the proportion loaded by Suzanne differs from that loaded by Ted, which would mean that p differs from 0.5. SOLVE: We assume that the 30 songs sampled are an SRS. With 30 songs sampled, we expect $30(0.50) = 15$ successes and $30(0.50) = 15$ failures, so conditions for use of the large sample z test are satisfied. We have $\hat{p} = \dfrac{22}{30} = 0.7333$, so $z = \dfrac{0.7333 - 0.50}{\sqrt{\dfrac{0.50(1-0.50)}{30}}} = 2.556$ and $P = 0.0106$.

There is strong evidence that the proportion of songs downloaded by Suzanne differs from 0.50. CONCLUDE: We conclude that the proportions of songs downloaded by Ted and Suzanne differ.

20.39: PLAN: We will give a 95% confidence interval for p, the proportion of American adults who think that humans developed from earlier species of animals. SOLVE: We have an SRS with a very large sample size, so both large-sample and plus-four methods can be used. We have $\hat{p} = \dfrac{594}{1484} = 0.4003$, $\mathrm{SE}_{\hat{p}} = 0.01272$, margin of error $1.96\,\mathrm{SE}_{\hat{p}} = 0.02493$, and the 95% confidence interval is 0.3754 to 0.4252. Using the plus four method, we have $\tilde{p} = \dfrac{594+2}{1484+4} = 0.4005$, $\mathrm{SE}_{\tilde{p}} = 0.01270$, margin of error $1.96\,\mathrm{SE}_{\tilde{p}} = 0.02489$. Hence the plus four 95% confidence interval is 0.3756 to 0.4254. CONCLUDE: We are 95% confident that the percent of American adults thinking that humans developed from earlier species of animals is between about 37.5% and 42.5%.

20.40: (a) PLAN: We will give a 95% confidence interval for p, the proportion of subjects who would select the first choice presented. SOLVE: We assume we have an SRS from the population. With 32 subjects, we have 22 successes (people that picked the first wine) and 10 failures (people that picked the second wine). We use the plus-four method: $\tilde{p} = \dfrac{22+2}{32+4} = 0.6667$, $SE_{\tilde{p}} = 0.0786$, margin of error $1.96\,SE_{\tilde{p}} = 0.1540$, and the 95% confidence interval is 0.5127 and 0.8207, or 51.27% and 82.07%. CONCLUDE: We are 95% confident that the proportion of subjects that would select the first wine is between about 0.513 and 0.821. (b) People that would go out of their way to participate in such a study are presumed to represent the population of all wine drinkers (or adults). This assumption that we have a simple random sample may not be reasonable.

20.41: PLAN: Let p represent the proportion of American adults who think that humans developed from earlier species of animals. In order to assess the evidence for the claim that less than half of adults hold this belief, we will test $H_0 : p = 0.50$ vs. $H_a : p < 0.50$. SOLVE: We have an SRS with a very large sample size, so expected counts (successes and failures) are easily large enough to apply the large sample z test. We have $\hat{p} = \dfrac{594}{1484} = 0.4003$, so

$z = \dfrac{0.4003 - 0.50}{\sqrt{\dfrac{0.50(1-0.50)}{1484}}} = -7.68$, for which $P < 0.0001$. CONCLUDE: We have very strong

evidence that fewer than half of adults believe that humans developed from earlier species of animals.

20.42: PLAN: Let p represent the proportion of the proportion of subjects who would select the first choice presented. In order to assess the evidence for the claim that subjects are not equally likely to choose either position, we will test $H_0 : p = 0.50$ vs. $H_a : p \neq 0.50$. SOLVE: We assume we have an SRS from the population of all wine tasters (see below). With 32 subjects, we expect 16 to choose the first sample, and 16 to choose the second sample. Conditions for use of the large-sample z test are satisfied. With $\hat{p} = \dfrac{22}{32} = 0.6875$, so $z = \dfrac{0.6875 - 0.50}{\sqrt{\dfrac{0.50(1-0.50)}{32}}} = 2.121$,

for which $P = 0.0340$. CONCLUDE: We have fairly strong evidence that wine tasters are not equally likely to select the first or second wine. Given that the sample was obtained by recruiting volunteers to participate in a wine-tasting study, it isn't likely that this sample represents all wine drinkers or wine tasters.

20.43: PLAN: We will give a 95% confidence interval for p, the proportion of Chick-fil-A orders correctly filled. SOLVE: We will assume that the 196 visits constitute a random sample of all possible visits. In our sample, we have 182 successes (correctly filled orders) and 14 failures (incorrectly filled orders). We will use the plus four method, since we do not have at least 15 failures: We have $\tilde{p} = \dfrac{182+2}{196+4} = 0.92$, $SE_{\tilde{p}} = 0.0192$, margin of error $1.96\,SE_{\tilde{p}} = 0.0376$, and the 95% confidence interval is 0.8824 to 0.9576. CONCLUDE: We are 95% confident that the proportion of orders filled correctly by Chick-fil-A is between 0.882 and 0.958, or 88.2% to 95.8%.

20.44: PLAN: We obtain the sample size required to estimate the proportion of wine tasters that select the first choice to within ±0.05 with 95% confidence. SOLVE: We guess that the unknown value of p is 0.6667, as computed in Exercise 20.40. Hence, $n = \left(\dfrac{z^*}{m}\right)^2 p^*(1-p^*) = \left(\dfrac{1.96}{0.05}\right)^2 (0.6667)(1-0.6667) = 341.46$, so take $n = 342$. CONCLUDE: We require a sample of at least 342 wine tasters in order to estimate the proportion that would choose the first option to within 0.05 with 95% confidence.

20.45 and 20.46 are Web-based exercises.

Chapter 21 Solutions

21.1: PLAN: We construct a 95% confidence interval for $p_1 - p_2$, where p_1 denotes the proportion of younger people that text often, and p_2 denotes the proportion for older people. SOLVE: We have two large samples: 625 younger people and 1917 older people. The number of successes in each sample (475 and 786, respectively) and the number of failures in each sample (150 and 1131) are large enough to use large-sample methods. We have $\hat{p}_1 = \dfrac{475}{625} = 0.76$, and $\hat{p}_2 = \dfrac{786}{1917} = 0.41$. Now SE $= \sqrt{\dfrac{\hat{p}_1(1-\hat{p}_1)}{625} + \dfrac{\hat{p}_2(1-\hat{p}_2)}{1917}} = 0.0204$, so the margin of error for 95% confidence is 1.96(0.0204) = 0.0400 and a 95% confidence interval for the difference in proportions is 0.3100 to 0.3900, or 31% to 39%. CONCLUDE: With 95% confidence, the proportion of teenagers that text exceeds that of persons 18 and over by somewhere between 0.31 and 0.39.

21.2: PLAN: We construct a 95% confidence interval for $p_1 - p_2$, where p_1 denotes the proportion of Democrats that believe a person should be able to speak, and p_2 denotes the proportion of Republicans that believe a person should be able to speak. SOLVE: We have two large samples: 464 Democrats and 340 Republicans. The number of successes in each sample (362 and 254, respectively) and the number of failures in each sample (102 and 86) are large enough to use large-sample methods. We have $\hat{p}_1 = \dfrac{362}{464} = 0.7802$, and $\hat{p}_2 = \dfrac{254}{340} = 0.7471$. Now SE $= \sqrt{\dfrac{\hat{p}_1(1-\hat{p}_1)}{464} + \dfrac{\hat{p}_2(1-\hat{p}_2)}{340}} = 0.0304$, so the margin of error for 95% confidence is 1.96(0.0304) = 0.0596 and a 95% confidence interval for the difference in proportions is –0.0265 to 0.0927, or –2.6% to 9.3%. CONCLUDE: With 95% confidence, the increase in proportion of Democrats (over Republicans) that believe somebody with "dangerous" or "bad" ideas should be able to speak is between is between –0.0265 and 0.0927.

21.3: Let p_1 denote the proportion of males that meet recommended levels, and let p_2 denote the proportion for females. We have many successes and failures in both samples, so large sample methods are reasonable. Then $\hat{p}_1 = \dfrac{3594}{7881} = 0.4560$, and $\hat{p}_2 = \dfrac{2261}{8164} = 0.2769$. Then SE = 0.0075, and the margin of error is 2.576 SE = 0.0193. A 99% confidence interval for the difference in proportions between males and females meeting recommended levels of physical activity is 0.1598 to 0.1984, or 16.0% to 19.8%.

21.4: (a) One count is only 6, and the guidelines for using the large-sample method call for all counts to be at least 10. (b) For the plus four method, the sample sizes are 55 and 110, and the success counts are 7 and 46. (c) We have $\tilde{p}_1 = \dfrac{6+1}{53+2} = 0.1273$ and $\tilde{p}_2 = \dfrac{45+1}{108+2} = 0.4182$. Hence, a plus four 95% confidence interval for $p_1 - p_2$ is $(0.1273 - 0.4182) \pm$

$1.96\sqrt{\dfrac{\tilde{p}_1(1-\tilde{p}_1)}{55} + \dfrac{\tilde{p}_2(1-\tilde{p}_2)}{110}} = -0.2909 \pm 0.1275 = \qquad -0.4184$ to -0.1634. Since the first population is for injured skaters with wrist guards, the proportion for skaters with wrist guards is seen to be lower than the proportion for skaters without wrist guards. With 95% confidence, among injured skaters, the difference between proportion with wrist guards and those without is between -41.8% and -16.3%. That is, more injured skaters fail to wear wrist guards.

21.5: STATE: How much does microwaving crackers reduce checking? PLAN: Let p_1 denote the proportion of checking in the control group, and let p_2 denote the proportion of checking in the microwaved group. We give a 95% (plus four) confidence interval for $p_1 - p_2$. SOLVE: To use plus four methods, we want samples of at least size 5; this condition is easily met here. The plus four estimates are $\tilde{p}_1 = \dfrac{16+1}{65+2} = 0.2537$ and $\tilde{p}_2 = \dfrac{0+1}{65+2} = 0.0149$. Hence, a plus four 95%

confidence interval for $p_1 - p_2$ is $\tilde{p}_1 - \tilde{p}_2 \pm 1.96\sqrt{\dfrac{\tilde{p}_1(1-\tilde{p}_1)}{67} + \dfrac{\tilde{p}_2(1-\tilde{p}_2)}{67}} = 0.2388 \pm 0.1082 =$ 0.1306 to 0.3470. CONCLUDE: We are 95% confident that microwaving reduces checking by between about 13% and 35%.

21.6: (a) This is an observational study: no treatment was imposed; we simply observed drivers in the two cities. (b) PLAN: Let p_1 be the proportion of New York female Hispanic drivers who wear seat belts, and let p_2 be that proportion for Boston. The comparison of local laws suggests a one-sided alternative: $H_0 : p_1 = p_2$ vs. $H_a : p_1 > p_2$. SOLVE: All counts are greater than 5, so the significance test should be safe. We find $\hat{p}_1 = \dfrac{183}{220} = 0.8318$ and $\hat{p}_2 = \dfrac{68}{117} = 0.5812$. The pooled proportion is $\hat{p} = \dfrac{183+68}{220+117} = 0.7448$, and SE = 0.04989. The test statistic is therefore z $= \dfrac{0.8318-0.5812}{\text{SE}} = 5.02$, for which P is very small (< 0.001). CONCLUDE: We conclude that female Hispanic drivers in Boston are less likely to wear seat belts.

21.7: STATE: Is helmet use less common among skiers and snowboarders with head injuries than skiers and snowboarders without head injuries? PLAN: Let p_1 and p_2 be (respectively) the proportions of injured skiers and injured snowboarders who wear helmets. We test $H_0 : p_1 = p_2$ vs. $H_a : p_1 < p_2$. SOLVE: The smallest count is 96, so the significance testing procedure is safe. We find $\hat{p}_1 = \dfrac{96}{578} = 0.1661$ and $\hat{p}_2 = \dfrac{656}{2992} = 0.2193$. The pooled proportion is $\hat{p} = \dfrac{96 + 656}{578 + 2992}$ $= 0.2106$. Then for the significance test, $\mathrm{SE} = \sqrt{\hat{p}(1 - \hat{p})\left(\dfrac{1}{578} + \dfrac{1}{2992}\right)} = 0.01853$. The test statistic is therefore $z = \dfrac{0.1661 - 0.2193}{\mathrm{SE}} = -2.87$, and $P = 0.0021$. CONCLUDE: We have strong evidence (significant at $\alpha = 0.01$) that skiers and snowboarders with head injuries are less likely to use helmets than skiers and snowboarders without head injuries.

21.8: STATE: Is the proportion of disease-free patients after five years using ALND different from that for those using SLND alone? PLAN: Let p_1 and p_2 be (respectively) the proportions of patients using ALND and using SLND alone. We test $H_0 : p_1 = p_2$ vs. $H_a : p_1 \neq p_2$. SOLVE: The smallest count is 70 (number of failures in the SLND alone group), so the large sample significance testing procedure is safe. We find $\hat{p}_1 = \dfrac{345}{420} = 0.8214$ and $\hat{p}_2 = \dfrac{366}{436} = 0.8394$. The pooled proportion is $\hat{p} = \dfrac{345 + 366}{420 + 436} = 0.8306$. Then for the significance test, $\mathrm{SE} = \sqrt{\hat{p}(1 - \hat{p})\left(\dfrac{1}{420} + \dfrac{1}{436}\right)} = 0.0256$. The test statistic is therefore $z = \dfrac{0.8214 - 0.8394}{\mathrm{SE}} = -0.7018$, and $P = 0.4840$. CONCLUDE: There is virtually no evidence of a difference in proportions disease-free five years later between patients on ALND and those using SLND alone. Random chance easily explains a difference in the observed sample proportions.

21.9: (b) We look for evidence that the proportion for 2009 is lower than for 1999.

21.10: (b) For example, $\hat{p}_{1999} = \dfrac{592}{2045} = 0.2895$, which rounds to 0.29.

21.11: (b) $\hat{p} = \dfrac{511 + 592}{2411 + 2045} = 0.2475$, which rounds to 0.25.

21.12: (a) Using values above, $z = \dfrac{\hat{p}_{1999} - \hat{p}_{2009}}{\sqrt{\hat{p}(1 - \hat{p})\left(\dfrac{1}{2411} + \dfrac{1}{2045}\right)}} = 5.98$, yielding $P < 0.01$.

21.13: (c) For a 95% confidence interval, the margin of error is

$1.96 \sqrt{\dfrac{\hat{p}_{1999}(1 - \hat{p}_{1999})}{2411} + \dfrac{\hat{p}_{2009}(1 - \hat{p}_{2009})}{2045}} = 0.026.$

21.14: (c) $z = \dfrac{\hat{p}_1 - \hat{p}_2}{\sqrt{\hat{p}(1-\hat{p})\left(\dfrac{1}{n_1}+\dfrac{1}{n_2}\right)}} = \dfrac{0.70-0.20}{\sqrt{0.45(1-0.45)\left(\dfrac{1}{10}+\dfrac{1}{10}\right)}} = 2.25$, and the *P*-value is one-

sided and less than 0.02.

21.15: (b) We have only three failures in the treatment group, and only two successes in the control group.

21.16: (b) $\tilde{p}_1 = \dfrac{7+1}{10+2} = 0.667$, $\tilde{p}_2 = \dfrac{2+1}{10+2} = 0.25$, and the margin of error is

$1.645\sqrt{\dfrac{\tilde{p}_1(1-\tilde{p}_1)}{12}+\dfrac{\tilde{p}_2(1-\tilde{p}_2)}{12}} = 0.304$.

21.17: (a) The four counts are 117, 53, 152, and 165, so all counts are large enough. (b) Using the plus four method, $\tilde{p}_1 = \dfrac{117+1}{170+2} = 0.6860$ and $\tilde{p}_2 = \dfrac{152+1}{317+2} = 0.4796$, and the 95%

confidence interval is $\tilde{p}_1 - \tilde{p}_2 \pm 1.96\sqrt{\dfrac{\tilde{p}_1(1-\tilde{p}_1)}{172}+\dfrac{\tilde{p}_2(1-\tilde{p}_2)}{319}} = 0.2064 \pm 0.08841 = 0.1180$ to

0.2948. Using the large-sample method, $\hat{p}_1 = \dfrac{117}{170} = 0.6882$, and $\hat{p}_2 = \dfrac{152}{317} = 0.4795$, and the

95% confidence interval is $\hat{p}_1 - \hat{p}_2 \pm 1.96\sqrt{\dfrac{\hat{p}_1(1-\hat{p}_1)}{170}+\dfrac{\hat{p}_2(1-\hat{p}_2)}{317}} = 0.2087 \pm 0.08873 = 0.1200$

to 0.2974.

21.18: (a) For the subitramine group, $\hat{p}_1 = \dfrac{561}{4906} = 0.114$. For the control (placebo) group, $\hat{p}_2 = \dfrac{490}{4898} = 0.100$. (b) The counts are 561, 4345, 490, and 4408 — easily large enough for use of the large sample confidence interval procedure. (c) Using the plus-four method anyway, $\tilde{p}_1 = \dfrac{561+1}{4906+2} = 0.114$ and $\tilde{p}_2 = \dfrac{490+1}{4898+2} = 0.100$ (the plus-four estimates are the same to three or four decimal places because the samples are so large). The 95% confidence interval is $\tilde{p}_1 - \tilde{p}_2 \pm$

$1.96\sqrt{\dfrac{\tilde{p}_1(1-\tilde{p}_1)}{4908}+\dfrac{\tilde{p}_2(1-\tilde{p}_2)}{4900}} = 0.014 \pm 0.012 = 0.002$ to 0.026, or 0.2% to 2.6%.

Using the large-sample method, the 95% confidence interval is $\hat{p}_1 - \hat{p}_2 \pm 1.96$

$\sqrt{\dfrac{\hat{p}_1(1-\hat{p}_1)}{4906}+\dfrac{\hat{p}_2(1-\hat{p}_2)}{4898}} = 0.014 \pm 0.012 = 0.002$ to 0.026, or 0.2% to 2.6%. Note that the two

methods produce the same confidence interval up to four decimal places of precision because the samples are so large.

21.19: (a) One of the counts is 0; for large-sample intervals, we want all counts to be at least 10, and for significance testing, we want all counts to be at least 5. (b) The sample size for the treatment group is 35, 24 of which have tumors; the sample size for the control group is 20, 1 of which has a tumor. (c) $\tilde{p}_1 = \dfrac{23+1}{33+2} = 0.6857$ and $\tilde{p}_2 = \dfrac{0+1}{18+2} = 0.05$. The plus four 99% confidence interval is

$$\tilde{p}_1 - \tilde{p}_2 \pm 2.576 \sqrt{\frac{\tilde{p}_1(1-\tilde{p}_1)}{35} + \frac{\tilde{p}_2(1-\tilde{p}_2)}{20}} = 0.6357 \pm 0.2380 = 0.3977 \text{ to } 0.8737.$$

We are 99% confidence that lowering DNA methylation increases the incidence of tumors by between about 40% and 87%.

21.20: Let p_1 and p_2 be (respectively) the proportions of subjects in the treatment and control groups experiencing a primary outcome. We test $H_0 : p_1 = p_2$ vs. $H_a : p_1 \neq p_2$. For the treatment group $\hat{p}_1 = \dfrac{561}{4906} = 0.114$. For the control (placebo) group, $\hat{p}_2 = \dfrac{490}{4898} = 0.100$. The pooled estimate is $\hat{p} = \dfrac{561+490}{4906+4898} = 0.1072$. Hence,

$$z = \frac{\hat{p}_1 - \hat{p}_2}{\sqrt{\hat{p}(1-\hat{p})\left(\dfrac{1}{4906} + \dfrac{1}{4898}\right)}} = 2.24 \text{ and } P = 0.025.$$ We have strong evidence that the proportion of subjects on subitramine suffering a primary outcome differs from that on the placebo. (b) A comparison group is important because we want to learn about the difference in rate of primary outcome due to subitramine. A placebo should be used in order to blind patients to which group they are in, and to account for any possible placebo effect.

21.21: (a) Let p_1 and p_2 be (respectively) the proportions of subjects in the music and no music groups that receive a passing grade on the Maryland HSA. We test $H_0 : p_1 = p_2$ vs. $H_a : p_1 \neq p_2$. For the music group $\hat{p}_1 = \dfrac{2818}{3239} = 0.870$. For the no music group, $\hat{p}_2 = \dfrac{2091}{2787} = 0.750$. The pooled estimate is $\hat{p} = \dfrac{2818+2091}{3239+2787} = 0.815$.

Hence, $z = \dfrac{\hat{p}_1 - \hat{p}_2}{\sqrt{\hat{p}(1-\hat{p})\left(\dfrac{1}{3239}+\dfrac{1}{2787}\right)}} = 11.94$. An observed difference of $0.87 - 0.75 = 0.12$ in

group proportions is much too large to be explained by chance alone, and $P < 0.001$. We have overwhelming evidence (or do we? See part (b).) that the proportion of music students passing the Maryland HSA is greater than that for the no music group. (b) and (c) This is an observational study — people that choose to (or can afford to) take music lessons differ in many ways from those that do not. Hence, we cannot conclude that music causes an improvement in Maryland HSA achievement.

21.22: We estimate the overall proportion of ninth graders that passed the HSA test. As computed in Exercise 21.21, $\hat{p} = \dfrac{2{,}818+2{,}091}{3{,}239+2{,}787} = \dfrac{4{,}909}{6{,}026} = 0.815$. A 95% confidence interval

for the proportion p is given by $\hat{p} \pm 1.96\sqrt{\dfrac{\hat{p}(1-\hat{p})}{6{,}026}} = 0.815 \pm 0.010 = 0.805$ to 0.825, or 80.5% to

82.5%. Using the plus four method, there is just a slight change since the sample size is so

large: Here, $\tilde{p} = \dfrac{4{,}909+2}{6{,}026+4} = 0.814$, and the 95% confidence interval is given by

$\tilde{p} \pm 1.96\sqrt{\dfrac{\tilde{p}(1-\tilde{p})}{6{,}026+4}} = 0.814 \pm 0.010 = 0.804$ to 0.824, or 80.4% to 82.4%.

21.23: The samples are so large, either confidence interval procedure is appropriate. Using the

plus four method, we have $\tilde{p}_1 = \dfrac{2{,}818+1}{3{,}239+2} = 0.870$. and $\tilde{p}_2 = \dfrac{2{,}091+1}{2{,}787+2} = 0.750$. A 95%

confidence interval for $p_1 - p_2$ is then $\tilde{p}_1 - \tilde{p}_2 \pm 1.96\sqrt{\dfrac{\tilde{p}_1(1-\tilde{p}_1)}{3{,}241}+\dfrac{\tilde{p}_2(1-\tilde{p}_2)}{2{,}789}} = 0.100$ to 0.140,

or 10.0% to 14.0%. With such large samples, the large sample methods are appropriate also, but

will yield virtually identical results: With $\hat{p}_1 = \dfrac{2{,}818}{3{,}239} = 0.870$. For the no music group, $\hat{p}_2 =$

$\dfrac{2{,}091}{2{,}787} = 0.750$. $\hat{p}_1 - \hat{p}_2 \pm 1.96\sqrt{\dfrac{\hat{p}_1(1-\hat{p}_1)}{3{,}239}+\dfrac{\hat{p}_2(1-\hat{p}_2)}{2{,}787}} = 0.100$ to 0.140, or 10.0% to 14.0%.

21.24: The two samples are not independent because the same 23 facilities were used for both. In particular, a facility that fails to detect the 1% GM beans almost certainly will not detect the 0.1% GM beans.

21.25: (a) To test $H_0 : p_M = p_F$ vs. $H_a : p_M \neq p_F$, we find $\hat{p}_M = \dfrac{15}{106} = 0.1415$, $\hat{p}_F = \dfrac{7}{42} =$

0.1667, and $\hat{p} = 0.1486$. Then $SE = \sqrt{\hat{p}(1-\hat{p})\left(\dfrac{1}{106} + \dfrac{1}{42}\right)} = 0.06485$, so $z = \dfrac{\hat{p}_M - \hat{p}_F}{SE} = -0.39$.

This gives $P = 0.6966$, which provides virtually no evidence of a difference in failure rates. (b)
We have $\hat{p}_M = \dfrac{450}{3180} = 0.1415$, $\hat{p}_F = \dfrac{210}{1260} = 0.1667$, and $\hat{p} = 0.1486$, but now

$SE = \sqrt{\hat{p}(1-\hat{p})\left(\dfrac{1}{3180} + \dfrac{1}{1260}\right)} = 0.01184$, so $z = \dfrac{\hat{p}_M - \hat{p}_F}{SE} = -2.13$ and $P = 0.0332$. (c) We are

asked to construct two confidence intervals – one based on the smaller samples of part (a) and
one based on the larger samples of part (b). In each case, we provide both large sample and plus
four intervals, which are both appropriate here. First, for case (a), $\hat{p}_M = 0.1415$ and $\hat{p}_F = 0.1667$,

so a 95% confidence interval for the difference is $\hat{p}_M - \hat{p}_F \pm 1.96\sqrt{\dfrac{\hat{p}_M(1-\hat{p}_M)}{106} + \dfrac{\hat{p}_F(1-\hat{p}_F)}{42}} =$

-0.1560 to 0.1056. Using the plus four method, $\tilde{p}_M = \dfrac{15+1}{106+2} = 0.1481$ and $\tilde{p}_F = \dfrac{7+1}{42+2} =$

0.1818, so a 95% confidence interval for the difference is $\tilde{p}_M - \tilde{p}_F \pm$

$1.96\sqrt{\dfrac{\tilde{p}_M(1-\tilde{p}_M)}{108} + \dfrac{\tilde{p}_F(1-\tilde{p}_F)}{44}} = -0.0337 \pm 0.1322 = -0.1659$ to 0.0985.

For case (b), $\hat{p}_M = 0.1415$ and $\hat{p}_F = 0.1667$, but now $\tilde{p}_M = \dfrac{450+1}{3,180+2} = 0.1417$ and $\tilde{p}_F =$

$\dfrac{210+1}{1,260+2} = 0.1672$. The resulting confidence intervals are then $\hat{p}_M - \hat{p}_F \pm$

$1.96\sqrt{\dfrac{\hat{p}_M(1-\hat{p}_M)}{3,180} + \dfrac{\hat{p}_F(1-\hat{p}_F)}{1,260}} = -0.0491$ to -0.0013. The plus four interval is $\tilde{p}_M - \tilde{p}_F \pm$

$1.96\sqrt{\dfrac{\tilde{p}_M(1-\tilde{p}_M)}{3,182} + \dfrac{\tilde{p}_F(1-\tilde{p}_F)}{1,262}} = -0.0494$ to -0.0016.

21.26: PLAN: Let p_1 be the proportion of students from urban/suburban backgrounds who
succeed, and let p_2 be that proportion for students from rural/small-town backgrounds. We test
$H_0 : p_1 = p_2$ vs. $H_a : p_1 \neq p_2$. SOLVE: All counts are greater than 5, so the significance test
should be safe. We find $\hat{p}_1 = \dfrac{52}{65} = 0.8$ and $\hat{p}_2 = \dfrac{30}{55} = 0.5455$. The pooled proportion is $\hat{p} =$

$\dfrac{52+30}{65+55} = 0.6833$, and $SE = \sqrt{\hat{p}(1-\hat{p})\left(\dfrac{1}{65} + \dfrac{1}{55}\right)} = 0.08523$. The test statistic is therefore $z =$

$\dfrac{0.8 - 0.5455}{SE} = 2.99$, for which $P = 0.0028$. CONCLUDE: We have strong evidence that there is
a difference in success rates between urban/suburban students and rural/small-town students.

21.27: PLAN: Let p_1 be the proportion of women who succeed, and let p_2 be that proportion of men who succeed. We test $H_0 : p_1 = p_2$ vs. $H_a : p_1 \neq p_2$. SOLVE: The smallest count is 11, so the significance test should be safe. We find $\hat{p}_1 = \dfrac{23}{34} = 0.6765$ and $\hat{p}_2 = \dfrac{60}{89} = 0.6742$. The pooled proportion is $\hat{p} = \dfrac{23+60}{34+89} = 0.6748$, and SE $= \sqrt{\hat{p}(1-\hat{p})\left(\dfrac{1}{34}+\dfrac{1}{89}\right)} = 0.09445$. The test statistic is therefore $z = \dfrac{0.6765-0.6742}{\text{SE}} = 0.02$, for which $P = 0.9840$. CONCLUDE: We have no evidence to support a conclusion that women's and men's success rates differ.

21.28: PLAN: We construct a 90% confidence interval for $p_1 - p_2$, as defined as in the solution to Exercise 21.26. SOLVE: The smallest count is 13, so the large-sample procedures are safe. Still, we will apply the plus four procedure: $\tilde{p}_1 = \dfrac{52+1}{65+2} = 0.7910$, $\tilde{p}_2 = \dfrac{30+1}{55+2} = 0.5439$, and the 90% confidence interval is $\tilde{p}_1 - \tilde{p}_2 \pm 1.645\sqrt{\dfrac{\tilde{p}_1(1-\tilde{p}_1)}{67}+\dfrac{\tilde{p}_2(1-\tilde{p}_2)}{57}} = 0.2471 \pm 0.1358 = 0.1113$ to 0.3829. Using the large-sample method, $\hat{p}_1 = \dfrac{52}{65} = 0.8$, and $\hat{p}_2 = \dfrac{30}{55} = 0.5455$, and the 90% confidence interval is $\hat{p}_1 - \hat{p}_2 \pm 1.645\sqrt{\dfrac{\hat{p}_1(1-\hat{p}_1)}{65}+\dfrac{\hat{p}_2(1-\hat{p}_2)}{55}} = 0.2545 \pm 0.13733 = 0.1172$ to 0.3918. CONCLUDE: We are 90% confident that the success rate for urban/suburban students is between about 11.4 and 38.3 percentage points higher than for rural/small-town students.

21.29: PLAN: We construct a 99% confidence interval for $p_1 - p_2$, where p_1 denotes the proportion of people on Chantix who abstained from smoking, and p_2 is the corresponding proportion for the placebo population. SOLVE: The sample counts are 155 and 61 (successes for treatment and control, respectively) and 197 and 283 (failures for the groups), so the large-sample procedures are safe. We will apply the plus four procedure: $\tilde{p}_1 = \dfrac{155+1}{352+2} = 0.4407$, $\tilde{p}_2 = \dfrac{61+1}{344+2} = 0.1792$, and the 99% confidence interval is $\tilde{p}_1 - \tilde{p}_2 \pm 2.576\sqrt{\dfrac{\tilde{p}_1(1-\tilde{p}_1)}{354}+\dfrac{\tilde{p}_2(1-\tilde{p}_2)}{346}} = 0.2615 \pm 0.0863 = 0.1752$ to 0.3478.

Using the large-sample method, $\hat{p}_1 = \dfrac{155}{352} = 0.4403$, and $\hat{p}_2 = \dfrac{61}{344} = 0.1773$, and the 99% confidence interval is $\hat{p}_1 - \hat{p}_2 \pm 2.576\sqrt{\dfrac{\hat{p}_1(1-\hat{p}_1)}{352}+\dfrac{\hat{p}_2(1-\hat{p}_2)}{344}} = 0.2630 \pm 0.0864 = 0.1766$ to 0.3494. CONCLUDE: We are 99% confident that the success rate for abstaining from smoking is between 17.5 and 34.8 percentage points higher for smokers using Chantix than for smokers on a placebo.

21.30: PLAN: Let p_1 be the proportion of deaths among African miners, and p_2 be the proportion among European miners. We test $H_0 : p_1 = p_2$ vs. $H_a : p_1 > p_2$, where, presumably, these hypotheses were determined before looking at the data. SOLVE: The smallest success/failure count is 7, so the conditions for a significance test are met. The sample proportions are $\hat{p}_1 = \dfrac{223}{33,809} = 0.006596$ and $\hat{p}_2 = \dfrac{7}{1541} = 0.004543$. The pooled proportion is $\hat{p} = \dfrac{223+7}{33,809+1541} = 0.006506$, and $SE = \sqrt{\hat{p}(1-\hat{p})\left(\dfrac{1}{33,809} + \dfrac{1}{1541}\right)} = 0.002094$. The test statistic is therefore $z = \dfrac{0.006596 - 0.004543}{SE} = 0.98$, for which $P = 0.1635$. CONCLUDE: We do not have enough evidence to conclude that the death rates are higher for European miners than for African miners.

21.31: PLAN: Let p_1 be the proportion of people that will reject an unfair offer from another person, and p_2 be the proportion for offers from a computer. We test $H_0 : p_1 = p_2$ vs. $H_a : p_1 > p_2$. SOLVE: All counts are greater than 5, so the conditions for a significance test are met. The sample proportions are $\hat{p}_1 = \dfrac{18}{38} = 0.4737$ and $\hat{p}_2 = \dfrac{6}{38} = 0.1579$. The pooled proportion is $\hat{p} = \dfrac{18+6}{38+38} = 0.3158$, and $SE = \sqrt{\hat{p}(1-\hat{p})\left(\dfrac{1}{38} + \dfrac{1}{38}\right)} = 0.1066$. The test statistic is therefore $z = \dfrac{0.4737 - 0.1579}{SE}$ $(0.4737 - 0.1579)/SE = 2.96$, for which $P = 0.0015$. CONCLUDE: There is very strong evidence that people are more likely to reject an unfair offer from another person than from a computer.

21.32: STATE: Is there evidence of a difference in the proportion of women with a family history of breast cancer between the treatment and control groups? PLAN: With p_1 the proportion for the treatment population, and p_2 the proportion for control population, we test $H_0 : p_1 = p_2$ vs. $H_a : p_1 \neq p_2$. SOLVE: All counts are large enough to use the significance testing procedure safely. $\hat{p}_1 = \dfrac{3396}{19,541} = 0.1738$, $\hat{p}_2 = \dfrac{4929}{29294} = 0.1683$, and $\hat{p} = \dfrac{3,396+4,929}{19,541+29,294} = 0.1705$. Hence, $SE = \sqrt{\hat{p}(1-\hat{p})\left(\dfrac{1}{19,541} + \dfrac{1}{29,294}\right)} = 0.00347$. The test statistic is therefore $z = \dfrac{0.1738 - 0.1683}{SE} = 1.58$, for which $P = 0.1142$. CONCLUDE: We do not have enough evidence to reject the null hypothesis. Comparing treatment and control groups, there is little evidence of a difference in proportions of women with family history of breast cancer.

21.33: Let p_1 and p_2 be (respectively) the proportions of mice ready to breed in good acorn years and bad acorn years. We give a 90% confidence interval for $p_1 - p_2$. SOLVE: One count is only 7, and the guidelines for using the large-sample method call for all counts to be at least 10, so we use the plus-four method. We have $\tilde{p}_1 = \dfrac{54+1}{72+2} = 0.7432$, and $\tilde{p}_2 = \dfrac{10+1}{17+2} = 0.5789$, so

the plus-four 90% confidence interval is $\tilde{p}_1 - \tilde{p}_2 \pm 1.645 \sqrt{\dfrac{\tilde{p}_1(1-\tilde{p}_1)}{74} + \dfrac{\tilde{p}_2(1-\tilde{p}_2)}{19}} = 0.1643 \pm$

$0.2042 = -0.0399$ to 0.3685. CONCLUDE: We are 90% confident that the proportion of mice ready to breed in good acorn years is between 0.04 lower than and 0.37 higher than the proportion in bad acorn years.

21.34: PLAN: Let p_1 and p_2 be (respectively) the proportions of preschool and non-preschool populations that require social services. We test $H_0 : p_1 = p_2$ vs. $H_a : p_1 < p_2$, and find a 95% confidence interval for $p_2 - p_1$. SOLVE: All counts are large enough for both a significance test and a large-sample confidence interval. We find $\hat{p}_1 = \dfrac{38}{62} = 0.6129$, $\hat{p}_2 = \dfrac{49}{61} = 0.8033$, and $\hat{p} =$

$\dfrac{38+49}{62+61} = 0.7073$. Hence, SE $= \sqrt{\hat{p}(1-\hat{p})\left(\dfrac{1}{62} + \dfrac{1}{61}\right)} = 0.08205$. The test statistic is therefore z

$= \dfrac{0.6129-0.8033}{SE} = -2.32$, which yields $P = 0.0102$. Now $\tilde{p}_1 = 0.6094$ and $\tilde{p}_2 = 0.7937$. A plus-

four 95% confidence interval for the difference $p_2 - p_1$ is then given by $\tilde{p}_2 - \tilde{p}_1 \pm$

$1.96 \sqrt{\dfrac{\tilde{p}_1(1-\tilde{p}_1)}{64} + \dfrac{\tilde{p}_2(1-\tilde{p}_2)}{63}} = 0.1843 \pm 0.1558 = 0.0285$ to 0.3401. If we use the large sample

method, we obtain $\hat{p}_2 - \hat{p}_1 \pm 1.96 \sqrt{\dfrac{\hat{p}_1(1-\hat{p}_1)}{62} + \dfrac{\hat{p}_2(1-\hat{p}_2)}{61}} = 0.1904 \pm 0.1570 = 0.0334$ to

0.3474. CONCLUDE: The sample gives strong evidence that the preschool population has less need for social services than the non-preschool population. We are 95% confident that these proportions differ by between 0.03 and 0.34.

21.35: (a) This is an experiment because the researchers assigned subjects to the groups being compared. (b) PLAN: Let p_1 and p_2 be (respectively) the proportions that have an RV infection for the HL+ group and control group. We test $H_0 : p_1 = p_2$ vs. $H_a : p_1 < p_2$. SOLVE: We have

large enough counts to use large-sample significance testing procedure safely. Now $\hat{p}_1 = \dfrac{49}{49+67}$

$= 0.4224$, $\hat{p}_2 = \dfrac{49}{49+47} = 0.5104$, and $\hat{p} = \dfrac{49+49}{116+96} = 0.4623$. Hence,

SE $= \sqrt{\hat{p}(1-\hat{p})\left(\dfrac{1}{116} + \dfrac{1}{96}\right)} = 0.0688$. The test statistic is therefore $z = \dfrac{0.4224-0.5104}{SE} = -1.28$,

for which $P = 0.1003$. CONCLUDE: We do not have enough evidence to reject the null hypothesis; there is little evidence to conclude that the proportion of HL+ users with a rhinovirus infection is less than that for non-HL+ users.

21.36 and 21.37 are Web-based exercises.

Chapter 22 Solutions

Test Yourself Exercise Solutions contain only answers or sketches of answers. All of these problems are similar to ones found in Chapters 18–21, for which the solutions in this manual provide more detail.

22.1: (c) The margin of error is $2.056(9.3)/\sqrt{27} = 3.7$.

22.2: The sample has to be an SRS taken from the population. Also, the sample should be free of outliers. The SRS condition is important for the validity of the procedure.

22.3: (b) $t = 2.023$, df $= 13$.

22.4: A 99% confidence interval is given by –2.79 to 14.21 micrometers.

22.5: (d) Our estimate is $\hat{p} = 1926/7028 = 0.274$.

22.6: (a) Similarly, our estimate is $\hat{p} = 1020/6889 = 0.148$.

22.7: (d) The standard error is $SE = \sqrt{\dfrac{0.148(1-0.148)}{6889} + \dfrac{0.274(1-0.274)}{7028}} = 0.0068$.

22.8: (c) The margin of error is $2.576(0.0068) = 0.0175$.

22.9: (a) The standard error is 0.0124. (b) A 95% confidence interval is 0.336 to 0.384.

22.10: (b) The margin of error is $1.972(2.5)/\sqrt{200} = 0.349$.

22.11: (b) The margin of error is $2.005(3.2)/\sqrt{55} = 0.865$.

22.12: (d) $t = \dfrac{2.35 - 1.20}{\sqrt{\dfrac{2.5^2}{200} + \dfrac{3.2^2}{55}}} = 2.47$.

22.13: (a) df is the lesser of $(55 - 1)$ and $(200 - 1)$.

22.14: (a) $t = 10.417$. Note that it is surprising that the two sample standard deviations are so small, suggesting that wait times for next mating times for butterflies are remarkably consistent with very little variation.

22.15: With such large samples, t procedures are reasonable.

22.16: (b) With df $= 134$ (the lesser of $135 - 1$ and $162 - 1$), using Table C with df $= 100$, $t^* = 1.660$. With software, $t^* = 1.654$. Using software df, the margin of error is $1.654(26.09)/\sqrt{162} = 3.39$.

22.17: (b) With SE $= \sqrt{\dfrac{26.09^2}{162}+\dfrac{6.69^2}{135}} = 2.129$, the margin of error is $t^*(SE) = (1.656)(2.129) =$ 3.52. The point estimate is $11.4 - 6.7 = 4.7$. Hence, a 90% confidence interval is given by $4.7 \pm$ 3.52 minutes.

22.18: We test $H_0 : \mu_M = \mu_F$ against $H_a : \mu_M < \mu_F$. With SE $= \sqrt{\dfrac{26.09^2}{162}+\dfrac{6.69^2}{135}} = 2.129$, the test statistic is $t = \dfrac{11.4-6.7}{2.129} = 2.208$. With df $= 134$, $P = 0.014$. There is very strong evidence that female mice have mean endurance greater than that of male mice.

22.19: (c) Plus four confidence intervals are reliable for samples of 5 or more in each group.

22.20: (c) Use $p^* = 0.5$ and $z^* = 2.576$.

2.21: (b) $\hat{p} = 225/757 = 0.297$.

2.22: (b) $\sqrt{\dfrac{0.297(1-0.297)}{757}} = 0.0166$.

22.23: (b) $0.297 \pm 1.645(0.017)$

22.24: (a) Subjects (babies) were not assigned to groups being compared.

22.25: (c) It seems reasonable that the researchers suspect that VLBW babies are less likely to graduate from high school.

22.26: (b) $\hat{p} = \dfrac{179+193}{242+233} = 0.78$.

22.27: (b) $z = \dfrac{0.7397-0.8283}{\sqrt{\hat{p}(1-\hat{p})\left(\dfrac{1}{242}+\dfrac{1}{233}\right)}} = -2.34$.

22.28: (b) $t = \dfrac{87.6-94.7}{\sqrt{\dfrac{15.1^2}{113}+\dfrac{14.9^2}{106}}} = -3.50$.

22.29: (d) $t = \dfrac{86.2-89.8}{\sqrt{\dfrac{13.4^2}{38}+\dfrac{14^2}{54}}} = -1.25$, and the test is two-sided.

22.30: (a) The 95% confidence interval is computed as $0.379 \pm 1.96\sqrt{\dfrac{0.379(1-0.379)}{378}}$.

22.31: (b) $z = \dfrac{0.379 - 0.41}{\sqrt{0.41(1 - 0.41)/348}} = -1.18$, so $P = 0.1190$.

22.32: (a) Random chance easily explains the observed difference.

22.33: $0.58 \pm 1.645\sqrt{\dfrac{0.58(1 - 0.58)}{634}} = 0.58 \pm 0.03 = 0.55$ to 0.61. A plus four interval will agree to three decimal places and would also be appropriate.

22.34: $(0.45 - 0.23) \pm 1.645\sqrt{\dfrac{0.45(1 - 0.45)}{314} + \dfrac{0.23(1 - 0.23)}{567}} = 0.22 \pm 0.055 = 0.165$ to 0.275. The plus four method would also be appropriate, and will agree to three decimal places.

22.35: $H_0 : p_b = p_w$ vs. $H_a : p_b \neq p_w$. With $\hat{p} = [0.72(634) + 0.68(567)]/(634 + 567) = 0.701$,

$z = \dfrac{0.72 - 0.68}{\sqrt{0.70(1 - 0.70)\left(\dfrac{1}{634} + \dfrac{1}{567}\right)}} = 1.51$ and $P = 2P(Z > 1.51) = 0.131$. There is little evidence of a difference between black and white young people in the proportion believing that rap music videos contain too many references to sex.

22.36: (c) $193 \pm 2.060\dfrac{68}{\sqrt{26}} = 165.5$ to 220.5.

22.37: $t = \dfrac{193 - 174}{\sqrt{\dfrac{68^2}{26} + \dfrac{44^2}{23}}} = 1.174$, and df $= 22$, the lesser of $23 - 1 = 22$ and $26 - 1 = 25$.

22.38: (b) $(193 - 174) \pm 2.074\sqrt{\dfrac{68^2}{26} + \dfrac{44^2}{23}} = 19 \pm 33.6 = -14.6$ to 52.6

22.39: We must assume that each sample is an SRS taken from its respective populations (clinic dogs and pet dogs). We must also assume that the populations (cholesterol levels of pet dogs and cholesterol levels of clinic dogs) are Normal.

22.40: The problem description makes clear that the sample of clinic dogs is not an SRS. The sample of pets also is not likely to represent an SRS.

22.41: Two-sample test for difference in means.

22.42: Large-sample or plus four confidence interval for proportion.

22.43: If the sample can be viewed as an SRS, a *t* confidence interval for a population mean.

22.44: This is the entire population of Chicago Cubs players. Statistical inference is not appropriate.

22.45: Matched pairs *t* test or confidence interval.

22.46: (a) Two-sample test or confidence interval for difference of proportions. (b) Two-sample test or confidence interval for difference of means. (c) Two-sample test or confidence interval for difference in proportions.

22.47: The response rate for the survey was only about 20% (427/2100 = 0.203), which might make the conclusions unreliable.

22.48: (a) This is a matched-pairs situation: the responses of each subject under both conditions (control and treatment) are not independent. (b) We need to know the standard deviation of the differences, not the two individual sample standard deviations.

22.49: Each of a monkey's six trials are not independent. If a monkey prefers silence, it will almost certainly spend more time in the silent arm of the cage each time it is tested.

22.50: $\hat{p} = 80/80 = 1$, and the margin of error for 95% confidence (or any level of confidence) is 0: $z^* \sqrt{\dfrac{(1)(1-1)}{n}} = 0$. Almost certainly, if more trials were performed, a rat would eventually make a mistake, so the actual success rate is less than 1. (b) The plus-four estimate is $\tilde{p} = 82/84 = 0.9762$, and the plus-four 95% confidence interval is $\tilde{p} \pm z^* \sqrt{\dfrac{\tilde{p}(1-\tilde{p})}{n+4}} = 0.9762 \pm 0.0326 = 0.9436$ to 1.0088. Ignoring the upper limit, we are 95% confident that the actual success rate is 0.9436 or greater.

22.51: (a) PLAN: We will find a 99% confidence interval for $p_2 - p_1$, where p_1 is the proportion of subjects on Gardasin that get cancer, and p_2 is the corresponding proportion for the control group. SOLVE: We assume that we have SRSs from each population. Because there were no cases of cervical cancer in the Gardasil group, we should use the plus-four procedure. We have $\tilde{p}_1 = \dfrac{0+1}{8487+2} = 0.000118$, and $\tilde{p}_2 = \dfrac{32+1}{8460+2} = 0.003900$. A 99% confidence interval for $p_2 - p_1$ is then given by $\tilde{p}_2 - \tilde{p}_1 \pm 2.576 \sqrt{\dfrac{\tilde{p}_1(1-\tilde{p}_1)}{8489} + \dfrac{\tilde{p}_2(1-\tilde{p}_2)}{8462}} = 0.003782 \pm 0.001772 = 0.0020$ to 0.0056. (b) PLAN: Now let p_1 denote the proportion in the Gardasil group with genital warts, and let p_2 be the corresponding proportion for the control group. We find a 99% confidence interval for $p_2 - p_1$. SOLVE: Because we have fewer than 10 "successes" in the Gardasil group, conditions for using the large-sample interval are not met. However, we can use the plus four interval. We find that $\tilde{p}_1 = 0.000253$ and $\tilde{p}_2 = 0.011644$. A 99% confidence interval for $p_2 - p_1$ is then 0.0082 to 0.0145. (c) CONCLUDE: Gardasil is seen to be effective in reducing the risk of both cervical cancer (by between 0.0020 and 0.0056, with 99% confidence) and genital warts (by between 0.0082 and 0.0145, with 99% confidence).

22.52: PLAN: We test $H_0 : \mu = 12$ vs. $H_a : \mu > 12$, where μ denotes the mean age at first word, measured in months. SOLVE: We regard the sample as an SRS; a stemplot (not shown) shows that the data are right-skewed with a high outlier (26 months). If we proceed with the t procedures in spite of this, we find $\bar{x} = 13$ and $s = 4.9311$ months. Hence, $t = \dfrac{13-12}{4.9311/\sqrt{20}} = 0.907$, with df $= 19$, and $P = 0.1879$. Note: If you delete the outlier mentioned above, $\bar{x} = 12.3158$, $s = 3.9729$, and $t = 0.346$, yielding $P = 0.3665$. CONCLUDE: We cannot conclude that the mean age at first word is greater than one year.

22.53: PLAN: We test $H_0 : \mu_1 = \mu_2$ vs. $H_a : \mu_1 < \mu_2$, where μ_1 is the mean number of new leaves on plants from the control population, and μ_2 is the mean for the nitrogen population. SOLVE: With $\bar{x}_1 = 13.2857$, $\bar{x}_2 = 15.6250$, $s_1 = 2.0587$, $s_2 = 1.6850$, $n_1 = 7$ and $n_2 = 8$, we find SE $= \sqrt{\dfrac{2.0587^2}{7} + \dfrac{1.6850^2}{8}} = 0.9800$ and $t = \dfrac{13.3857 - 15.6250}{SE} = -2.387$. With Option 2, df $= 6$ and $P = 0.0271$. Or, using Option 1, df $= 11.66$ and $P = 0.0175$. CONCLUDE: We have strong evidence that nitrogen increases the formation of new leaves.

22.54: PLAN: We give a 90% confidence interval for μ, the mean age at first word, measured in months. SOLVE: See results from Exercise 22.52. For df $= 19$, $t^* = 1.729$, so the 90% confidence interval is $13 \pm 1.729 \dfrac{4.9311}{\sqrt{20}} = 11.09$ to 14.91 months. CONCLUDE: We are 90% confident that the mean age at first word for normal children is between 11 and 15 months.

22.55: PLAN: Do a two-sided test because we have no advance claim about the direction of the difference: $H_0 : \mu_1 = \mu_2$ vs. $H_a : \mu_1 \neq \mu_2$. SOLVE: We view the data as coming from two SRSs; the distributions show no strong departures from Normality. The means and standard deviations of the lightness scores are: $\bar{x}_1 = 48.9513$ and $s_1 = 0.2154$ (cotton) and $\bar{x}_2 = 41.6488$ and $s_2 = 0.3922$ (ramie). Ramie is darker, having a lower score for lightness. We find SE $= 0.1582$ and $t = 46.16$. With either df $= 7$ or df $= 10.87$ (software), $P \approx 0$. CONCLUDE: There is overwhelming evidence that cotton is lighter than ramie.

22.56: (a) The design is shown below. (b) PLAN: We test $H_0 : \mu_B = \mu_C$ vs. $H_a : \mu_B \neq \mu_C$. SOLVE: We have $\bar{x}_B = 41.2825$ and $s_B = 0.2550$, and $\bar{x}_C = 42.4925$ and $s_C = 0.2939$; $n_B = n_C = 8$. Hence, SE $= 0.1376$ and $t = \dfrac{\bar{x}_B - \bar{x}_C}{SE} = -8.79$. With df $= 7$ (or 13.73 from software), $P < 0.001$. Using software, with df $= 13.73$, $P = 0.0000$ to four places. There is overwhelming evidence that method B gives darker color on average. However, the magnitude of this difference may be too small to be important in practice.

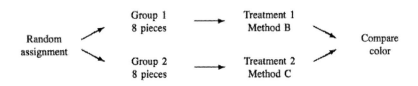

22.57: PLAN: We test $H_0 : \mu_1 = \mu_2$ vs. $H_a : \mu_1 \neq \mu_2$. **SOLVE:** We are told that the samples may be regarded as SRSs from their respective populations. Back-to-back stemplots show that t procedures are reasonably safe, since both distributions are only slightly skewed, with no outliers, and with fairly large sample sizes. We have $\bar{x}_1 = 4.1769$, $s_1 = 2.0261$ and $n_1 = 65$ (parent allows drinking) and $\bar{x}_2 = 4.5517$ and $s_2 = 2.4251$ and $n_2 = 29$ (parent does not allow drinking). Hence, SE = 0.5157 and $t = \dfrac{\bar{x}_1 - \bar{x}_2}{\text{SE}} = -0.727$. This is very close to zero, so we will certainly not reject the null hypothesis. Indeed, with df = 46.19 (software), $P = 0.47$. **CONCLUDE:** There is no significant difference in the mean number of drinks between female students with a parent that allows drinking and those whose parents do not allow drinking.

Parent allows drinking		No parent allows drinking
00000	1	000
55555550000	2	0
5500000000000	3	00000055
500000000000	4	000000
00000000	5	000
5000000	6	0
00000	7	000
00	8	0
0	9	00
0	10	0

22.58: PLAN: We give a 95% confidence interval for p, the proportion of female students with at least one parent that allows drinking. **SOLVE:** We are told that the sample represents an SRS. Large sample methods may be used. With $\hat{p} = 0.6915$, we have SE = 0.04764, so the margin of error is 1.96SE = 0.09337, and the interval is 0.5981 to 0.7849. **Note:** *Using a plus-four estimate, the interval is 0.5916 to 0.7757.* **CONCLUDE:** With 95% confidence, the proportion of female students who have at least one parent that allows drinking is 0.598 to 0.785 (or 0.592 to 0.776).

22.59: (a) Stemplots are provided. The diabetic potentials appear to be larger. (b) **PLAN:** We test $H_0 : \mu_1 = \mu_2$ vs. $H_a : \mu_1 \neq \mu_2$, where μ_1 is the mean potential for diabetics, and μ_2 is the mean for the normal population. **SOLVE:** We assume we have two SRSs; the distributions appear to be safe for t procedures. With $\bar{x}_1 = 13.0896$, $\bar{x}_2 = 9.5222$, $s_1 = 4.8391$, $s_2 = 2.5765$, $n_1 = 24$ and $n_2 = 18$, we find SE = 1.1595 and $t = 3.077$. With Option 2, df = 17 and $0.005 < P < 0.01$. Or, using Option 1, df = 36.6, and $P = 0.0040$. **CONCLUDE:** We have strong evidence that the electric potential in diabetic mice is greater than the potential in normal mice. (c) If we remove the outlier, the diabetic mouse statistics change: $\bar{x}_1 = 13.6130$, $s_1 = 4.1959$, $n_1 = 23$. Now SE = 1.065 and $t = 3.841$. With df = 16, $0.001 < P < 0.002$. With df = 37.15, $P = 0.0005$. **CONCLUDE:** With the outlier removed, the evidence that diabetic mice have higher mean electric potential is even stronger.

Diabetic		Normal
1	0	
	0	
	0	4
7	0	6777
988	0	8888999
100000	1	00
3	1	233
5444	1	4
76	1	
9988	1	
	2	
2	2	

22.60: (a) PLAN: We want to compare the proportions p_1 (microwave crackers that show checking) and p_2 (control crackers that show checking). We can do this either by testing hypotheses or with a confidence interval, but since the "microwave checked" count is only 3, significance tests are not appropriate. We will use the plus-four procedure and construct a confidence interval for $p_1 - p_2$. SOLVE: We find that $\tilde{p}_1 = \dfrac{3+1}{65+2} = 0.0597$ and $\tilde{p}_2 = \dfrac{57+1}{65+2} = 0.8657$. Hence, SE $= \sqrt{\dfrac{\tilde{p}_1(1-\tilde{p}_1)}{67} + \dfrac{\tilde{p}_2(1-\tilde{p}_2)}{67}} = 0.05073$, and a 95% confidence interval is given by $\tilde{p}_1 - \tilde{p}_2 \pm 1.96(0.0507) = -0.9054$ to -0.7066. CONCLUDE: We are 95% confident that microwaving reduces the percentage of checked crackers by between 70.7% and 90.5%.
(b) PLAN: We want to compare μ_1 and μ_2, the mean breaking pressures of microwaved and control crackers. We test $H_0 : \mu_1 = \mu_2$ vs. $H_a : \mu_1 \neq \mu_2$ and construct a 95% confidence interval for $\mu_1 - \mu_2$. SOLVE: We assume the data can be considered SRSs from the two populations, and that the population distributions are not far from Normal. Now SE $= 9.0546$ and $t = 6.914$, so the P-value is very small, regardless of whether we use df $= 19$ or df $= 33.27$. A 95% confidence interval for the difference in mean breaking pressures between these cracker types is 43.65 to 81.55 psi (using df $= 19$ and $t^* = 2.093$), or 44.18 to 81.02 psi (using df $= 33.27$ and $t^* = 2.0339$). CONCLUDE: There is very strong evidence that microwaving crackers changes their mean breaking strength. We are 95% confident that microwaving crackers increases their mean breaking strength by between 43.65 and 81.55 psi.

22.61: PLAN: We give a 95% confidence interval for μ, the mean date on which the tripod falls through the ice. SOLVE: We assume that the data can be viewed as an SRS of fall-through times, and that the distribution is roughly Normal. We find $n = 91$, $\bar{x} = 15.3736$ and $s = 5.9789$ days. Using df $= 90$, a 95% confidence interval is given by 14.13 to 16.62 days. CONCLUDE: We are 95% confident that the mean number of days for the tripod to fall through the ice is 14.13 days to 16.62 days from April 20 or between May 3 and May 5.

22.62: Two of the counts are too small to perform a significance test safely.

22.63: (a) "SEM" stands for "standard error of the mean"; SEM $= s/\sqrt{n}$. (b) Two-sample t-tests were done, because there are two separate, independent groups of mice. (c) The observed differences between the two groups of mice were so large that it would be unlikely to occur by chance alone if the two groups were the same in average. Specifically, if the two population means were the same, if we repeated the experiment, an observed difference in sample means as large as this would occur by chance alone less than 0.5% of the time, which is less often than the 5% level of significance criterion. This is strong evidence that the two population means differ. We conclude that both the insulin and glucose levels in blood plasma of P2-/- mice and wild type mice differ.

22.64: The group means are $\bar{x}_1 = 5.9$ (insulin), $\bar{x}_2 = 0.75$ (glucose) ng/ml, and the standard deviations are $s_1 = 0.9\sqrt{10} = 2.85$ and $s_2 = 0.2\sqrt{10} = 0.632$ ng/ml. PLAN: We test $H_0 : \mu_1 = \mu_2$ vs. $H_a : \mu_1 \neq \mu_2$. SOLVE: The estimated standard error of the difference in sample means is $SE = \sqrt{0.9^2 + 0.2^2} = 0.922$, so $t = \dfrac{5.9 - 0.75}{SE} = 5.59$. With either df = 9 or df = 9.89, $P < 0.001$. CONCLUDE: The evidence is even stronger than the paper claimed.

Chapter 23 Solutions

23.1: (a) The table provided gives percentages in each category. As an example, there are 978 surveyed students from the University Park campus. Of these, the proportion of University Park campus students that do not use Facebook is $68/978 = 0.0695$, which rounds to 0.070 and is represented as 7% in the table. (b) The bar graph reveals that students on the main campus are much more likely to use Facebook at least daily, while commonwealth campus students are more likely not to use it at all.

	Univ. Park	Common-wealth
Do not use Facebook	7.0%	28.3%
Several times a month or less	5.6%	8.7%
At least once a week	22.0%	17.9%
At least once a day	65.4%	45.0%

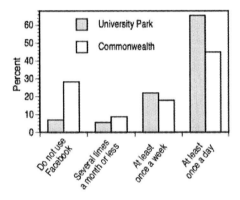

23.2: (a) For example, among those that played video games, the percentage that got A's and B's is $736/(736 + 450 + 193) = 736/1379 = 53.4\%$. The table below summarizes. The accompanying bar graph reveals a larger percentage of A's and B's, and a smaller percentage of D's and F's in the group of boys that played video games.

	A's and B's	C's	D's and F's
Played games	53.4%	32.6%	14.0%
Never played games	47.8%	33.6%	18.6%

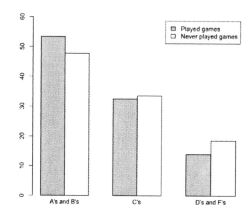

(b) We can't conclude that playing video games "causes" improved grades… this is an observational study so the boys who play video games may differ from those who do not in many ways. For example, perhaps boys who play video games live in households with higher income, and therefore have access to various resources (better schools, tutoring, etc.) that people with lower incomes do not have access to.

23.3: (a) To test $H_0 : p_1 = p_2$ vs. $H_a : p_1 \neq p_2$ for the proportions not using Facebook, we have $\hat{p}_1$ = 0.0695 (as illustrated in solution to Exercise 23.1) and $\hat{p}_2$ = 0.2834. The pooled proportion is $\hat{p} = \dfrac{68 + 248}{978 + 875} = 0.1705$, and the standard error is SE = 0.01750, so $z = -12.22$, for which P is close to zero. We conclude that the proportion of students using Facebook differs between these two campus locations   (b) To test $H_0 : p_1 = p_2$ vs. $H_a : p_1 \neq p_2$ for the proportions that use Facebook at least weekly, we have $\hat{p}_1$ = 0.2198 and $\hat{p}_2$ = 0.1794. The pooled proportion is $\hat{p}$ = 0.2008 and the standard error is SE = 0.01864, so $z = 2.17$, for which $P = 0.0300$. There is strong evidence that the proportion of students using Facebook at least weekly differs between these two campus locations. (c) If we did four individual tests, we would not know how confident we could be in all four results when taken together.

23.4: (a) For the Junior College sample, $\hat{p} = \dfrac{87}{87 + 43} = 0.669$, so the standard error is SE = $\sqrt{\dfrac{0.669(1 - 0.669)}{130}} = 0.041$. Hence, a 95% confidence interval for the proportion of all Junior College graduates that think astrology is not at all scientific is $0.669 \pm 1.96(0.041) = 0.589$ to 0.749, or 58.9% to 74.9%. The three confidence intervals are displayed:

Degree held	$\hat{p}$	SE	95% confidence Interval
Junior College	0.669	0.041	58.9% to 74.9%
Bachelor's	0.776	0.026	72.5% to 82.7%
Graduate	0.799	0.034	71.2% to 84.6%

(b) Before we take a random sample, there's a 95% chance that the sample we collect will lead to a confidence interval which captures the true, unknown proportion of people that believe astrology is not at all scientific. As we construct more confidence intervals, each based on a different random sample, the chance that at least one of them fails to capture the parameter of interest increases. The 95% confidence level specified refers to the construction of only one interval.

23.5: (a) Expected counts are below observed counts in the table provided. For example, for students at the Commonwealth campus using Facebook Monthly, the expected count is $\frac{(131)(627)}{1537} = 53.44$. The expected counts add up to the same values as the observed counts. (b) We find that Commonwealth students actually use Facebook less than once weekly more often than we would expect. Also, Commonwealth students use Facebook daily less often than we would expect.

Minitab output

	UPark	Cwlth	Total
Monthly	55	76	131
	77.56	53.44	
Weekly	215	157	372
	220.25	151.75	
Daily	640	394	1034
	612.19	421.81	
Total	910	627	1537

23.6: (a) The expected counts are shown in the table below. For example, for boys that play video games, the expected count earning A's and B's is $\frac{(1379)(941)}{1808} = 717.72$. We see that the expected cell counts add across rows or down columns to agree with the observed row and column totals. For example, $717.72 + 453.06 + 208.22 = 1379$, the total number of boys that play video games.

Minitab output

	AandB	C	DandF	Total
Plays	736	450	193	1379
	717.72	453.06	208.22	
Never plays	205	144	80	429
	223.28	140.94	64.78	
Total	941	594	273	1808

(b) By informal examination, there appear to be somewhat large differences between observed counts and expected counts, especially in a few of the cells. For example, for boys that get D's and F's and never play video games, the difference is $80 - 64.78 = 15.22$, which is fairly large relative to the expected cell count of 64.78.

23.7: (a) All expected counts are well above 5 (the smallest is 53.44). (b) We test H_0: there is no relationship between setting and Facebook use vs. H_a: There is a relationship between campus and Facebook use. Using software, we have $\chi^2 = 19.489$ and $P < 0.0005$. (c) The largest contributions come from the first row, reflecting the fact that monthly use is lower among University Park students and higher among commonwealth students.

23.8: (a) Inspecting Figure 23.4, we see that all expected cell counts are more than 5, and all individual observed cell counts are at least 1, so conditions required for use of the chi-square test are satisfied. (b) $\chi^2 = 6.739$ and $P = 0.034$, by inspection of the output. (c) There is strong evidence of an association between grades and video game playing. In the output, we see that of boys that played video games, more than expected earned A's and B's, while fewer than expected earned D's and F's. Conversely, for boys that do not play games, fewer than expected earned A's and B's, and more than expected earned D's and F's. For example, we expected 223.28 "never play" boys to earn A's and B's, while we observed only 205.

23.9: PLAN: We will carry out a chi-square test for association between education level and opinion about astrology. We test H_0: There is no relationship between education level and astrology opinion vs. H_a: There is some relationship between education level and astrology opinion. SOLVE: Examining the output provided in Figure 23.5, we see that all expected cell counts are greater than 5 and all observed cell counts are at least 1, so conditions for use of the chi-square test are satisfied. We see that $\chi^2 = 7.244$ and $P = 0.027$. CONCLUDE: There is strong evidence of an association between education level and opinion of astrology. Examining the table, we note that for people with Graduate degrees, more than expected felt that astrology is not scientific, while fewer than expected believed that astrology is scientific. For people with a Junior College degree, more than expected believed that astrology is scientific, and fewer than expected felt that astrology is not scientific.

23.10: PLAN: We will carry out a chi-square test for association between age and reliance on a cell phone. We test H_0: There is no relationship between age and reliance on a cell phone vs. H_a: There is some relationship between age and reliance on a cell phone. SOLVE: Minitab output is provided. Examining the output, we see that all expected cell counts are greater than 5 and all observed cell counts are at least 1, so conditions for use of the chi-square test are satisfied. We see that $\chi^2 = 132.399$ on df $= 3$, and $P = 0.000$ to three decimal places. CONCLUDE: We have strong evidence that there is a relationship between age and reliance on cell phone. Specifically, the table shows that 48% of the youngest age group rely entirely on a cell phone, while that proportion drops to 20.9% for the next age group, then to 11.3%, and then to only 4.3% for the over-65 group.

```
Minitab output
          Landline CellOnly   Total
Age1829      108       96      204
           161.14    42.86
Age3049      264       70      334
           263.83    70.17
Age5064      202       26      228
           180.10    47.90
Age65up      178        8      186
           146.92    39.08
Total        752      200      952

ChiSq =   17.526 + 65.897 +
           0.000 +  0.000 +
           2.663 + 10.012 +
           6.573 + 24.713 = 127.385
df = 3, p = 0.000
```

23.11: (a) df $= (r - 1)(c - 1) = (3 - 1)(2 - 1) = 2$. (b) The largest critical value shown for df $= 2$ is 15.20; since the computed value (19.489) is greater than this, we conclude that $P < 0.0005$. (c) With $r = 4$ and $c = 2$, the appropriate degrees of freedom would be df $= 3$.

23.12: (a) df $= (r - 1)(c - 1) = (2 - 1)(3 - 1) = 2$. (b) The computed value (6.739) is between the table values 5.99 and 7.38, we conclude that $0.025 < P < 0.05$, which is consistent with output's reported $P = 0.034$. (c) Under the null hypothesis of no association, the mean value of χ^2 is df $= 2$. Our computed value is larger than this. The small P-value suggests that random chance does not easily explain the larger than expected value of χ^2.

23.13: We test $H_0 : p_1 = p_2 = p_3 = \dfrac{1}{3}$ vs. H_a: Not all three are equally likely. There were 53 bird strikes in all, so the expected counts are each $53 \times \dfrac{1}{3} = 17.67$. The chi-square statistic is then

$$\chi^2 = \sum \frac{(\text{observed count} - 17.67)^2}{17.67} = \frac{(31-17.67)^2}{17.67} + \frac{(14-17.67)^2}{17.67} + \frac{(8-17.67)^2}{17.67} = 10.06 +$$

$0.76 + 5.29 = 16.11$. The degrees of freedom are df $= 2$. From Table D, $\chi^2 = 16.11$ falls beyond the 0.005 critical value, so $P < 0.005$. There is very strong evidence that the three tilts differ. The data and terms of the statistic show that more birds than expected strike the vertical window and fewer than expected strike the 40-degree window.

23.14: (a) If all days were equally likely, we would have $p_1 = p_2 = ... = p_7 = \dfrac{1}{7}$, and we would expect 100 births on each day. (b) The chi-square statistic is then

$$\chi^2 = \frac{(84-100)^2}{100} + \frac{(110-100)^2}{100} + L + \frac{(72-100)^2}{100} = 19.12.$$ (c) The degrees of freedom are df $= 7 - 1 = 6$. From Table D, $\chi^2 = 19.12$ yields $0.0025 < P < 0.005$. Software gives $P = 0.004$. We have strong evidence that births are not spread evenly across the week.

23.15: Letting p_1 denote the proportion of people aged 16 to 29 not wearing seatbelts, and similarly defining p_2 and p_3 for the other age groups, we test $H_0 : p_1 = p_2 = p_3$, vs. H_a: Not all proportions are equal. The details of the computation are shown below. The expected counts are found by multiplying the expected frequencies by 803 (the total number of observations).

	Expected Frequency	Observed Count	Expected Count	$O - E$	$\dfrac{(O-E)^2}{E}$
16 to 29	0.328	401	263.384	137.616	71.9032
30 to 59	0.594	382	476.982	−94.982	18.9139
60 or older	0.078	20	62.634	−42.634	29.0203
		803			119.8374

The difference is significant: $\chi^2 = 119.84$, df = 2, and $P < 0.0005$ (using software, $P = 0.000$ to three decimal places). The largest contribution to the statistic comes from the youngest age group, which is cited more frequently than we would have expected under the hypothesis of no association. The other two age groups, which are cited less frequently than would be expected, also have large contributions.

23.16: (a) 15/33 = 0.455, or 45.5% of subjects chose position 1. Similarly, the percentages for each position are: 15.2% for position 2, 6.1% for position 3, and 33.3% for position 4. (b) If subjects are equally likely to select any position, then we would expect 33/4 = 8.25 subjects in each position. (c) STATE: Are positions equally likely to be selected by subjects? PLAN: We test $H_0 : p_1 = p_2 = p_3 = p_4 = \dfrac{1}{4}$ vs. H_a: The four order selection probabilities are not equally likely. SOLVE: As computed above, we expect 8.25 subjects per cell under the null hypothesis, so all expected cell counts exceed 5. Also, we have at least one observation per cell. Hence, conditions for the chi-square test are satisfied. Now

$$\chi^2 = \frac{(15-8.25)^2}{8.25} + \frac{(5-8.25)^2}{8.25} + \frac{(2-8.25)^2}{8.25} + \frac{(11-8.25)^2}{8.25} = 12.45.$$ The degrees of freedom are df = 4 − 1 = 3. From Table D, $\chi^2 = 12.45$ yields $0.005 < P < 0.01$.

CONCLUDE: There is strong evidence that positions are not selected with equal probability — some positions are more likely to be selected than others. (d) We see that the largest contributions to χ^2 are from the first and fourth positions. In both cases we have more observations than expected, and in the second and third positions we have fewer observations than expected. Hence, there is evidence of *both* primacy and recency effects.

23.17: STATE: Are all 12 astrological signs equally likely? PLAN: We test
$H_0 : p_1 = p_2 = ... = p_{12} = \dfrac{1}{12}$ vs. H_a: The 12 astrological sign birth probabilities are not equally
likely. SOLVE: There are 1960 subjects in this sample. Under H_0, we expect $1960/12 =$
163.33 subjects per sign. Hence, all cells have expected counts greater than 5, and all cells have
at least one observation. A chi-square test is appropriate. Hence, $\chi^2 =$
$\dfrac{(164-163.33)^2}{163.33} + \dfrac{(152-163.33)^2}{163.33} + ... + \dfrac{(177-163.33)^2}{163.33} = 16.09$. With df $= 12 - 1 = 11$, using
Table D, $0.10 < P < 0.15$. CONCLUDE: There is little evidence that some astrological signs are
more likely in birth than others. That is, there is little to no support for a conclusion that
astrological signs are not equally likely.

23.18: (a) $295 + 655 + 239 + 363 = 1552$.

23.19: (b) $655/(655 + 916) = 655/1571 = 0.4169$.

23.20: (a) For 23- to 30-year-olds, the percentage is 26.5%.

23.21: (a) The expected cell count is $(1571)(1552)/4111 = 593.09$.

23.22: (c) The contribution of this cell to χ^2 is $(655 - 593.09)^2/593.09 = 6.46$.

23.23: (a) df $= (r - 1)(c - 1) = (4 - 1)(2 - 1) = 3$.

23.24: (b) This is the hypothesis of no association between "age" and "type of injury."

23.25: (b) This is the hypothesis of association between "age" and "type of injury."

23.26: (c) The largest entry in the table corresponding to df $= 3$ is 17.73.

23.27: (b) We assume that the sample is an SRS, or essentially an SRS from all weightlifting
injuries.

23.28: (a)–(b) STATE: We compare rates of success at smoking cessation in three groups.
PLAN: B denotes the Bupropion group, P the placebo group, and C the Chantix group. First,
we'll construct a confidence interval for the difference in success proportions between the
Bupropion group and the placebo group. Then, we'll conduct a test for equality of success rates.

SOLVE: The sample proportions are $\hat{p}_B = 0.2948$ and $\hat{p}_P = 0.1773$. The standard error is SE = 0.0325, so the large sample 95% confidence interval for $p_B - p_P$ is $\hat{p}_B - \hat{p}_P \pm 1.96\text{SE} = 0.1175 \pm 0.0637 = 0.0538$ to 0.1812. Now, to test $H_0: p_C = p_B = p_P$ vs. H_a: Not all proportions are equal, we carry out a Chi-square test. Note that all of the cell counts are more than 10, and trials are clearly independent, so such a test is appropriate. We have $\chi^2 = 139.16$, df = 2, and $P < 0.0005$ (from software, $P = 0.000$ to three places), so the evidence for a relationship between treatment (placebo, Bupropion, or Chantix) and cessation of smoking is overwhelming. Examining the output, we see that more Chantix users than expected and fewer placebo users than expected were successful. CONCLUDE: The treatments are not equally successful at helping people to quit smoking. The Chantix group, in particular has a higher success rate. We also conclude that the placebo and Bupropion success rates are not the same.

Minitab output

	Chantix	Bupropion	Placebo	Total
No smoke	155	97	61	313
	107.49	100.47	105.04	
Smoke	197	232	283	712
	244.51	228.53	238.96	
Total	352	329	344	1025

ChiSq = 20.999 + 0.120 + 18.465 +
        9.232 + 44.170 + 46.173 = 139.159

df = 2, p = 0.000

23.29: (a) The table below summarizes conditional distributions of opinion for each type of consumer. For example, there are $20 + 7 + 9 = 36$ buyers, so the proportion of buyers that think the quality of the recycled product is higher is $20/36 = 0.556$, or 55.6%.

	Think the quality of recycled product is		
	Higher	Same	Lower
Buyers	55.6%	19.4%	25.0%
Nonbuyers	29.9%	25.8%	44.3%

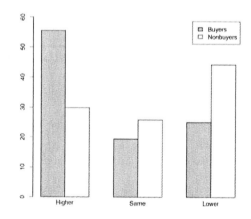

It seems that buyers of recycled products are more likely to feel that recycled products are of higher quality, while nonbuyers are more likely to feel that recycled products are of lower quality.

(b) We test H_0: No association between "opinion of quality" and "buyer status" vs. H_a: There is some association between buyer status and opinion of quality. All expected cell counts are more than 5, so the guidelines for the chi-square test are satisfied. We have $\chi^2 = 7.64$, df = 2, and $0.01 < P < 0.025$ There is strong evidence of an association between buyer status and opinion of quality.

```
Minitab output

             Better    Same    Lower    Total
Buyers         20        7        9        36
              13.26     8.66    14.08


Nonbuyers      29       25       43        97
              35.74    23.34    37.92

Total          49       32       52       133
```

(c) We see that there is a relationship between opinion of quality and whether somebody buys the recycled product. However, it is impossible to determine whether (i) prior opinion on quality drives the decision to buy or not to buy; or (ii) perhaps quality of both types of products are excellent, and whichever product you happen to buy drives your opinion of that product... for example, if you buy a nonrecycled product and think it is of high quality, you might conclude (erroneously, perhaps) that the recycled product is of lower quality.

23.30: We test H_0: All proportions are equal vs. H_a: Not all proportions are equal. To find the entries in the table, take (0.21)(800), (0.25)(800), and (0.28)(800). We find that $\chi^2 = 10.619$ with df = 2, so $P < 0.005$. There is strong evidence that contact method makes a difference in response.

	Yes	No
Phone	168	632
One-on-one	200	600
Anonymous	224	576

22.31: (a) The diagram is shown below. To perform the randomization, label the infants 01 to 77, and choose pairs of random digits. (b) See the Minitab output for the two-way table. We find $\chi^2 = 0.568$, df = 3, and $P = 0.904$. There is no reason to doubt that the randomization "worked."

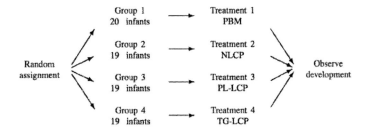

```
            Female    Male    Total
    PBM       11        9       20
             10.91     9.09

    NLCP      11        8       19
             10.36     8.64

   PL-LCP     11        8       19
             10.36     8.64

   TG-LCP      9       10       19
             10.36     8.64

   Total      42       35       77

   ChiSq =  0.001 +  0.001 +
            0.039 +  0.047 +
            0.039 +  0.047 +
            0.179 +  0.215 = 0.568
   df = 3, p = 0.904
```

22.32: (a) We test $H_0 : p_G = p_{NG}$ vs. $H_a : p_G \neq p_{NG}$. With $\hat{p}_G = \dfrac{36}{91} = 0.395604$ and $\hat{p}_{NG} = \dfrac{578}{2014}$ = 0.286991, the pooled proportion is $\hat{p} = 0.291686$. The standard error is SE = 0.048713. Hence, $z = \dfrac{\hat{p}_G - \hat{p}_{NG}}{\text{SE}} = 2.22965$ and $P = 0.0258$. (b) By inspection of the output, we see that all expected cell counts exceed 5, and use of a chi-square test is appropriate. We find $\chi^2 = 4.975$ with df = 1. From software, $P = 0.0257$. (c) $z^2 = (2.22965)^2 = 4.971$, which is equal to χ^2 up to rounding error. Obviously, P-values agree to rounding error, also. (d) We would use a one-sided z test. The chi-square test is inherently two-sided since it tests for association generally, rather than for a particular direction of association.

Minitab output

```
              Fights    No Fight    Total
   Games        36         55         91

               26.54      64.46


  NoGames       578       1436       2014

               587.46    1426.54

   Total        614       1491       2105


   ChiSq = 3.372 +  1.388 +
           0.152 +  0.063 = 4.975

   df = 1, p = 0.0257
```

23.33: (a) We test $H_0 : p_1 = p_2$ vs. $H_a : p_1 < p_2$. (b) The z test must be used because the chi-square procedure measures evidence in support of evidence of any association, and is implicitly two-sided. We have $\hat{p}_1 = 0.3667$ and $\hat{p}_2 = 0.7333$. The pooled proportion is $\hat{p} = (11 + 22)/(30 + 30) = 0.55$, and the standard error is SE = 0.12845, so $z = -2.85$ and $P = 0.0022$. We have strong evidence that rats that can stop the shock (and therefore presumably have better attitudes) develop tumors less often than rats that cannot (and therefore are presumably depressed).

	Tumor	No tumor
Group 1	11	19
Group 2	22	8

23.34: STATE: Is there a difference between how men and women assess their chances of being rich by age 30? PLAN: We test H_0: There is no relationship between gender and self-assessment of chances of being rich vs. H_a: There is some relationship between these factors. SOLVE: Examining the Minitab output in Figure 23.8, we see that conditions for use of the chi-square test are satisfied, since all expected cell counts exceed 5. We obtain $\chi^2 = 43.946$ with df = 4, leading to $P < 0.0005$. CONCLUDE: Overall, men give themselves a better chance of being rich. This difference shows up most noticeably in the second and fifth rows of the table: Women were more likely to say "some chance, but probably not," while men more often responded "almost certain." There was virtually no difference between men and women in the "almost no chance" and "a 50-50 chance" responses, and little difference in the "a good chance" response.

23.35: STATE: Does sexual content of ads differ in magazines aimed at different audiences? PLAN: We test H_0: There is no relationship between sexual content of ads and magazine audience vs. H_a: There is some relationship between sexual content of ads and magazine audience. SOLVE: Examining the Minitab output, we see that conditions for use of the chi-square test are satisfied since all expected cell counts exceed 5. We obtain $\chi^2 = 80.874$ with df = 2, leading to $P < 0.0005$. CONCLUDE: Magazines aimed at women are much more likely to have sexual depictions of models than the other two types of magazines. Specifically, about 39% of ads in women's magazines show sexual depictions of models, compared with 21% and 17% of ads in general-audience and men's magazines, respectively. The two women's chi-squared terms account for over half of the total chi-square value.

23.36: (a) We compare the percentage of dogs in each "condition type" (I, II, III) making specified number of errors. The table summarizes. We see that under Type I condition (social-communicative), dogs tend to make more errors, while under Type III condition (nonsocial), dogs tend to make fewer errors.

	0	1	2	3
Type I	0%	25%	25%	50%
Type II	41.7%	25%	8.3%	25%
Type III	66.7%	16.7%	16.7%	0%

(b) We have many cells with expected cell counts lower than 5. We also have a 0 in the table. (c) Software should warn users against using the chi-square test. The software package Minitab does provide such a warning.

23.37: We need cell counts, not just percents. If we had been given the number of travelers in each group — leisure and business — we could have estimated this.

22.38: Each respondent could have participated in more than one — or even none — of the categories of Internet use.

22.39: In order to do a chi-square test, each subject can only be counted once.

22.40: (a) $\hat{p} = \dfrac{404}{4310} = 0.0938$, and SE = 0.0044. Hence, a 99% confidence interval for the proportion of smokers is $0.0938 \pm 2.576(0.0044) = 0.0938 \pm 0.0114 = 0.0824$ to 0.1052, or

8.24% to 10.52%. (b) A table of conditional distributions and a corresponding bar graph are provided. Notice that smokers feel less optimistic about their own health than do nonsmokers: Smokers are more likely to view their health as Good, Fair, or Poor, while nonsmokers are more likely to view their health as Excellent or Very good.

	Excellent	Very good	Good	Fair	Poor
Smokers	6.19%	28.47%	35.89%	22.28%	7.18%
Nonsmokers	12.39%	39.86%	33.51%	13.95%	0.28%

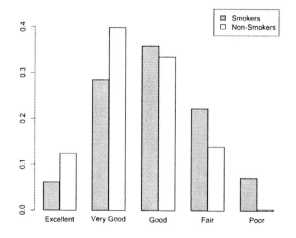

(c) Output is attached. Notice the very large differences between expected cell counts and observed cell counts. Indeed, we see from software that

$$\chi^2 = \frac{(25-47.7)^2}{47.7} + \frac{(484-461.3)^2}{461.3} + \frac{(115-156.7)^2}{156.7} + ... + \frac{(11-36.3)^2}{36.3} = 229.66.$$ With df = (5 − 1)(2 − 1) = 4, we attain $P < 0.0005$.

Minitab output

	Smokers	Nonsmokers	Total
Excellent	25	484	509
	47.7	461.3	
VeryGood	115	1557	1672
	156.7	1515.3	
Good	145	1309	1454
	136.3	1317.7	
Fair	90	545	635
	59.5	575.5	
Poor	29	11	40
	3.7	36.3	
Total	404	3906	4310

```
ChiSq =  10.803 +   1.117 +
         11.097 +   1.148 +
          0.555 +   0.057 +
         15.634 +   1.616 +
        172.997 +  17.633  =  229.66
 df = 4,  p = 0.000
```

(d) Examining the terms of the chi-square statistic, or by comparing the differences between observed counts and expected counts (relative to expected) in the table above, we see that the greatest contributions to χ^2 are due to differences at both extremes of the conditional distributions: More than the expected number of smokers and fewer than expected nonsmokers were observed in the Poor and Fair categories, while the opposite trend occurs for the Very good and Excellent categories.

23.41: (a) We test H_0: There is no relationship between degree held and service attendance vs. H_a: There is some relationship between degree held and service attendance. Examining the Minitab output, $\chi^2 = 14.19$ with df = 3, yielding *P*-value = 0.0027. There is strong evidence of an association between degree held and service attendance.

Minitab output

	HSchool	JColl	Bach	Grad	Total
Attend	400	62	146	76	684
	437.3	55.7	129.2	61.8	
NoAttend	880	101	232	105	1318
	842.7	107.3	248.9	119.1	
Total	1280	163	378	181	2002

```
ChiSq =  3.182 + 0.713 + 2.185 + 3.263 +
         1.651 + 0.370 + 1.147 + 1.669 = 14.19
 df = 3,  p = 0.0027
```

(b) The new table is shown below. We attain $\chi^2 = 0.73$ on df = 2. Hence, *P* = 0.694. In this table, we find no evidence of association between religious service attendance and degree held.

Minitab output

	JColl	Bach	Grad	Total
Attend	62	146	76	284
	64.1	148.7	71.2	
NoAttend	101	232	105	438
	98.9	229.3	109.8	
Total	163	378	181	722

```
ChiSq =  0.069 + 0.049 + 0.324 +
         0.045 + 0.032 + 0.210 = 0.729
 df = 2,  p = 0.694
```

(c) The new table is shown: We attain $\chi^2 = 13.40$ on df = 1. Hence, *P* = 0.000 to three places (it's actually 0.0002). There is overwhelming evidence of association between level of education (High school versus Beyond high school) and religious service attendance.

Minitab output

	HSchool	BeyondHS	Total
Attend	400	284	684
	437.3	246.7	
NoAttend	880	438	1318
	842.7	475.3	
Total	1280	722	2002

ChiSq = 3.182 + 5.640 +
         1.651 + 2.927 = 13.400
df = 1, p = 0.000

(d) In general, we find that people with degrees beyond high school attend service more often than expected, while people with high school degrees attend services less often than expected. Of those with high school degrees, 31.3% attended services, while the percentages are 38.0%, 38.6% and 42.0%, respectively, for people with Junior College, Bachelor's, and Graduate degrees.

23.42: STATE: Is there a relationship between condom use and grade? PLAN: We carry out a chi-square test of $H_0 : p_9 = p_{10} = p_{11} = p_{12}$ vs. H_a: Not all proportions are equal. SOLVE: Examination of the Minitab output provided suggests that a chi-square test is appropriate since all expected cell counts are more than 5. We attain $\chi^2 = 53.0$. On df = 3, we find $P = 0.000$ ($P < 0.005$ using the table) to three places. CONCLUDE: There is overwhelming evidence of an association between grade level and condom use. Examining the table, we see that more than the expected number of 12th graders use condoms, while in all other grades, fewer than expected use condoms.

Minitab output

	Condom	NoCondom	Total
Nine	300	532	832
	326.3	505.7	
Ten	350	736	1086
	425.9	660.1	
Eleven	601	956	1557
	610.6	946.4	
Twelve	873	1068	1941
	761.2	1179.8	
Total	2124	3292	5416

ChiSq = 2.120 +   1.368 +
        13.526 +   8.727 +
         0.151 +   0.097 +
        16.420 + 10.594 = 53.004
df = 3, p = 0.000

23.43: STATE: Is there a relationship between race and parental opinion of schools? PLAN: We use a chi-square test to test H_0: There is no relationship between race and opinion about schools vs. H_a: There is some relationship between race and opinion about schools. SOLVE: All expected cell counts exceed 5, so use of a chi-square test is appropriate. We find that $\chi^2 = 22.426$ with df = 8 and $P = 0.004$. Nearly half of the total chi-square comes from the first two terms; most of the rest comes from the second and fifth rows. CONCLUDE: We have strong evidence of a relationship between race and opinion of schools. Specifically, according to the sample (as illustrated in the table), blacks are less likely and Hispanics are more likely to consider schools to be excellent, while Hispanics and whites differ in the percent considering schools good. Also, a higher percentage of blacks rated schools as "fair."

```
Minitab output
           Black    Hisp   White    Total
         Black   Hisp  White    Total
Exclnt     12      34     22        68
         22.70   22.70  22.59

Good       69      55     81       205
         68.45   68.45  68.11

Fair       75      61     60       196
         65.44   65.44  65.12

Poor       24      24     24        72
         24.04   24.04  23.92

DontKnow   22      28     14        64
         21.37   21.37  21.26

Total     202     202    201       605

ChiSq =  5.047 + 5.620 + 0.015 +
         0.004 + 2.642 + 2.441 +
         1.396 + 0.301 + 0.402 +
         0.000 + 0.000 + 0.000 +
         0.019 + 2.058 + 2.481 = 22.426
df = 8, p = 0.004
```

23.44: (a) This is an experiment in the sense that subjects were assigned to treatments — but it is not a randomized experiment, and it may well be the case that certain types of patients (e.g., high risk patients) are more likely to be assigned to particular treatments. In this sense, it is easy to believe that patients within treatment groups differ in more ways than one. One might also argue that patients select treatments in concert with their doctors… and in this sense it is an observational study. (b) STATE: Is there a relationship between complication and surgery type? PLAN: We use a chi-square test to test H_0: There is no relationship between surgery type and complications vs. H_a: There is some relationship between surgery type and complications. SOLVE: All expected cell counts exceed 5, so use of a chi-square test is appropriate. We find that $\chi^2 = 318.668$ with df = 4 and $P = 0.000$ to three places. CONCLUDE: There is overwhelming evidence of an association between surgery type and complication. Note that the greatest contributions to χ^2 come from more than the expected number of non life-threatening complications in bypass patients, and fewer non-life-threatening complications in banding patients. Banding had fewer non life-threatening and serious complications, and fewer "no complication" cases than expected.

```
Minitab output
              NonLfThrt   Serious    None      Total
  Banding        81         46       5253       5380

               252.9       137.4    4989.8

  Gastrect       31         19        804        854

                40.1        21.8     792.0

  Bypass        606        325       8110       9041

               425.0       230.8    8385.2

  Total         718        390      14167      15275

ChiSq = 116.831 + 60.766 + 13.888 +

         2.082 +  0.361 +  0.180 +

        77.114 + 38.414 +  9.032   = 318.668

df = 4, p = 0.000
```

23.45: PLAN: We compare how detergent preferences vary by laundry habits. We use a chi-square test to test H_0: There is no relationship between laundry habits and preference vs. H_a: There is some relationship between laundry habits and preference. SOLVE: To compare people with different laundry habits, we compare the percent in each class who prefer the new product.

	Soft water, warm wash	Soft water, hot wash	Hard water, warm wash	Hard water, hot wash
Prefer new product	54.3%	51.8%	61.8%	58.3%

The differences are not large, but the "hard water, warm wash" group is most likely to prefer the new detergent. With expected cell counts exceeding 5, a chi-square test is appropriate. We observe $\chi^2 = 2.058$ with df = 3, so that $P = 0.560$. CONCLUDE: The data provide no evidence to conclude that laundry habits and brand preference are related.

Minitab output

```
              S/W      S/H      H/W      H/H    Total
  Standard    53       27       42       30      152
              49.81    24.05    47.23    30.92

  New         63       29       68       42      202
              66.19    31.95    62.77    41.08

  Total       116      56       110      72      354

ChiSq =  0.205 + 0.363 + 0.579 + 0.027
         0.154 + 0.273 + 0.436 + 0.020 = 2.058
df = 3, p = 0.560
```

23.46: There are 2009 adults in the sample. Of these, 322 are Independent. Therefore, $\hat{p} = 322/2009 = 0.1603$. Hence, SE $= \sqrt{\dfrac{0.1603(1-0.1603)}{2009}} = 0.0082$. A 95% confidence interval for the proportion of Independents is $0.1603 \pm 1.96(0.0082) = 0.144$ to 0.176, or 14.4% to 17.6%.

23.47: STATE: How do the conditional distributions of political leaning, given education compare? PLAN: We compare the percentages leaning toward each party within each education group. SOLVE: The requested table is provided. At each education level, we compute the percentage leaning each party. For example, among Bachelor degree holders, $157/(157 + 154) =$ 50.5% lean Democrat, while the other 49.5% lean Republican.

	None	HS	JC	Bachelor	Grad	Total
Democrat	142	500	81	157	103	983
	68.9%	60.8%	55.1%	50.5%	63.6%	
Republican	64	323	66	154	59	666
	31.1%	39.2%	44.9%	49.5%	36.4%	

CONCLUDE: At every education level, people leaning Democrat outweigh people leaning Republican. The difference is greatest at the "None" level of education, then decreases until the party support is nearly equal for Bachelor holders. Among graduate degree holders, Democrats strongly outnumber Republicans.

23.48: PLAN: We will find conditional distributions for political leaning at each level of education, and perform a chi-square test on the full table, testing the null hypothesis of no relationship between education level and political preference. SOLVE: The conditional distributions are tabulated below, and summarized in a bar graph. Expected cell counts are all greater than 5, so using a chi-square test is appropriate. Using software, the chi-square statistic is $\chi^2 = 111.01$ on df $= 28$. The corresponding P-value is $P = 0.000$ to three decimal places. CONCLUDE: Student observations about the full table will vary. Notice that among the "None" education group, there is a much larger proportion of Independents, and in the "Grad" education group there is a very high percentage of Democrats and people that lean Democrat. Republican support is strongest in the Bachelor group. The general result of this exercise, where we find that the differences between party affiliation vary across levels of education is consistent with our conclusion in Exercise 23.47.

	None	HS	JC	Bachelor	Grad
Strong Democrat	21.4%	18.6%	18.5%	15.9%	28.0%
Not strong Dem.	15.3%	18.4%	17.3%	12.5%	15.0%
Near Democrat	11.5%	13.3%	11.0%	16.1%	10.4%
Independent	29.5%	15.7%	12.7%	8.8%	13.5%
Near Republican	6.4%	7.8%	11.6%	9.9%	5.2%
Not strong Repub.	6.8%	14.8%	19.1%	21.5%	14.0%
Strong Republican	8.5%	9.9%	7.5%	12.2%	11.4%
Other party	0.7%	1.6%	2.3%	3.1%	2.6%

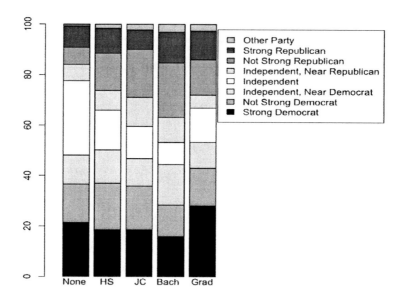

23.49 and 23.50 are Web-based exercises.

Chapter 24 Solutions

24.1: (a) A scatterplot of the data is provided, along with the least-squares regression line (students were not asked to add the regression line). We see that there is a strong linear relationship between wine intake and relative risk. From software, the correlation is $r = 0.985$.

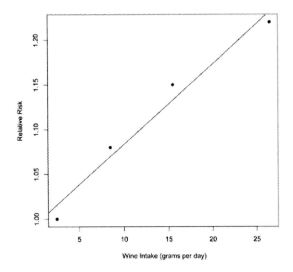

(b) The estimate of β is $b = 0.0009$ (see output). We estimate that an increase in intake of 1 gram per day increases relative risk of breast cancer by 0.0009. The estimate of α is $a = 0.9931$. According to our estimate, wine intake of 0 grams per day is associated with a relative risk of breast cancer of 0.9931 (about 1).

```
Regression Analysis: RRisk versus Intake

The regression equation is RRisk = 0.993 + 0.009 Intake

Predictor     Coef       SE Coef        T            P
Constant    0.993094    0.017771     55.884      0.00032
Intake      0.009012    0.001112      8.102      0.01489

S = 0.01986    R-Sq = 97.0%    R-Sq(adj) = 95.6%
```

(c) The least-squares regression line is given by $\hat{y} = 0.9931 + 0.0009x$. The table below summarizes computed residuals, which sum to zero, as demonstrated. We also have $s^2 = 0.00079/2 = 0.000395$, which provides an estimate of σ^2. Hence, we estimate σ by $s = \sqrt{0.000395} = 0.01987$, which agrees (up to rounding error) with "S" in the output above.

x	y	$\hat{y}$	Residual $y - \hat{y}$	$(y - \hat{y})^2$
2.5	1.00	1.0156	−0.0156	0.00024
8.5	1.08	1.0697	0.0103	0.00011
15.5	1.15	1.1328	0.0172	0.00030
26.5	1.22	1.2319	−0.0119	0.00014
			0	0.00079

24.2: (a) A scatterplot of the data is provided, with the least-squares regression line added (asked for in part (c)). From the output provided, $r^2 = 0.207$. Our model explains 20.7% of the observed variability in Aroc. (b) Reading directly from the output in Figure 24.4, we estimate α by $a = 8.91$. We estimate β by $b = 87.76$. We estimate σ by $s = 7.9$. Units are not defined in the problem. (c) The least-squares regression line is given by $\hat{y} = 8.9 + 87.8\,x$. This line has been added to the scatterplot drawn in part (a).

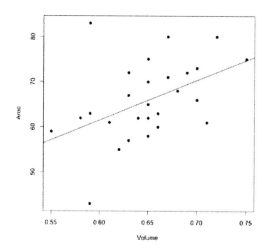

24.3: (a) A scatterplot of discharge by year is provided, along with the fitted regression line, which is requested in part (b). Discharge seems to be increasing over time, but there is also a lot of variation in this trend, and our impression is easily influenced by the most recent years' data. From the output provided below, $r^2 = 0.225$, so the least-squares regression line explains 22.5% of the total observed variability in arctic discharge. (b) The regression line has been added to the scatterplot provided. The least-squares regression line is given by $\hat{y} = -3690.08 + 2.80x$. We see from the output that $s = 111$.

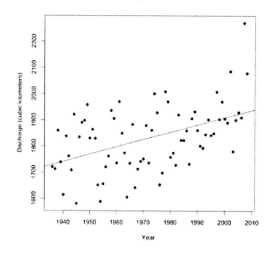

```
Regression Analysis: Discarge versus Year

The regression equation is Discharge = -3690.08 + 2.80Year

Predictor    Coef     SE Coef      T         P
Constant   -3690.078  3.29586    8.338    0.0000
Year           2.800  0.6168     4.539    0.0002

S = 111    R-Sq = 22.5%    R-Sq(adj) = 21.4%
```

24.4: (a) For testing $H_0 : \beta = 0$ vs. $H_a : \beta > 0$, $t = \dfrac{b}{SE_b} = \dfrac{0.009012}{0.001112} = 8.104$. (b) The sample size is $n = 4$, so df $= 4 - 2 = 2$. Using Table C, for a one-sided alternative, $0.005 < P < 0.01$. Don't forget that this data involved averaging over individuals. The data points provided are averages at each value of wine intake. No doubt, there would be far more variation between individuals.

24.5: Refer to the output provided with the solution to Exercise 24.3. We test $H_0 : \beta = 0$ vs. $H_a : \beta > 0$. We compute $t = \dfrac{b}{SE_b} = \dfrac{2.800}{0.6168} = 4.539$. Here, df $= n - 2 = 73 - 2 = 71$. In referring to Table C, we round df down to df $= 60$. Using Table C, we obtain $P < 0.0005$. Using software, we obtain $P = 0.0002$. There is strong evidence of an increase in arctic discharge over time.

24.6: Minitab output is provided.

```
Regression Analysis: Fuel versus Speed

The regression equation is Discharge = 11.06 - 0.0147Speed

Predictor    Coef     SE Coef      T         P
Constant   11.05790   2.12168    5.212    0.0001
Speed      -0.01466   0.02334   -0.628    0.5408

S = 3.905    R-Sq = 2.95%    R-Sq(adj) = -4.52%
```

We test $H_0 : \beta = 0$ vs. $H_a : \beta \neq 0$. We observe $t = \dfrac{b}{SE_b} = \dfrac{-0.01466}{0.02334} = -0.628$. We clearly will not reject the null hypothesis. With df $= 15 - 2 = 13$, using Table C we obtain $P > 0.50$. From software, $P = 0.5408$. There is little evidence of a straight-line relationship between fuel consumption and speed. However, examining the scatterplot, we see that there is, in fact, a very strong (non-straight-line) relationship between speed and fuel consumption. One should always plot data.

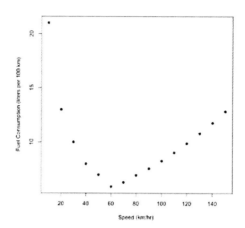

24.7: (a) Refer to the solution of Exercise 24.4. For testing $H_0 : \beta = 0$ vs. $H_a : \beta > 0$, we have $t = 8.104$ with df = 2. For the one-sided alternative suggested, we obtained $0.005 < P < 0.01$. This test is equivalent to testing H_0 : Population correlation = 0 vs. H_a : Population correlation > 0. (b) Using software, $r = 0.985$. This can also be computed by referring to the Minitab output provided with Exercise 24.1, with $r = +\sqrt{r^2} = +\sqrt{0.97}$. Referring to Table E with $n = 4$, we find that $0.005 < P < 0.01$, just as in part (a). These tests are equivalent.

24.8: Refer to the scatterplot provided with the solution to Exercise 4.45. We have $r = 0.878$, and $n = 13$. Hence, for testing H_0 : Population correlation = 0 vs. H_a : Population correlation > 0, using Table E, $P < 0.0005$. There is overwhelming evidence of a positive linear relationship between social distress score and activity in the part of the brain known to be activated by physical pain.

24.9: Referring to Table C, $t^* = 2.920$ (df = 4 – 2 = 2, with 90% confidence). Hence, a 90% confidence interval for β is given by $0.009012 \pm 2.920(0.001112) = 0.009012 \pm 0.003247 = 0.00577$ to 0.01226. With 90% confidence, the increase in relative risk of breast cancer associated with an increase in alcohol consumption by 1 gram per day is between 0.00577 and 0.01226.

24.10: There are $n = 29$ observations, so df = 29 – 2 = 27. From Table C, $t^* = 2.052$. From the output provided in Figure 24.4, b = 87.76 and $SE_b = 33.02$. Hence, a 95% confidence interval for the increase in Aroc per unit increase in volume is given by $87.76 \pm 2.052(33.02) = 87.76 \pm 67.76 = 20.00$ to 155.52. With 95% confidence, each unit increase in Brodmann area results in an increase of introspective ability (as measured by Aroc) of between 20.00 and 155.52 units.

24.11: Refer to the output provided in the solution to Exercise 24.3. We have b = 2.800 and $SE_b = 0.6168$. With 73 observations, df = 71. Using Table C, we look under the row corresponding to df = 60 (the nearest smaller value of df in the table). We obtain $t^* = 1.671$. Hence, a 90% confidence interval for β is given by $2.8000 \pm 1.671(0.6168) = 2.8000 \pm 1.0307 = 1.7693$ to 3.8307 cubic kilometers per year. With 90% confidence, the yearly increase in arctic discharge is between 1.7693 and 3.8307 cubic kilometers. This confidence interval excludes "0," so there is evidence arctic discharge is increasing over time.

24.12: (a) If we wish to predict the relative risk of breast cancer for a single group of women for which $x^* = 10$, then we should use a prediction interval. This is denoted "95% PI" in the output provided. With 95% confidence, the relative risk of breast cancer for women drinking 10 mg of red wine per day is 0.98643 to 1.18000. (b) From the output, $\hat{\mu} = 1.08321$ and $SE_{\hat{\mu}} = 0.01057$. For df $= 4 - 2 = 2$ and 90% confidence, $t^* = 2.920$. Hence, a 90% confidence interval for the mean relative risk of breast cancer in all women drinking 10 mg of red wine per day is $1.08321 \pm 2.920(0.01057) = 1.052$ to 1.114.

24.13: (a) If $x^* = 0.60$, then our prediction for mean Aroc is $\hat{\mu} = 8.91 + 87.76(0.60) = 61.57$. (b) We have $SE_{\hat{\mu}} = 2.184$. For df $= 29 - 2 = 27$ and 95% confidence, we have $t^* = 2.052$. Hence, a 95% confidence interval for mean Aroc in people with 0.6 volume of the Brodmann area is given by $61.57 \pm 2.052(2.184) = 57.088$ to 66.052.

24.14: (a) A stemplot of the residuals is provided after rounding each residual to the nearest whole number. The distribution of residuals appears close to Normal, with perhaps one outlier in the right tail (a residual of "51").

```
-3 | 1
-2 | 433
-1 | 975532
-0 | 99997666322
 0 | 00339
 1 | 01114899
 2 | 14
 3 | 3
 4 |
 5 | 1
```

(b) The residual plot is provided. There appears to be roughly equal spread in the residuals about the line. Notice the outlier mentioned in (a).

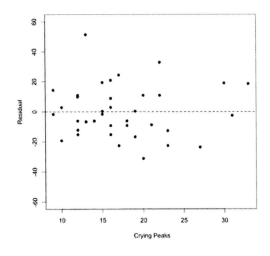

(c) The residuals sum to zero, so only $n - 1$ observations are independent. Here, there are $n = 38$ observations, but because they have to sum to zero, 1 of them is constrained, given the others. Hence, there are 37 degrees of freedom.

24.15: (a) The residual plot provided does not suggest any deviation from a straight-line relationship between volume and Aroc score, although there are two residuals of larger magnitude present, both for Aroc scores slightly lower than 0.60.

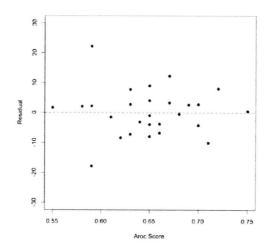

(b) A stemplot of residuals, provided below, does not suggest that the distribution of residuals departs strongly from Normality. There are two possible outliers, which agrees with the output provided by Minitab referenced in the problem statement.

```
-1 | 8
-1 | 0
-0 | 88777
-0 | 4443211
 0 | 0222333334
 0 | 889
 1 | 2
 1 |
 2 | 2
```

(c) It is reasonable to assume that observations are independent since we have 29 different subjects, measured separately. (d) Referring to the residual plot of (b), it may be the case that spread is larger for smaller values of Aroc, but these happen to be the two outliers. It is difficult to make a definitive argument either way.

24.16: (a) From the output provided, $a = 86.0$ and $b = 1.2699$.

24.17: (a) With a positive association, $r = +\sqrt{r^2} = +\sqrt{0.623} = 0.789$.

24.18: (b) Individual price increases vary, so answer (c) is inappropriate. The regression line provides all predicted mean prices, given appraised value.

24.19: (a) This is a one-sided alternative, because we wonder if larger appraisal values are associated with larger selling prices.

24.20: (c) less than 0.001. Note that the output shows that $P = 0.000$ to three decimal places.

24.21: (c) $s = 235.41$.

24.22: (c) There are 28 observations, so df $= 28 - 2 = 26$.

24.23: (c) With 26 degrees of freedom, $t^* = 2.056$, so the margin of error is $2.056(0.1938) = 0.3985$.

24.24: (a) The prediction interval is appropriate.

24.25: (a) Scientists estimate that each additional 1% increase in the percentage of Bt cotton plants results in an increase of 6.81 mirid bugs per 100 plants. (b) The regression model explains 90% of the variability in mirid bug density. That is, knowledge of the proportion of Bt cotton plants explains most of the variation in mired bug density. (c) Recall that the test $H_0 : \beta = 0$ vs. $H_a : \beta > 0$ is exactly the same as the test H_0 : Population correlation $= 0$ vs. H_a : Population correlation > 0. As $P < 0.0001$, there is strong evidence of a positive linear relationship between the proportion of Bt cotton plants and the density of mirid bugs. (d) We may conclude that denser mirid bug populations are associated with larger proportions of Bt cotton plants. However, it seems plausible that a reduced use of pesticides (an indirect cause), rather than more Bt cotton plants (a direct cause) is the reason for this increase.

24.26: We test $H_0 : \beta = 0$ vs. $H_a : \beta \neq 0$ and observe $t = \dfrac{b}{\text{SE}_b} = \dfrac{274.78}{88.18} = 3.116$ with df $= 12 - 2 = 10$. The two-sided P-value is between 0.01 and 0.02. There is strong evidence of a linear relationship between thickness and gate velocity.

24.27: For 90% intervals with df $= 10$, use $t^* = 1.812$. (a) Use the estimated slope and standard error given in Figure 24.13. The confidence interval for β is $b \pm t^* \text{SE}_b = 274.78 \pm 1.812(88.18) = 274.78 \pm 159.78 = 115.0$ to 434.6 fps/inch. (b) This is the "90% CI" given in Figure 24.13: 176.2 to 239.4 fps. To confirm this, we can use the given values of $\hat{y} = 207.8$ and $\text{SE}_{\hat{\mu}} = 17.4$, labeled "Fit" and "SE Fit" in the output:

$\hat{y} \pm t^* \text{SE}_{\hat{\mu}} = 207.8 \pm 1.812(17.4) = 176.3$ to 239.3 fps, which agrees with the output up to rounding error.

24.28: (a) The scatterplot shows no obvious nonlinearity or change in spread. (b) A histogram is quite spread out, but not strikingly non-Normal. (c) Student opinions about whether this point is influential may vary. There are some changes, but they might not be considered substantial: The regression standard error is about 25% smaller, the prediction for $x = 0.5$ inch is about 8 fps larger, and the confidence interval is narrower, due to the reduced standard error.

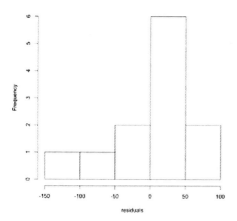
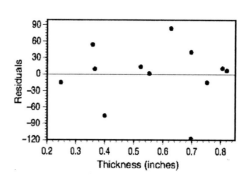

24.29: (a) The stemplot has split stems. There is little evidence of non-Normality in the residuals, and there don't appear to be any strong outliers. (b) The scatterplot confirms the comments made in the text: There is no clear pattern, but the spread about the line may be slightly greater when x is large. (c) Presumably, close inspection of a manatee's corpse will reveal non-subtle clues when cause of death is from collision with a boat rotor. Hence, it seems reasonable that the number of kills listed in the table are mostly not caused by pollution.

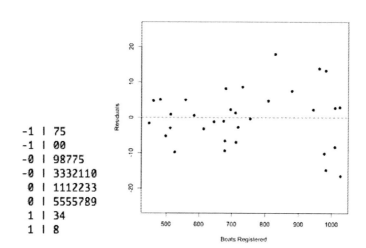

```
-1 | 75
-1 | 00
-0 | 98775
-0 | 3332110
 0 | 1112233
 0 | 5555789
 1 | 34
 1 | 8
```

24.30: We test $H_0 : \beta = 0$ vs. $H_a : \beta > 0$. With df $= 33 - 2 = 31$, we have $t = \dfrac{b}{\text{SE}_b} = \dfrac{0.129232}{0.00752} =$ 17.185. Hence, $P < 0.0005$. There is overwhelming evidence that manatee kills increase with boats registered.

24.31: (a) This is a confidence interval for β. With df = 31, using the table (and rounding degrees of freedom down to 30) we have $t^* = 2.042$ so a 95% confidence interval for β is $b \pm t^* \text{SE}_b = 0.129232 \pm 2.042(0.00752) = 0.129232 \pm 0.01536 = 0.11387$ to 0.14459 additional killed manatees per 1000 additional boats. (b) With 1,050,000 boats, we predict $\hat{y} = -43.17195 + 0.129232(1050) = 92.5217$ killed manatees, which agrees with the output in Figure 24.14 under "Fit." We need the prediction interval, since we are forecasting the number of manatees killed for a single year. According to the output provided, a 95% prediction interval for the number of killed manatees if 1,050,000 boats are registered is 75.18 to 109.87 kills.

24.32: (a) The Minitab output for this analysis is provided below. Recall that the test for $H_0 : \beta = 0$ is equivalent to the test of H_0 : Population correlation = 0. We have $t = -4.64$, and $P < 0.0005$ for testing $H_0 : \beta = 0$ vs. $H_a : \beta \neq 0$. For a one-sided test, P is half the size of Minitab's value. Hence, in order to test H_0 : Population correlation = 0 against H_a : Population correlation is negative, we have $P < 0.00025$. There is overwhelming evidence of a negative population correlation. (b) To find this interval, we need SE_b, which is seen to be 0.0007414. With df = 14, $t^* = 1.761$ for 90% confidence. Hence, a 90% confidence interval for β is $-0.0034415 \pm 1.761(0.0007414) = -0.0034415 \pm 0.00131 = -0.00475$ to -0.00213. (c) This question calls for a prediction interval. The Minitab output provided gives the interval as 0.488 to 3.769 kg.

Regression Analysis: Fat versus nea

The regression equation is Discharge = 3.51 − 0.00344nea

Predictor	Coef	SE Coef	T	P
Constant	3.5051	0.3036	11.54	0.000
nea	-0.0034415	0.0007414	-4.64	0.000

S = 0.7399   R-Sq = 60.6%   R-Sq(adj) = 57.8%

Fit	StError	95% C.I.	95% P.I
2.129	0.193	(1.714, 2.543)	(0.488, 3.769)

24.33: See the output corresponding to a regression analysis, below. (a) We test H_0 : Population correlation = 0 against H_a : Population correlation is positive. We see that $t = 3.88$ with df = 27 − 2 = 25. Hence, $P < 0.0005$. There is very strong evidence of a positive correlation between Gray's forecasted number of storms and the number of storms that actually occur. (b) The output provided provides the corresponding confidence interval for the mean number of storms in years for which Gray predicts 16 stores. Here, $\hat{\mu} = 1.022 + 0.9696(16) = 16.535$, and $\text{SE}_{\hat{\mu}} = 1.3070$ (obtained from output). With df = 25, $t^* = 2.060$ and the 95% confidence interval is given by $16.535 \pm 2.060(1.3070) = 13.843$ to 19.227 storms.

Regression Analysis: Observed versus Forecast

The regression equation is
Observed = 1.02 + 0.970 Forecast

Predictor	Coef	SE Coef	T	P
Constan	1.022	3.008	0.34	0.737
Forecast	0.9696	0.2501	3.88	0.001

S = 3.79361   R-Sq = 37.5%   R-Sq(adj) = 35.0%

Fit	SE Fit	95% CI	95% PI
16.535	1.307	(13.843, 19.226)	(8.271, 24.799)

24.34: See the output below, which provides a scatterplot with least-squares regression line added, along with Minitab output corresponding to the analysis.

(a) The scatterplot reveals a fairly strong negative linear relationship between SST and Coral growth. A formal test of $H_0 : \beta = 0$ vs. $H_a : \beta < 0$ reveals $t = 5.487$ on df = $7 - 2 = 5$. Hence, $P = 0.003$, using software (referring to the output). There is strong evidence of a negative linear relationship between SST and Coral growth. (b) The fit is $\hat{\mu} = 12.37587 - 0.32761(30) = 2.5476$ mm/year. According to the output, SE$_{\hat{\mu}} = 0.0362$. With df = 5, $t^* = 2.571$. Hence, a 95% confidence interval for the mean coral growth per year when water temperature is 30 degrees is $2.5476 \pm 2.571(0.0362) = 2.4545$ to 2.6407 mm per year.

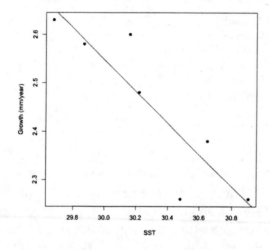

Regression Analysis: Growth versus SST

The regression equation is Growth = 12.376 − 0.328SST

Predictor	Coef	SE Coef	T	P
Constant	12.37587	2.25537	5.487	0.003
Forecast	−0.32761	0.07448	−4.399	0.007

S = 0.07837   R-Sq = 79.5%   R-Sq(adj) = 75.4%

Fit	StError	95% C.I.	95% P.I.
2.5476	0.0362	(2.4544, 2.6407)	(2.3256, 2.7698)

24.35: The stemplot is provided, where residuals are rounded to the nearest tenth. The plot suggests that the residuals do not follow a Normal distribution. Specifically, there are a number of rather extreme outliers. This makes regression inference and interval procedures unreliable.

```
 -7 | 5
 -6 |
 -5 |
 -4 | 7
 -3 | 75
 -2 | 88776
 -1 | 8
 -0 | 876
  0 | 3345
  1 | 334
  2 | 333
  3 | 23
  4 |
  5 |
  6 | 3
  7 |
  8 |
  9 |
 10 |
 11 | 4
```

24.36: The two requested plots are provided below. (a) There is a potential outlier, but with only 7 observations, and considering the scatterplot provided in the solution to Exercise 24.34, there is no evidence of a systematic departure from non-linearity in the relationship between SST and coral growth. (b) There is some evidence (albeit difficult to detect with only 7 observations) that residuals are non-Normal. (c) It is not clear that observations are independent. For example, perhaps temperatures one year are correlated with temperatures the next year. (d) There may be a trend in the residual plot — negative residuals are associated with low and high temperatures, while large positive residuals are associated with moderate temperatures.

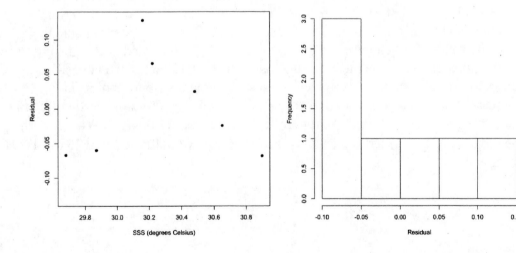

24.37: (a) Shown is the scatterplot with two (nearly identical) regression lines: One using all points, and tone with the outlier omitted. Minitab output for both regressions is provided below. (b) The correlation for all points is $r = 0.8486$. For testing the slope, $t = 6.00$, for which $P < 0.001$. (c) Without the outlier, $r = 0.7014$, the test statistic for the slope is $t = 3.55$, and $P = 0.004$. In both cases there is strong evidence of a linear relationship between neural loss aversion and behavioral loss aversion. However, omitting the outlier weakens this evidence somewhat.

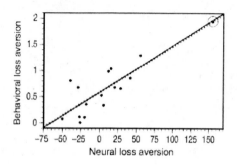

Minitab output: Regression for all points

```
The regression equation is Behave = 0.585 + 0.00879 Neural

Predictor      Coef       Stdev     t-ratio        p
Constant    0.58496     0.07093       8.25    0.000
Neural     0.008794    0.001465       6.00    0.000

s = 0.2797      R-sq = 72.0%     R-sq(adj) = 70.0%
```

Minitab output: Regression with outlier omitted

```
The regression equation is Behave = 0.586 + 0.00891 Neural

Predictor      Coef       Stdev     t-ratio        p
Constant    0.58581     0.07506       7.80    0.000
Neural     0.008909    0.002510       3.55    0.004

s = 0.2903      R-sq = 49.2%     R-sq(adj) = 45.3%
```

24.38: (a) The scatterplot and Minitab output are shown below. The regression equation is $\hat{y} = 560.65 - 3.0771x$, and the correlation is $r = -0.6492$. Generally, the longer a child remains at the table, the fewer calories he or she will consume. This relationship is moderately strong and linear. (b) All the conditions for inference appear to be upheld. First, it is reasonable to view the children as independent. The scatterplot appears to be roughly linear, and does not suggest that the standard deviation changes (the plot of residuals against time spent at the table also supports this later observation). The stemplot provided suggests that the distribution of residuals has a slightly irregular appearance, but is not markedly non-Normal. (c) The slope is significantly different from 0: $t = -3.62$, $P = 0.002$. Software reports that $SE_b = 0.8498$. With df = 18, $t^* = 2.101$, so the 95% confidence interval for β is $-3.0771 \pm 2.101(0.8498) = -4.8625$ to -1.2917 calories per minute.

```
-3 | 6
-2 | 7432
-1 | 8853
-0 | 21
 0 |
 1 | 3679
 2 | 028
 3 | 23
```

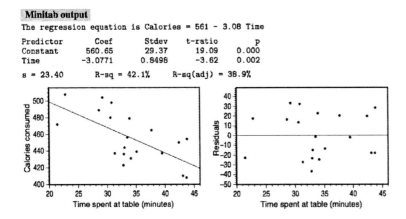

Minitab output

```
The regression equation is Calories = 561 - 3.08 Time

Predictor      Coef      Stdev    t-ratio      p
Constant     560.65      29.37     19.09    0.000
Time         -3.0771     0.8498    -3.62    0.002

s = 23.40     R-sq = 42.1%     R-sq(adj) = 38.9%
```

24.39: The distribution is skewed right, but the sample is large, so t procedures should be safe. We find $\bar{x} = 0.2781$ g/m^2 and $s = 0.1803$ g/m^2. Table C gives $t^* = 1.984$ for df $= 100$ (rounded down from 115). Hence, the 95% confidence interval for μ is 0.2449 to 0.3113 g/m^2.

```
 0 | 0067778999
 1 | 00001111222333455555556667777788889
 2 | 00000111122333444666667788889
 3 | 0000011122233456667788999
 4 | 01456667
 5 | 3589
 6 | 04
 7 |
 8 | 29
 9 | 0
10 | 5
```

24.40: Refer to the output provided with the solution to Exercise 24.38, above. We construct a prediction interval for the calories of a single child sitting at the table for 40 minutes, rather than a confidence interval for mean calories of all children sitting 40 minutes. We have $\hat{y} = 560.65 -$ 3.0771(40) = 437.57 calories. Then $SE_{\hat{y}} = s\sqrt{1 + \dfrac{1}{n} + \dfrac{(x^* - \bar{x})^2}{\sum(x - \bar{x})^2}} = 23.4\sqrt{1 + \dfrac{1}{20} + \dfrac{(40 - 34.01)^2}{758.07}}$

$= 24.51$ calories. Hence, a 95% prediction interval is given by $437.57 \pm 2.101(24.51) = 386$ to 489 calories. Note that it would be preferable simply to ask for this interval from software. Doing so, the following output would be appended to the output provided with Exercise 24.38.

Minitab output

```
   Fit  Stdev.Fit      95.0% C.I.            95.0% P.I.
437.57       7.30  ( 422.23,  452.91)  ( 386.06,  489.08)
```

24.41: PLAN: We examine the relationship between pine cone abundance and squirrel reproduction using a scatterplot and regression. **SOLVE:** Regression gives predicted offspring $\hat{y}$ $= 1.4146 + 0.4399x$. The slope is significantly different from zero ($t = 4.33$, $P = 0.001$). To assess the evidence that more cones leads to more offspring, we should use the one-sided alternative, $H_a : \beta > 0$, for which P is half as large (so $P < 0.001$). The conditions for inference seem to be satisfied. The year-to-year observations should be reasonably independent, a stemplot of the residuals against cone abundance does not show any obvious non-normality. The residual plot shows no departures from a linear pattern. One might also choose to find a confidence interval for β: With df = 14, $t^* = 2.145$ for 95% confidence. Hence, a 95% confidence interval for β is $0.4399 \pm 2.145(0.1016) = 0.2220$ to 0.6578 offspring per cone. CONCLUDE: We have strong evidence of a positive linear relationship between cone abundance and squirrel offspring. Specifically, we are 95% confidence that for each additional one-unit change in the cone index, the mean number of offspring increases by between 0.22 and 0.66 offspring per female.

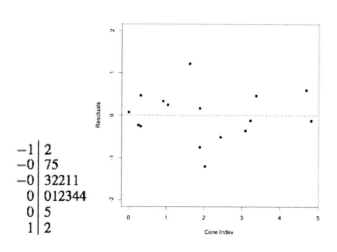

```
-1 | 2
-0 | 75
-0 | 32211
 0 | 012344
 0 | 5
 1 | 2
```

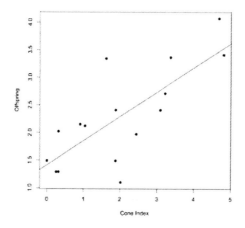

Minitab output: Regression of offspring on cones

The regression equation is Offspr = 1.41 + 0.440 Cones

Predictor	Coef	Stdev	t-ratio	p
Constant	1.4146	0.2517	5.62	0.000
Cones	0.4399	0.1016	4.33	0.001

s = 0.6003   R-sq = 57.2%   R-sq(adj) = 54.2%

24.42: PLAN: We examine the relationship between HAV angle and MA angle using a scatterplot and regression. SOLVE: Refer to solutions to Exercises 7.47 and 7.49 for scatterplot and regression line fit to the data. Although there was an outlier in the data, the data show a roughly linear relationship. From Exercise 7.49, we have $\hat{y} = 19.723 + 0.3388x$. The output provided below shows that for testing $H_0 : \beta = 0$ vs. $H_a : \beta \neq 0$, we find $t = 1.90$ and $P = 0.065$. We have some evidence of a linear relationship between MA angle and HAV, but not strong evidence. Note that perhaps the researchers were really interested in testing $H_0 : \beta = 0$ vs. $H_a : \beta > 0$ (as perhaps they felt that severe MA deformity is associated with larger MA angle). If so, then $P = 0.033$, half that for the two-sided test. We have strong evidence for such an assertion. An analysis of the residuals, both in a stemplot and a plot against MA angle, shows the same outlier visible in the original scatterplot; this might make us hesitate to use inference procedures. Other than the outlier, there are no great causes of concern: The rest of the stemplot appears to be roughly Normal, and the scatterplot has no clear pattern, although there is some suggestion that the spread about the line is slightly greater for small MA angle. It seems reasonable to believe that observations are independent here since the data concern different patients.

Note: *If we remove the outlier, then $\hat{y} = 17.7 + 0.419x$. In the absence of the outlier, there is strong evidence of a linear relationship between HAV and MA angle (t = 2.93, P = 0.006). Residual analysis shows little reason for concern, and all assumptions needed for inference appear to be met, as discussed above.*

CONCLUDE: The correlation is significantly positive with the full data set, and significantly different from zero with the outlier removed. In neither case is the relationship very useful for prediction since the model explains less than 20% of the total variation in HAV in either case.

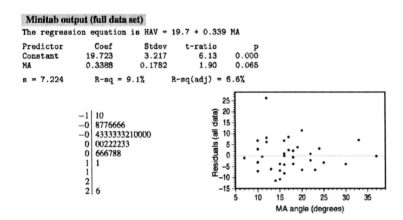

```
Minitab output (full data set)
The regression equation is HAV = 19.7 + 0.339 MA

Predictor      Coef      Stdev     t-ratio        p
Constant     19.723      3.217        6.13    0.000
MA           0.3388     0.1782        1.90    0.065

s = 7.224      R-sq = 9.1%      R-sq(adj) = 6.6%
```

Minitab output (outlier omitted)

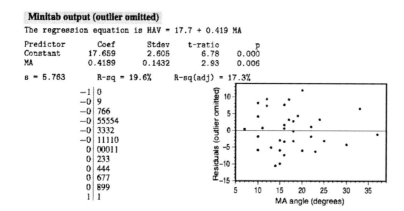

The regression equation is HAV = 17.7 + 0.419 MA

Predictor	Coef	Stdev	t-ratio	p
Constant	17.659	2.605	6.78	0.000
MA	0.4189	0.1432	2.93	0.006

s = 5.763   R-sq = 19.6%   R-sq(adj) = 17.3%

```
-1 | 0
-0 | 9
-0 | 766
-0 | 55554
-0 | 3332
-0 | 11110
 0 | 00011
 0 | 233
 0 | 444
 0 | 677
 0 | 899
 1 | 1
```

24.43: PLAN: We will examine the relationship between beaver stumps and beetle larvae using a scatterplot and regression. We specifically wish to test for a positive slope β, and find a confidence interval for β. SOLVE: The scatterplot shows a positive linear association; the regression line is $\hat{y} = -1.286 + 11.894x$. A stemplot of the residuals does not suggest non-normality of the residuals, the residual plot does not suggest non-linearity, and the problem description makes clear that observations are independent. To test $H_0 : \beta = 0$ vs. $H_a : \beta > 0$, the test statistic is $t = 10.47(\text{df}=21)$, for which Table C provides a one-sided P-value, $P < 0.0005$. For df = 21, $t^* = 2.080$ for 95% confidence, so with b and SE_b as given by Minitab, we are 95% confident that β is between 9.531 and 14.257. CONCLUDE: We have strong evidence that beetle larvae counts increase with beaver stump counts. Specifically, we are 95% confident that each additional stump is (on the average) accompanied by between 9.5 and 14.3 additional larvae clusters.

Minitab output

The regression equation is larvae = - 1.29 + 11.9 stumps

Predictor	Coef	Stdev	t-ratio	p
Constant	-1.286	2.853	-0.45	0.657
stumps	11.894	1.136	10.47	0.000

s = 6.419   R-sq = 83.9%   R-sq(adj) = 83.1%

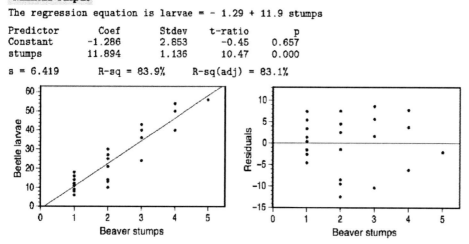

```
-1 | 2
-1 | 0
-0 | 98
-0 | 6
-0 | 4
-0 | 22
-0 | 11
 0 | 011
 0 | 233
 0 | 455
 0 | 777
 0 | 8
```

24.44: PLAN: We will examine the relationship between SRD and DMS using a scatterplot and regression. We will test $H_0 : \beta = 0$ vs. $H_a : \beta > 0$ and find a 90% confidence interval for β. SOLVE: The scatterplot shows a positive linear association; the regression line is $\hat{y} = 0.1385 + 0.0282x$. The stemplot of residuals may suggest slight non-normality, but not severely so. The residual plot does not provide any evidence of nonlinearity. Observations are clearly independent. To test $H_0 : \beta = 0$ vs. $H_a : \beta > 0$, the test statistic is $t = 14.03$ (df = 13), for which Table C tells us that the one-sided *P*-value is $P < 0.0005$. For df = 13, $t^* = 1.771$ for 90% confidence, so with $b = 0.028219$ and $SE_b = 0.002011$, as given by Minitab, we are 90% confident that β is between $0.028219 - 1.771(0.002011)$ and $0.028219 + 1.771(0.002011)$, or 0.0247 and 0.0318. CONCLUDE: We have strong evidence that DMS increases with SRD. Specifically, we are 90% confident that on the average, each additional unit increase in SRD raises surface DMS concentration by between 0.025 and 0.032 nanomolars.

```
-1 | 6
-1 |
-0 | 75
-0 | 4440
 0 | 1334
 0 | 557
 1 | 2
```

Minitab output

The regression equation is DMS = 0.138 + 0.0282 SRD

Predictor	Coef	Stdev	t-ratio	p
Constant	0.1385	0.2757	0.50	0.624
SRD	0.028219	0.002011	14.03	0.000

s = 0.7592   R-sq = 93.8%   R-sq(adj) = 93.3%

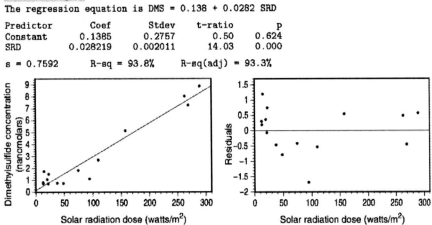

24.45: PLAN: Using a scatterplot and regression, we examine how well phytopigment concentration explains DNA concentration. SOLVE: The scatterplot shows a fairly strong linear positive association; the regression equation is $\hat{y} = 0.1523 + 8.1676x$. A stemplot of the residuals looks reasonably Normal, but the scatterplot suggests that the spread about the line is greater when phytopigment concentration is greater. This may make regression inference unreliable, but we will proceed. Finally, observations are independent, from the context of the problem. The slope is significantly different from 0 ($t = 13.25$, df = 114, $P < 0.001$). We might also construct a 95% confidence interval for β: $8.1676 \pm 1.984(0.6163) = 6.95$ to 9.39. CONCLUDE: The significant linear relationship between phytopigment and DNA concentrations is consistent with the belief that organic matter settling is a primary source of DNA. Starting from a measurement of phytopigment concentration, we could give a fairly accurate prediction of DNA concentration, as the relationship explains about $r^2 = 60.6\%$ of the variation in DNA concentration. We are 95% confident that each additional unit increase in phytopigment concentration increases DNA concentration by between 6.95 and 9.39 units (on the average).

Minitab output

```
The regression equation is dna = 0.152 + 8.17 phyto

Predictor       Coef      Stdev     t-ratio        p
Constant      0.15231    0.01419     10.73      0.000
phyto          8.1676     0.6163     13.25      0.000

s = 0.1136      R-sq = 60.6%      R-sq(adj) = 60.3%
```

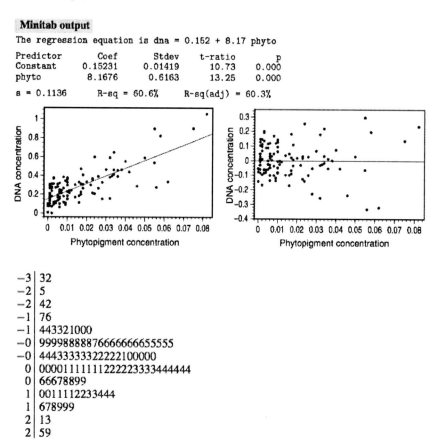

```
-3 | 32
-2 | 5
-2 | 42
-1 | 76
-1 | 443321000
-0 | 99998888876666666655555
-0 | 444333333322222100000
 0 | 000011111111222223333444444
 0 | 66678899
 1 | 0011112233444
 1 | 678999
 2 | 13
 2 | 59
```

24.46: (a) This plot is below; as usual, we add a horizontal line at residual zero, the mean of the residuals. This line corresponds to the regression line in the plot of selling price against appraised value. The residuals show a random scatter about the line, with roughly equal vertical spread across their range. This is what we expect when the conditions for regression inference hold. (b) The stemplot is shown below. (c) The plot of residuals against the month of the sale is below also. The pattern of steadily rising residuals shows that predicted prices are too high for early sales and too low for later sales. This is what we expect if selling prices are rising and appraised values aren't updated quickly enough to keep up. The prediction given in Exercise 24.24 (a selling price of $967.3 thousand) is almost certainly too low because it does not take rising prices into account.

```
—0 | 87765
—0 | 4222
 0 | 233
 0 | 68
 1 | 01
```

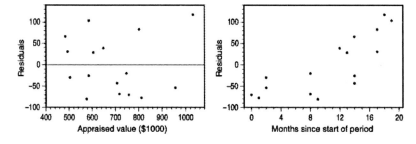

24.47: (a) The mean is $\bar{x} = -0.00333$, and the standard deviation is $s = 1.0233$. For a standardized set of values, we expect the mean and standard deviation to be (up to rounding error) 0 and 1, respectively. (b) The stemplot does not look particularly symmetric, but it is not strikingly non-Normal for such a small sample. (c) The probability that a standard Normal variable is as extreme as this is about 0.0272.

```
—2 | 2
—1 |
—1 | 4
—0 |
—0 | 32
 0 | 01122
 0 | 7
 1 | 0
 1 | 5
```

24.48: The t statistic given in Figure 24.7 is $-1.00 = \dfrac{a}{\mathrm{SE}_a} = \dfrac{-0.01270}{0.01264}$. The P-value is 0.332, so we do not have enough evidence to conclude that the intercept α differs from 0.

24.49: For df = 14 and a 95% confidence interval, we use $t^* = 2.145$, so the interval is $-0.01270 \pm 2.145(0.01264) = -0.0398$ to 0.0144. This interval does contain 0.

24.50 and 24.51 are Web-based exercises.

Chapter 25 Solutions

25.1: (a) We wish to test whether the average status measure in the four groups (men expressing anger, men expressing sadness, women expressing anger, women expressing sadness) differ. That is, we test $H_0 : \mu_A = \mu_B = \mu_C = \mu_D$ vs. H_a : Not all means agree. (b) Referring to Figure 25.2, comparing Groups A and C, we see that the mean status for men expressing anger is about 6.3, while the mean status for women expressing anger is about 4. Hence, with both groups expressing anger, men receive higher mean status scores than women, and the mean difference is about 2.3. Notice that comparing Groups B and D, we see that women expressing sadness receive higher status scores than men expressing sadness, but the difference is relatively small.

25.2: (a) The null hypothesis is "all age groups have the same (population) mean road-rage measurement," and the alternative is "at least one group has a different mean." (b) The F test is quite significant, giving strong evidence that the means are different. The sample means suggest that the degree of road rage decreases with age. (We assume that higher numbers indicate *more* road rage.)

25.3: (a) The stemplots appear to suggest that logging reduces the number of trees per plot and that recovery is slow (the 1-year-after and 8-years-after stemplots are similar). (b) The means lead one to the same conclusion as in (a): The first mean is much larger than the other two. (c) In testing $H_0 : \mu_1 = \mu_2 = \mu_3$ vs. H_a : Not all means are the same, we find that $F = 11.43$ with df = 2 and 30, which has $P = 0.000205$, so we conclude that these differences are significant: the number of trees per plot really is lower in logged areas.

```
Never logged   1 year ago      8 years ago
0 |            0 | 2           0 | 4
0 |            0 | 9           0 |
1 |            1 | 2244        1 | 22
1 | 699        1 | 57789       1 | 5889
2 | 0124       2 | 0           2 | 22
2 | 7789       2 |             2 |
3 | 3          3 |             3 |
```

25.4: (a) Examining the means provided in Figure 25.5, we see that liberals are notably younger than conservatives or moderates, and moderates are perhaps younger than conservatives (maybe this difference can be explained by chance). The mean ages of liberals, moderates and conservatives are, respectively, 43.97, 48.11, and 50.28 years. (b) We test $H_0 : \mu_L = \mu_M = \mu_C$ vs. H_a : Not all means are the same, we find that $F = 20.36$ with df = 2 and 1920, which has $P = 0.000$ to three places. There is overwhelming evidence that the three means differ. We can see that, indeed, at least liberals differ in mean age from conservatives and moderates.

25.5: (a) By moving the middle mean to the same level as the other two, it is possible to reduce F to about 0.02, which has a P-value very close to the left end of the scale (near 1). (b) By moving any mean about 1 centimeter up or down (or any two means about 0.5 cm in opposite directions), the value of F increases (and P decreases) until it moves to the right end of the scale.

25.6: (a) F can be made as small as 0.3174, for which $P > 0.5$. (b) F can be made quite large (and P small) by separating the means—for example, by moving two means all the way down, and one all the way up.

25.7: (a) We have $s_1^2 = 25.6591$, $s_2^2 = 24.8106$, and $s_3^2 = 33.1944$. Hence, $s_1 = 5.065$, $s_2 = 4.981$ and $s_3 = 5.761$. The ratio of largest to smallest standard deviation is $5.761/4.981 = 1.16$, which is less than 2. Conditions are satisfied. (b) The three standard deviations are $s_L = 16.61$, $s_M = 17.42$ and $s_C = 17.13$. Hence, the ratio of largest to smallest standard deviation is $17.42/16.61 = 1.05$, which is less than 2. Conditions are satisfied.

25.8: The standard deviations (0.1201, 0.1472, 0.1134) do not violate our rule of thumb. However, the distributions appear to be skewed and have outliers, especially the 1-year-ago group.

Never logged	1 year ago	8 years ago
4	4 | 2	4
4 | 8	4	4
5	5	5
5	5	5
6 | 3	6	6
6 | 57	6	6 | 8
7	7	7
7 | 5889	7 | 7	7 | 8
8 | 111	8 | 3	8 | 13
8	8 | 588	8
9	9 | 01123	9 | 34
9 | 5	9	9
10	10 | 0	10 | 000

25.9: STATE: How does the presence of nitrogen, phosphorus, or both affect the development of new leaves in bromeliads? PLAN: Examine the data to compare the effect of the treatments and check that we can safely use ANOVA. If the data allow ANOVA, assess the significance of observed differences in mean numbers of new leaves. SOLVE: Side-by-side stemplots shows some irregularity, but no outliers or strong skewness. The Minitab ANOVA output below shows that the group standard deviations easily satisfy our rule of thumb ($2.059/1.302 = 1.58 < 2$). The differences among the groups were significant at $\alpha = 0.05$: $F = 3.44$, df=3 and 27, $P = 0.031$. CONCLUDE: Nitrogen had a positive effect, the phosphorus and control groups were similar, and the plants that got both nutrients fell between the others.

Control	Nitrogen	Phosphorus	Both
11 | 00	11	11 | 0	11
12 | 0	12	12 | 0	12
13 | 0	13 | 0	13 | 0	13 | 0
14	14 | 0	14 | 000	14 | 0000
15 | 00	15 | 00	15 | 00	15 | 0
16 | 0	16 | 0	16	16 | 0
17	17 | 00	17	17 | 0
18	18 | 0	18	18

Minitab output

Source	DF	SS	MS	F	P
Treatment	3	27.21	9.07	3.44	0.031
Error	27	71.18	2.64		
Total	30	98.39			

Individual 95% CIs For Mean
Based on Pooled StDev

Level	N	Mean	StDev	
C	7	13.286	2.059	(---------*--------)
N	8	15.625	1.685	(-------*------)
P	8	13.500	1.414	(--------*--------)
NP	8	14.625	1.302	(------*--------)

Pooled StDev = 1.624   13.5   15.0   16.5

25.10: (a) The number of populations is $I = 3$; the sample sizes from each population are $n_1 = n_2 = 12$ and $n_3 = 9$; the total sample size is $N = 12 + 12 + 9 = 33$. (b) Numerator ("Between groups") df: $I - 1 = 2$, denominator ("Within groups") df: $N - I = 30$.

25.11: (a) $I = 3$ and $N = 96$, so df = 2 and 93. (b) $I = 3$ and $N = 90$, so df = 2 and 87.

25.12: (a) The sample sizes are quite large, and the F test is robust against non-Normality with large samples. (b) Yes (barely): The ratio is $3.11/1.60 = 1.94$. (c) We have $I = 3$ and $N = 1342$. The details of the computations are given here, where some of the fractional values have been rounded.

$$\bar{x} \doteq 1.31 \quad \doteq \frac{244 \times 2.22 + 734 \times 1.33 + 364 \times 0.66}{1342}$$

$$\text{SSG} \doteq 356.14 \quad \doteq 244(2.22 - 1.31)^2 + 734(1.33 - 1.31)^2 + 364(0.66 - 1.31)^2$$

$$\text{MSG} \doteq 178.07 \quad \doteq \frac{356.14}{3 - 1}$$

$$\text{SSE} \doteq 6859.65 \doteq 243 \times 3.11^2 + 733 \times 2.21^2 + 363 \times 1.60^2$$

$$\text{MSE} \doteq 5.12 \quad \doteq \frac{6859.65}{1342 - 3}$$

$$F \doteq 34.76 \quad \doteq \frac{178.07}{5.12}$$

(d) We compare to an F distribution with df $= 2$ and 1339. We have strong evidence that the means differ among the age groups; specifically, road rage decreases with age.

25.13: (a) No sample standard deviation is larger than twice any other. Specifically, the ratio of largest to smallest standard deviation is $2.25/1.61 = 1.40$, which is less than 2. Conditions are safe for use of ANOVA. (b) Calculations are provided:

$$\bar{x} = \frac{17 \times 6.47 + 17 \times 3.75 + 17 \times 4.05 + 17 \times 5.02}{68} = 4.8225$$

$$\text{MSG} = \frac{17(6.47 - 4.8225)^2 + 17(3.75 - 4.8225)^2 + 17(4.05 - 4.8225)^2 + 17(5.02 - 4.8225)^2}{4 - 1} = 25.502$$

$$\text{MSE} = \frac{(17 - 1)2.25^2 + (17 - 1)1.77^2(17 - 1)1.61^2 + (17 - 1)1.80^2}{68 - 4} = 3.507$$

$$F = \frac{\text{MSG}}{\text{MSE}} = \frac{25.502}{3.507} = 7.272$$

(c) We have df $= 4 - 1 = 3$ and $68 - 4 = 64$, so we refer to the F distribution with 3 and 64 degrees of freedom. Citing the output provided below, the P-value is 0.000 rounded to three decimal places. In fact, $P = 0.0003$ (obtained using software). There is strong evidence that the mean status scores between the four groups studied are not equal — a conclusion consistent with the solution to Exercise 25.1.

```
Minitab output

Source    DF     SS       MS       F        p
Factor    3      76.504   25.502   7.272    0.000
Error     64     224.440   3.507
Total     67     300.944
```

25.14: (a) We have independent samples from the five groups, and the standard deviations easily satisfy our rule of thumb. (b) The details of the computations, with $I = 5$ and $N = 4413$, are:

$$\bar{x} = 2.459 = \frac{(809)(2.57) + (1860)(2.32) + (654)(2.63) + (883)(2.51) + (207)(2.51)}{4413}$$

$$SSG = 67.86 = 809(2.57 - \bar{x})^2 + 1860(2.32 - \bar{x})^2 + 654(2.63 - \bar{x})^2 \\ + 883(2.51 - \bar{x})^2 + 207(2.51 - \bar{x})^2$$

$$MSG = 16.97 = \frac{67.86}{5 - 1}$$

$$SSE = 8010.98 = 808(1.40)^2 + 1859(1.36)^2 + 653(1.32)^2 \\ + 882(1.31)^2 + 206(1.28)^2$$

$$MSE = 1.82 = \frac{8010.98}{4413 - 5}$$

$$F = 9.34 = \frac{16.97}{1.82}$$

(c) The ANOVA is very significant ($P < 0.001$), but this is not surprising because the sample sizes were very large. The differences might not have practical importance. (The largest difference is 0.31, which is relatively small on a 5-point scale.)

25.15: (c) the means of several populations.

25.16: (b) a family of distributions that are right-skewed and take only values greater than 0.

25.17: (b) $I - 1 = 3 - 1 = 2$, and $N - I = 9 - 3 = 6$.

25.18: (a) The null hypothesis for an ANOVA test is always that the population means are equal.

25.19: (c) Since MSG = 22,598/(3–1) = 22,598/2 = 11,299, F = MSG/MSE = 11,299/1600 = 7.06.

25.20: (a) The test measures evidence against the null hypothesis stated in Exercise 25.18. We conclude that not all means are the same.

25.21: (c) The largest standard deviation is 62.02, and the smallest is 20.07. Hence, the largest standard deviation is more than twice the smallest.

25.22: (a) This is the problem of multiple comparisons.

25.23: (c) We do not have three independent samples from three populations.

25.24: The populations are morning people, evening people, and people who are neither. The response variable is the difference in memorization scores. $H_0 : \mu_1 = \mu_2 = \mu_3$ (all three groups have equal mean) vs. H_a : Not all means are equal. There are $I = 3$ populations; the sample sizes are $n_1 = 16$, $n_2 = 30$, and $n_3 = 54$, so the total sample size is $N = 100$. The degrees of freedom are therefore $I - 1 = 2$ and $N - I = 97$.

25.25: The populations are college students that might view the advertisement with art image, college students that might view the advertisement with a nonart image, and college students that might view the advertisement with no image. The response variable is student evaluation of the advertisement on the 1–7 scale. We test the hypothesis $H_0 : \mu_1 = \mu_2 = \mu_3$ (all three groups have equal mean advertisement evaluation) vs. H_a : not all means are equal. There are $I = 3$ populations; the samples sizes are $n_1 = n_2 = n_3 = 39$, so there are $N = 39 + 39 + 39 = 117$ individuals in the total sample. There are then $I - 1 = 3 - 1 = 2$ and $N - I = 117 - 3 = 114$ df.

25.26: There are $I = 4$ populations: learning-disabled children with each of the three accommodations plus a control group. The response variable is the scores on the state math exam. We test the hypothesis $H_0 : \mu_1 = \mu_2 = \mu_3 = \mu_4$ (all four groups have equal means) vs. H_a : Not all means are equal. The sample sizes are $n_1 = n_2 = n_3 = n_4 = 25$, with a total sample size of $N = 100$. The degrees of freedom are therefore $I - 1 = 3$ and $N - I = 96$.

25.27: The response variable is hemoglobin A1c level. We have $I = 4$ populations; a control (sedentary) population, an aerobic exercise population, a resistance training population, and a combined aerobic and resistance training population. We test hypothesis $H_0 : \mu_1 = \mu_2 = \mu_3 = \mu_4$ (all four groups have equal mean hemoglobin A1c levels) vs. H_a : Not all means are equal. Sample sizes are $n_1 = 41$, $n_2 = 73$, $n_3 = 72$, and $n_4 = 76$. Our total sample size is $N = 41 + 73 + 72 + 76 = 262$. We have $I - 1 = 4 - 1 = 3$ and $N - I = 262 - 4 = 258$ df.

25.28: (a) The ratio of largest to smallest standard deviation is $1.50/0.87 = 1.72$, which is less than 2. Hence, ANOVA is safe to use for comparing means. Comparing the means provided, males seeing a model are clearly more positive in their evaluation of the product. Among female subjects, there is little difference between the impact of model or student confederate. Notice that for both genders, seeing a model confederate scores higher on average than seeing a student confederate. (b) There are $I = 5$ populations being compared. We have $N = 22 + 23 + 24 + 23 + 27 = 119$ subjects in total. Hence, there are $I - 1 = 5 - 1 = 4$ and $N - I = 119 - 5 = 114$ df. With $F = 8.30$, using software $P = 0.00007$, so there is overwhelming evidence of a difference in population means.

25.29: (a) The graph suggests that emissions rise when a plant is attacked because the mean control emission rate is half the smallest of the other rates. (b) The null hypothesis is "all groups have the same mean emission rate." The alternative is "at least one group has a different mean emission rate." (c) The most important piece of additional information would be whether the data are sufficiently close to Normally distributed. (From the description, it seems reasonably safe to assume that these are more or less random samples.) (d) The SEM equals $s/\sqrt{8}$, so we can find the standard deviations by multiplying by $\sqrt{8}$; they are 16.77, 24.75, 18.78, and 24.38. However, this factor of $\sqrt{8}$ would cancel out in the process of finding the ratio of the largest and smallest standard deviations, so we can simply find this ratio directly from the SEMs: $\dfrac{8.75}{5.93} = \dfrac{24.75}{16.77} =$ 1.48, which satisfies our rule of thumb.

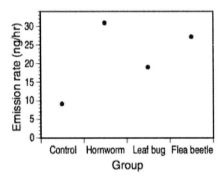

25.30: Only Design A would allow use of one-way ANOVA, because it produces four independent sets of numbers. The data resulting from Design B would be dependent (a subject's responses to the first list would be related to that same subject's responses to the other lists), so that ANOVA would not be appropriate for comparison.

25.31: (a) The stemplots are provided, and means and standard deviations are in the Minitab output. The means suggest that extra water in the spring has the greatest effect on biomass, with a lesser effect from added water in the winter. ANOVA is risky with these data; the standard deviation ratio is nearly 3, and the winter and spring distributions may have skewness or outliers (although it is difficult to judge with such small samples). (b) We wish to test whether the mean biomass from any group differs from the others: $H_0 : \mu_w = \mu_s = \mu_c$ vs. H_a: At least one mean is different. (c) ANOVA gives a statistically significant result ($F = 27.52$, df 2 and 15, $P <$ 0.0005), but as noted in (a), the conditions for ANOVA are not satisfied. Based on the stemplots and the means, however, we should still be safe is concluding that added water increases biomass.

Minitab output

Source	DF	SS	MS	F	p
Treatment	2	97583	48791	27.52	0.000
Error	15	26593	1773		
Total	17	124176			

Individual 95% CIs For Mean
Based on Pooled StDev

Level	N	Mean	StDev	
winter	6	205.17	58.77	(----*-----)
spring	6	315.39	37.34	(----*----)
control	6	136.65	21.69	(-----*----)

Pooled StDev = 42.11   140   210   280   350

Winter	Spring	Control
1	1	1	11
1	1	1	2
1	4	1	1	44
1	67	1	1	7
1	8	1	1
2	2	2
2	2	2
2	6	2	2
2	9	2	889	2
3	3	1	3
3	3	2	3
3	3	3
3	3	3
3	3	8	3

25.32: The ANOVA test statistic is $F = 4.92$ (df = 3 and 92), which has $P = 0.003$, so there is strong evidence that the means are not all the same. In particular, list 1 seems to be the easiest, and lists 3 and 4 are the most difficult.

25.33: (a) The design, with four treatments, is shown. **(b) PLAN:** We compare the mean lightness of the four methods using a plot of the means and ANOVA. **SOLVE:** ANOVA should be safe: It is reasonable to view the samples as SRSs from the four populations, the distributions do not show drastic deviations from Normality, and the standard deviations satisfy our rule of thumb ($0.392/0.250 = 1.568$). The Minitab output below includes a table of the means, and a display that is equivalent to a plot of the means. The means have rather small differences in lightness score; Method C is lightest and Method B is darkest. The differences in mean lightness are nonetheless highly significant ($F = 22.77$, $P < 0.001$). **CONCLUDE:** The manufacturer will prefer Method B. Whether these differences are large enough to be important in practice requires more information about the scale of lightness scores.

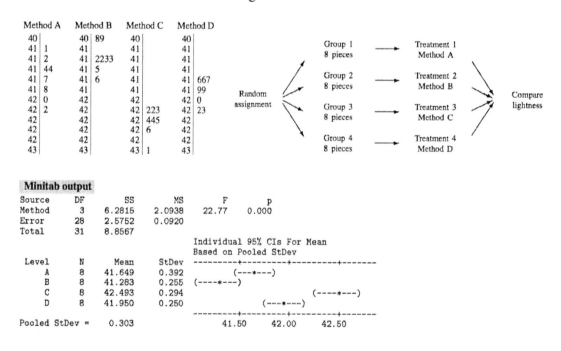

Minitab output

Source	DF	SS	MS	F	p
Method	3	6.2815	2.0938	22.77	0.000
Error	28	2.5752	0.0920		
Total	31	8.8567			

Individual 95% CIs For Mean
Based on Pooled StDev

Level	N	Mean	StDev	
A	8	41.649	0.392	(---*---)
B	8	41.283	0.255	(----*---)
C	8	42.493	0.294	(----*---)
D	8	41.950	0.250	(---*---)

Pooled StDev = 0.303   41.50   42.00   42.50

25.34: (a) Stemplots are provided. There is some degree of left skew in the data corresponding to lemon odor, but it is not strong. At least there is not strong evidence of non-Normality in any of the population distributions based on these stemplots. There are no real outliers. (b) STATE: Do customer times differ on average depending on the odor present? PLAN: We will compare mean times spent in the restaurant by using ANOVA. SOLVE: As discussed in (a), there is little evidence of non-Normality in any of the three distributions. Also, the three standard deviations are reasonably close: The ratio of largest standard deviation to smallest standard deviation is $15.44/13.10 = 1.18$, which is less than 2. It is safe to apply ANOVA procedures. Minitab output follows. We have $F = 10.861$ on degrees of freedom 2 and 85, yielding $P = 0.000$. There is overwhelming evidence of a difference in the mean time customers spend in the restaurant, depending on the odor present. Lavender odor yields the longest mean time, while lemon odor reduces time spent on average compared with no odor at all.

```
    Lavender            Lemon            No odor

  7 | 6             5 | 6            6 | 89
  8 | 89            6 | 03           7 | 223569
  9 | 234578        7 | 3458         8 | 445677
 10 | 12345566788999 8 | 338889      9 | 1222368
 11 | 46            9 | 0144677     10 | 136779
 12 | 1469         10 | 145688      11 | 58
 13 | 7            11 | 23          12 | 1
```

```
Minitab output

Source   DF      SS         MS       F       p
Scent     2    4569.01    2284.51   10.861   0.000
Error    85   17878.87     210.34
Total    87   22447.88
```

```
            Mean    SD    n
Lavender  105.70  13.10   30
Lemon      89.79  15.44   28
Odorless   91.27  14.93   30
```

25.35: STATE: Are the mean tip percentages constant for all types of weather forecasts (no forecast, good forecast, bad forecast)? PLAN: We will carry out an ANOVA test for the equality of means. SOLVE: First, we see that the ratio of largest standard deviation to smallest standard deviation is $2.388/1.959 = 1.219$, which is less than 2. Histograms of the samples are provided. There is some evidence of non-Normality, and perhaps one outlier in the "No Weather Report" group. We proceed, as the samples are reasonably large. From the output, we have $F = 20.679$ on $3 - 1 = 2$ and $60 - 3 = 57$ df. Hence, $P = 0.000$. CONCLUDE: There is overwhelming evidence that the mean tip percentages are not the same for all three groups. Examination of the summary statistics and the histograms provided suggests that while mean tip for the Bad report group is similar to that of the No report group, the mean tip for Good weather report is higher.

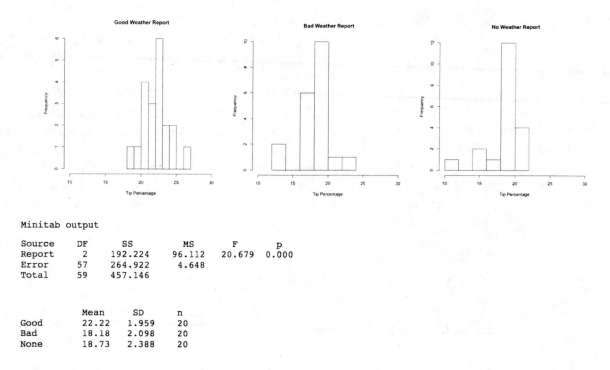

Minitab output

Source	DF	SS	MS	F	p
Report	2	192.224	96.112	20.679	0.000
Error	57	264.922	4.648		
Total	59	457.146			

	Mean	SD	n
Good	22.22	1.959	20
Bad	18.18	2.098	20
None	18.73	2.388	20

25.36: First, we note that ANOVA with all four groups shows large differences, as expected. The untreated mean is 58.56, roughly double the means for the other groups; the differences are highly significant ($F = 236.68$, $P < 0.001$). PLAN: We compare the mean strengths of the three durable press treatments using a plot of the means and ANOVA. SOLVE: It is reasonable to view the samples as SRSs from the three populations. The distributions show no severe deviations from Normality. (Stemplots are not shown; with only five observations in each group, they are not very informative.) The standard deviations do not satisfy our rule of thumb; the largest to smallest ratio is $2.669/1.167 = 2.29$. Because this is slightly more than 2, ANOVA is somewhat risky, but we proceed anyway. The Minitab output below includes a table of the means, and a display that is equivalent to a plot of the means. There is a highly significant ($F = 5.02$, df = 2 and 12, $P = 0.026$) difference among the mean breaking strengths for the three durable press treatments. CONCLUDE: Fabrics treated with Permafresh 55 have considerably higher strength than fabrics treated with Permafresh 48 or Hylite.

```
Minitab output
Source  DF      SS      MS       F       p
treat    2    47.50   23.75    5.02    0.026
Error   12    56.74    4.73
Total   14   104.24
                               Individual 95% CIs For Mean
                               Based on Pooled StDev
Level    N    Mean    StDev    --------+---------+---------+---------
  P55    5   29.540   1.167                     (-------*--------)
  P48    5   27.020   2.387             (-------*---------)
   HY    5   25.200   2.669    (---------*-------)
                               --------+---------+---------+---------
Pooled StDev =   2.174            25.0      27.5      30.0
```

25.37: First, we note that the mean angle for untreated fabric is 79 degrees, showing much less wrinkle resistance than any of the treated fabrics. ANOVA on four groups gives $F = 153.76$ and $P < 0.001$. A comparison of wrinkle recovery angle for the three durable press treatments is more interesting. The ANOVA results are shown in the Minitab output below. Hylite LF, which in Exercise 25.36 was seen to have the lowest breaking strength, has the highest wrinkle resistance. There is almost no difference between the means for two versions of Permafresh, even though we saw in Exercise 25.36 that Permafresh 55 appears to be stronger than Permafresh 48.

The ANOVA F-test cannot be trusted because the standard deviations violate our rule of thumb: $10.16/1.92 = 5.29$. This is much larger than 2. In particular, Permafresh 48 shows much more variability from piece to piece than either of the other treatments. Large variability in performance is a serious defect in a commercial product, so it appears that Permafresh 48 is unsuited for use on these grounds. The data are very helpful to a maker of durable press fabrics despite the fact that the formal test is not valid.

```
Minitab output
Source     DF      SS      MS       F       p
treat       2    253.2   126.6    3.39   0.068
Error      12    448.4    37.4
Total      14    701.6
                                Individual 95% CIs For Mean
                                Based on Pooled StDev
Level    N     Mean    StDev   --------+---------+---------+---------+
 P55     5    134.80    1.92     (---------*---------)
 P48     5    134.20   10.16   (---------*---------)
 HY      5    143.20    2.28                     (---------*---------)
                                --------+---------+---------+---------+
Pooled StDev =   6.11           132.0     138.0     144.0
```

25.38: (a) The table is given in the Minitab output below; because $4.500/3.529 = 1.28$, ANOVA should be safe. The means appear to suggest that logging reduces the number of species per plot and that recovery takes more than 8 years. (b) ANOVA gives $F = 6.02$ with df $= 2$ and 30, so $P < 0.01$ (software gives 0.006). We conclude that these differences are significant; the number of species per plot really is lower in logged areas.

```
Minitab output
Source     DF      SS      MS       F       p
Code        2    204.4   102.2    6.02   0.006
Error      30    509.2    17.0
Total      32    713.6
                                Individual 95% CIs For Mean
                                Based on Pooled StDev
Level    N     Mean    StDev   ---------+---------+---------+--------
Never   12    17.500   3.529                  (-------*-------)
1year   12    11.750   4.372   (-------*-------)
8years   9    13.667   4.500        (---------*--------)
                                ---------+---------+---------+--------
Pooled StDev =   4.120           12.0      15.0      18.0
```

25.39: (a) There is a slight increase in growth when water is added in the wet season, but a much greater increase when it is added during the dry season. (b) The means differ significantly during the first three years. (c) The year 2005 is the only one for which the winter biomass was higher than the spring biomass.

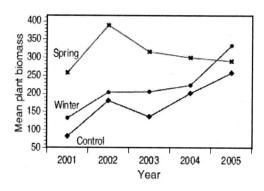

25.40: PLAN: We compare the mean biomass of the three groups using a plot of the means and ANOVA, testing $H_0 : \mu_w = \mu_s = \mu_c$ vs. H_a : At least one mean is different.

SOLVE: It is reasonable to view the samples as SRSs from the three populations, but the standard deviation ratio is high ($49.59/11.22 = 4.42$), so ANOVA is risky. The Minitab output below includes a table of the means, and a display that is equivalent to a plot of the means. As with the 2003 data, the means suggest that extra water in the spring has the greatest effect on biomass, with a lesser effect from added water in the winter. ANOVA gives a statistically significant result ($F = 43.79$, df 2 and 15, $P < 0.0005$). **CONCLUDE:** The combination of the (questionable) ANOVA results and the means supports the conclusion that added water in the spring increases biomass. The benefit of additional water in the winter is not so clear, especially when taking the plot of means in the solution to the previous exercise.

```
 Minitab output
Source     DF      SS      MS       F        p
Treatment   2    98451   49225    43.79    0.000
Error      15    16863    1124
Total      17   115314
                                  Individual 95% CIs For Mean
                                  Based on Pooled StDev
  Level    N     Mean    StDev   ---+---------+---------+---------+---
  winter   6   132.58    11.22                (---*---)
  spring   6   257.69    49.59                          (---*---)
  control  6    81.67    28.07   (----*---)
                                  ---+---------+---------+---------+---
Pooled StDev =    33.53           70       140       210       280
```

25.41: In addition to a high standard deviation ratio ($117.18/35.57 = 3.29$), the spring biomass distribution has a high outlier.

25.42: (a) This is a comparison of two means, so it requires a *t* test. (b) This is a comparison of three means, so it requires ANOVA. (c) This is a comparison of three proportions, so it requires a chi-square test.

25.43 and 25.44 are Web-based Exercises.